AND THERE'S ANOTHER COUNTRY

AND THERE'S ANOTHER COUNTRY

David C. Warren

Matador
Unit E2 Airfield Business Park,
Harrison Road, Market Harborough,
Leicestershire. LE16 7UL
Tel: 0116 2792299
Email: books@troubador.co.uk
Web: www.troubador.co.uk/matador
Twitter: @matadorbooks

ISBN 978 1803130 347

British Library Cataloguing in Publication Data.
A catalogue record for this book is available from the British Library.

Printed and bound by CPI Group (UK) Ltd, Croydon, CR0 4YY
Typeset in 12pt Minion Pro by Troubador Publishing Ltd, Leicester, UK

Matador is an imprint of Troubador Publishing Ltd

FOR ALL those who serve their countries, their parents who bring them up, their friends and relations who know and love them and their descendants who are proud of them.

CONTENTS

Foreword

> 'The past is a foreign country:
> they do things differently there.'
> ***The Go-Between* – Leslie Poles Hartley**

For a long time, I had thought about writing a book featuring my ancestors. Not necessarily because I feel that others would be particularly fascinated by my family, more because their circumstances, how events affected them, how they lived, how and where they worked, their trials and tribulations and how and why they died, were typical of so many other people at the time. As a result, their lives could have been the lives lived by almost any 'ordinary' person's ancestors, certainly with regard to the challenges they had to face.

Being based, as it is, on personal and public records, and stories and anecdotes passed down through the years by family members and friends, though, the additional research required meant that I was unable, due to pressure of work, to devote anything like enough time to the project until I took early retirement in 2008.

Although I have tried to record events as accurately and as completely as possible, obviously, since I was not there, I cannot possibly know for sure the exact turn of events in every detail. For continuity purposes, therefore, I have occasionally had to portray events in the most likely way that they would have occurred and/or also to introduce fictional characters whose existence is logical, but I do not and cannot know their exact identity. Where this has been done, however, I have tried not to 'massage' things to the extent that they become implausible and hope that I am not too far out.

I did not set out to judge, criticise, demean or ridicule in any way whatsoever anybody described or referred to in this book, and if it appears to any reader that I have, then I sincerely apologise. It will have been entirely unintended.

According to my father the family name 'Warren' comes from the De Warenne family, closely associated with William the Conqueror, though I have not (as yet) managed to get back anything like as far as them. Through what I have unearthed about the lives and fates of my ancestors, however, I have been repeatedly fascinated and would certainly encourage anybody who has the opportunity and the time, at least to dabble a little into their roots. Be warned, though, it can become addictive, especially to the curious, and of course, be careful what you wish for: I came upon one record that mentions a John Warren from Leicester being 'transported to the Colonies' in 1850. The entry is very summary and does not say what he had done to deserve this punishment. Sometimes you did not have to do a great deal then and in any event, he may well have no connection to me whatsoever. On the other hand, I have a 4x-Great-Uncle John Warren who was born in Leicester in 1797. (Not to be confused with his nephew, also John, my great-great-grandfather, written about later in this story.) Could it have been him? I hope not as the sentence was for seven years and he would have been well into his fifties at the start of it! At that age and in those days, could many survive such an ordeal? Especially since the ship, the *Blenheim*, was bound for Van Diemen's Land (Tasmania) and Norfolk Island (way out in the South Pacific between Australia and New Zealand), both very desolate places back then, I would imagine.

Apart from this and a murderer described later in this book (with whom I share a surname but can find no family connection I am pleased to say) I have not, as yet, discovered anything else along these lines and certainly no dreadful 'skeletons' but as I go on, who knows…

Genealogy is a continuum as, in theory at least, you can always go one more generation back but there is a 'wall' that all researchers have to climb when they go back beyond the 1830s, because the General Register of Births, Deaths and Marriages was only begun during that decade. Anybody wanting to go back further will need access to the Parish Records, which, although far from inaccessible, require a bit more input. In my case I hit the wall with my 4x-great-grandparents: William Warren and his wife Mary. I knew that they were around at the turn of the nineteenth century because of the parish record of my 3x-great-grandfather's birth and I knew William's (approximate*[see next paragraph]) birth date because burial records record his age at the date of his death, but I could not locate his birth within the same parish. Naturally there are many records relating to William Warrens being born around the time that he must have been but, with some effort, many can be discounted by 'triangulation', that is to say, where other associated records do not fit. And so, after eliminating all these impossible alternatives, I think I now know where he came from and so, if I am correct, the details of several of my other ancestors who came before him. The critical assumption here, of course, is that the records are complete and any alternative 'better fits' are not lost or missing for one reason or another. But what can anyone do about this possibility other than keep an open mind? Perhaps any missing or incomplete documentation may reveal itself at some point in the future. Until or unless it does, unlike with the relations after William, about whom I am sure beyond reasonable doubt, his origins must remain in question and there is a possibility that they always will; to me at least.

*I have bracketed and denoted 'approximate' because the exact dates in these records can never be, and should never be, relied on absolutely. Bear in mind that they are all based on declarations made at the time: and the further back you go, the greater the degree of illiteracy. For example, in the places where documents require a signature, the earlier the entry the more likely you will find written 'X' or 'X – his [or her] mark'. It would have been of limited use, therefore, to ask such a person to check that a written date was accurate. By the same token do not rely on the spelling always being totally accurate, particularly surnames, which, the further back you go, may be spelt in a variety of curious ways.

Records can be inaccurate for a variety of other reasons too, including errors of recall: an elderly person may well be confused about their exact date of birth and, more often than you may think, even the actual year is suspect. Additionally, what people were told about when, or even where, they were born can be suspect. For example, in one particular census return, my great-grandfather appears to have been confused about whether he was born in Leicester or Lancaster. A mere error of transcription, you may think, as the names of the two places can easily be confused if written in a hand difficult to read, but the fact that his father died in Lancaster when my great-grandfather was very young may, on the other hand, have led him to believe that he had been born there.

You can even come across cases where it is very hard to discount good, old-fashioned hoodwinking, as in the case of my great-grandmother. When she married a younger man, her declared age on the marriage lines at the time differed significantly from what I knew it must have been. But then, on censuses down the subsequent years, she gradually catches up by ageing something like twelve years in every ten!

There is very little difficulty, these days, in finding books that will guide you through the process of starting to research your family history, but it is an inescapable fact that the biggest single development that has facilitated the process is the Internet. Brilliant tool or slave-master, depending on how you see it, the personal computer is certainly not everybody's cup of tea but its ability to connect to and share massive amounts of information with other computers means that you can do almost all your research without leaving the comfort of your own home.

With many family historians beginning their research 'a bit late in life', though, they may not be very (that contrived phrase) 'computer literate' and, although I do not wish to sound patronising, we all know at least one such person who has given up entirely on the concept and screw their faces up in horror at the mere mention of terms like 'website' or 'email'. But what you have never had you never miss, of course, and I must admit that part of me envies the more halcyon lives that many of these people must lead, especially just after raging at a printer that simply refuses to print! However, this will, no doubt, change as more people who have grown up with computers 'come of age'.

Whatever, there is no doubt now that the Internet is here to stay and, as with other successful innovations, has turned from a curiosity into an almost universal essential. If you are at all able, therefore, do make the most of it because when it comes to family history research, in the foreseeable future I, at least, feel that there is unlikely to be another single more powerful tool.

This in mind, to trace the records of those born after the creation of the General Register requires only the very basic of computer skills and entries can be searched and certificates ordered through consulting only a few sites. For prior events there is now an increasing number of websites that have amassed large collections of parish records. It has to be said, however, that some are better than others, and many charge a fee, so it rests with the individual researcher to decide what is affordable and what best suits their needs.

Another of the many drawbacks to getting older is that you are much more likely to have lost most, or all, of your older relatives and so are deprived of all those priceless first-hand accounts from long ago. Sadly, here there is no alternative but to resign yourself to the fact that you will never know for sure the answers to all those questions that you now realise you should have asked when they were alive.

With the Internet as your main starting point then, from what I have already said, rule number one has to be: never take anything you read on it as 'gospel', even on sites that you may consider as highly reliable sources. My rule of thumb is to confirm the details by checking on at least three different and independent sites and then once more, ideally through a source completely unconnected with the Internet (if such a thing exists these days).

The next most valuable tool has to be the local record offices. Always well worth a visit (or more often than not, a series of visits), these places are amazing 'squirrel's nests' of information where, as well as the 'hatches, matches and dispatches', you can access a myriad of other historical collections such as newspapers, copies of wills, school records and even prison records, to name but a few. I myself have spent many a happy hour not only at Wigston, which houses the Leicester, Leicestershire and Rutland collections, but also the Lichfield (for Staffordshire) and the Matlock (for Derbyshire) Record Offices as and when my research has led me. In all cases I found the facilities warm and comfortable to work in and remain indebted to the dedicated staff, all of whom I found extremely helpful and understanding.

In the absence of discovering a famous ancestor or infamous murderer or highwayman, etc. in your family, there are a few things that are almost inevitable. Although the Second World War claimed many more lives internationally, it was the First World War that deprived the most British families of loved ones, with over twice as many British military deaths as those in the second World War. The sheer scale of the carnage throughout this bloody conflict means that the discovery of at least one member of your family, if not several, involved in the action, is virtually guaranteed, and it follows, therefore, that almost as likely as not, these ancestors would also have been casualties.

It is important to bear in mind, though, that regarding war records there may be factors, over and above those already mentioned, that can conspire to draw their accuracy into question. Although mistranscriptions can arise at the best of times, with the despair that war brings and where matters are pressing, details are often sketchy, levels of secrecy increase, and less experienced record keepers may be involved.

There are yet other matters that can lead to confusion, not least the various 'taboos' that tend to differ with time, in some cases very different from or altered or exaggerated forms of similar prejudices that may exist today. Whatever your political views, it is an inescapable fact that certain afflictions or affectations, possibly as a result of a more limited understanding of cause and effect, then unacceptable, are now completely accepted by all but the most zealous. In the past any suggestion that a member of the family was, say, a 'lunatic', could easily lead to 'stigmatisation' – not only towards the person concerned but also their entire family and even beyond, including anybody else who had anything to do with them. Although a much less widely used term today, being 'stigmatised' is essentially someone or some group being defined as disgraceful, the perceived cause being 'hushed up' and hardly ever, if at all, disclosed to anybody outside the immediate family. It is easy nowadays to regard these sorts of attitudes as quaint or ignorant, but they were very real at the time, that is to say, born out of narrower ideas of pride and decorum in a time when the mere sight of table or piano legs was considered provocative and so had to be covered up by valances or the like. As a result, certain afflictions, often acquired through mere misfortune and perhaps less easily treated as they may nowadays be, may then have been regarded as a result of poor hygiene, bad habits, or even 'visitation of God'! In many cases these issues would have been 'swept under the carpet' and only confronted, even within the family, when absolutely necessary and even then, only being spoken of with a grimace, in shameful, whispered euphemisms.

All these sorts of things affected my family and I have no reason to believe that they were, in any way, vastly different from the next family. So, if some of those stories about old so and so, which you believed to be 'the gospel truth' and would have challenged anybody who tried to say otherwise, do not always stack up, even sometimes to the extent that they simply cannot have occurred as you were led to believe, you are not alone.

Along similar lines, other conundrums may arise where different members of families, especially large, extended families, do not always see 'eye to eye' or, for some reason, lose contact with each other. I have absolutely no idea why my family lost contact with some of my great-uncles who must have lived on until well after I was born, but they did.

Remember, just as perceptions today are different from those of the past, in the future they will be different from today. Although disparities may at first appear confusing and may even challenge your respect for those cherished family anecdotes, unless you are unfortunate enough to uncover a 'hornet's nest', there is no reason to be concerned. After all, who does not harbour secrets that they would rather others did not know about, even though it may not be exactly the same thing as something our ancestors may have hidden? As we judge our ancestors, so shall our descendants judge us.

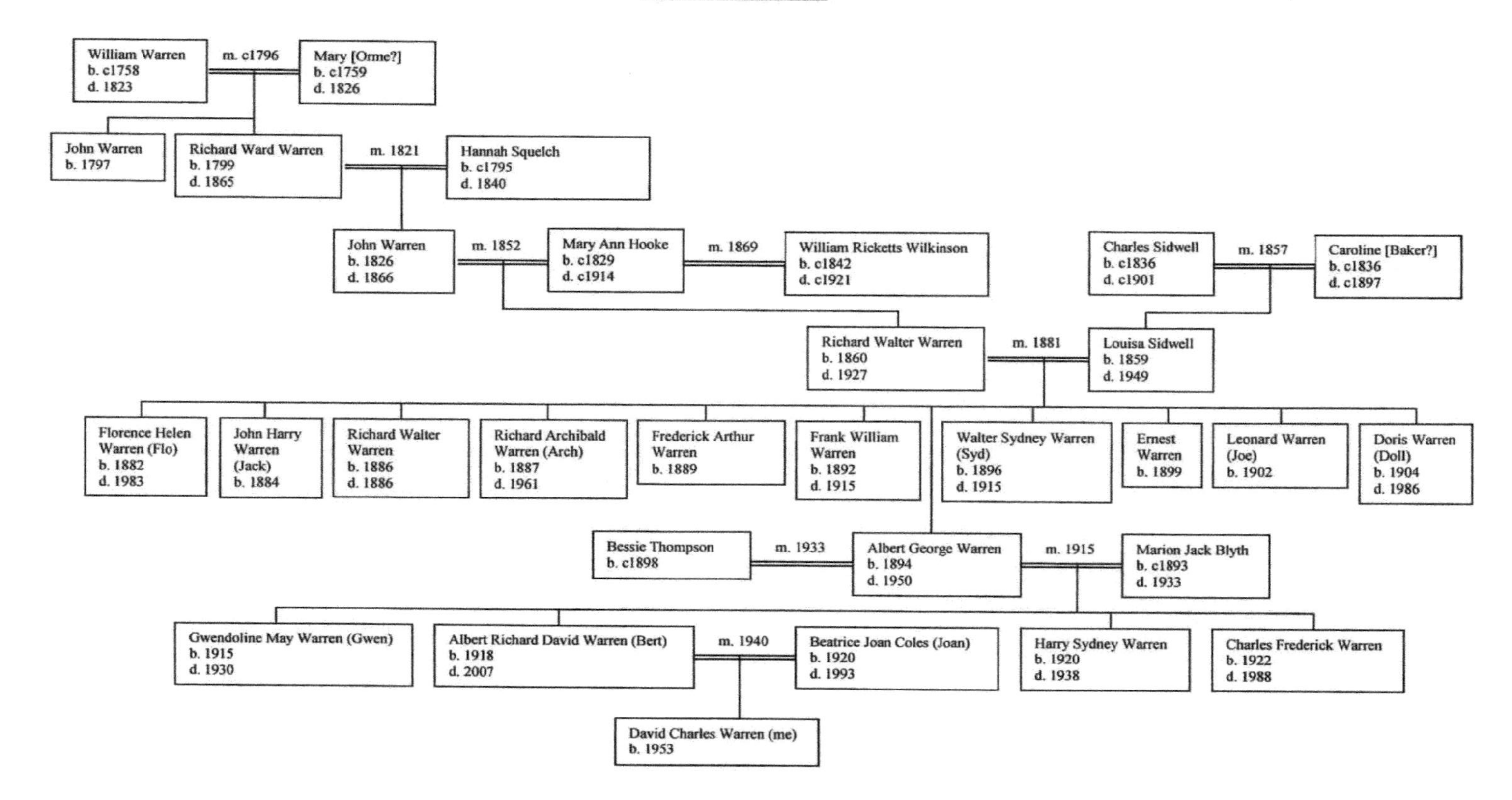
FAMILY TREE
William Warren
b. c1758
d. 1823
m. c1796
Mary [Orme?]
b. c1759
d. 1826
John Warren
b. 1797
Richard Ward Warren
b. 1799
d. 1865
m. 1821
Hannah Squelch
b. c1795
d. 1840
John Warren
b. 1826
d. 1866
m. 1852
Mary Ann Hooke
b. c1829
d. c1914
m. 1869
William Ricketts Wilkinson
b. c1842
d. c1921
Charles Sidwell
b. c1836
d. c1901
m. 1857
Caroline [Baker?]
b. c1836
d. c1897
Richard Walter Warren
b. 1860
d. 1927
m. 1881
Louisa Sidwell
b. 1859
d. 1949
Florence Helen Warren (Flo)
b. 1882
d. 1983
John Harry Warren (Jack)
b. 1884
Richard Walter Warren
b. 1886
d. 1886
Richard Archibald Warren (Arch)
b. 1887
d. 1961
Frederick Arthur Warren
b. 1889
Frank William Warren
b. 1892
d. 1915
Walter Sydney Warren (Syd)
b. 1896
d. 1915
Ernest Warren
b. 1899
Leonard Warren (Joe)
b. 1902
Doris Warren (Doll)
b. 1904
d. 1986
Bessie Thompson
b. c1898
m. 1933
Albert George Warren
b. 1894
d. 1950
m. 1915
Marion Jack Blyth
b. c1893
d. 1933
Gwendoline May Warren (Gwen)
b. 1915
d. 1930
Albert Richard David Warren (Bert)
b. 1918
d. 2007
m. 1940
Beatrice Joan Coles (Joan)
b. 1920
d. 1993
Harry Sydney Warren
b. 1920
d. 1938
Charles Frederick Warren
b. 1922
d. 1988
David Charles Warren (me)
b. 1953

Chapter 1

Beginnings, Middles and Ends

'A story should have a beginning, a middle and an end, but not necessarily in that order.'

Jean-Luc Godard

There are so many beginnings middles and ends to this story that you might say it never really begins or ends. Beginnings for some are ends and middles for others, like the story of life itself, I suppose. In Britain today we expect, rather than hope for, 'a better life' with enough time between the beginnings and the endings for middles to be the long, sweet, enjoyable experiences of which memories are meant to be made. We give the knowing nod of acknowledgement when regaled with stories of past austerity, but can we really imagine life without its modern comforts – waking each day to a cold, damp house, sleeping five and six to a bed, working for long hours on basic food and with basic sanitation? Life was extremely hard and ahead lay a war, the like of which the world had never before seen. That was the way it was for them, but as far as my family is concerned, I'll not venture to add 'and without complaint' unless, that is, there has been a weighty shift in their temperament over the last few generations.

The first disjointed rumblings of the twentieth century were drowned under the hubbub of daily life; slowly and surely, though, the storm gathered strength, and almost without warning, as if from around a corner somewhere, blew a whirlwind that would wreak disaster on a scale that could never have been foreseen, least of all by the eager but unsuspecting youth of the time. And then, afterwards, came many different sorts of wars, private battles fought in minds rather than on fields, bombs of psychological shrapnel every bit as burning, piercing and destroying as the physical kind, battles against despair, and the cost of defiance: insanity. The so-called 'Great War' continued to take prisoners, cause casualties and fill graves long after the guns had fallen silent.

It is perhaps somewhat ironic, then, to say that, in relation to many large towns of the time, Leicester in late Victorian times scored better than average as a place to live. There was a plentiful supply of labour and comparative wealth, first from the 'life blood' hosiery industry and latterly the boot and shoe industry which had, by this time, begun to gather significant momentum. In effect, everything had fallen into place. Urbanisation was consolidating production into factories at the expense of the previously small and scattered cottage industries, machines were bigger, faster, and more efficient, and, perhaps most importantly, steam power had arrived. What's more, the steam was relatively cheap as Leicester was fed with ample coal by its rich seams in the west of the county, readily linked to the city by railway. As a result, housing for the better off was more opulent and the familiar Victorian terraces were often built to a better standard than may have been the case elsewhere. So much so that a lot of the original street layouts survive today, and, left alone, will no doubt remain well beyond many a house constructed much later. Nowadays, though, standing on those same streets, it is not always easy to leap back over the last couple of hundred years in one's mind. The ever-present rows of parked vehicles seem to dwarf all proportion while the ubiquitous satellite dishes, road signs and various other street jumble all conspire to upstage the façades.

It was onto this stage then that my great-grandfather, Richard Walter Warren, was born on the 28th of October 1860 and, in the best Godard tradition, my tale begins with an ending, namely the untimely demise of his father, John Warren. John was born late in 1826; the second son of Richard Ward Warren and Hannah (née Squelch). He was baptised that New Year's Eve in the ancient church of St. Mary de Castro in the heart of the town (as it then was) of Leicester and I have every reason to believe that the family into which John was born was certainly not the poorest of the time. After serving an apprenticeship as a carpenter, John's father, Richard Ward Warren, was to become a fairly wealthy builder, and his will of 1865 contains many significant bequests of money and property to various members of his family and friends. He was also a Freeman of Leicester (a vestige of ancient times which once entitled the enrolled to various privileges including freedom from certain tolls, access to tenancies, common grazing and so on, following the swearing of an oath of allegiance to both the Crown and the civic authorities, not to be confused with Freemasonry). As his business progressed and Richard Ward Warren became more influential, he took on various municipal duties including becoming a 'Guardian of the Poor'. These were often 'well-to-do' members of society elected to administer the enactment of the Poor Laws aimed at protecting those who had fallen on hard times. Part of their role was to oversee the workhouses; perhaps ironically, in which Richard's descendants would, from time to time, come very near to finding themselves residents. On his death certificate, years later, Richard Ward Warren's occupation is given as 'Gentleman' and, although thickly overgrown with ivy now, the stone memorial above his grave in Welford Road Cemetery is certainly not that of a pauper. Later Richard's sons, including John, as well as both John's sons and various other descendants of Richard, would become Freemen too, many of whom were also in the building trade. Additionally, I believe that my great-grandfather, Richard Walter Warren, assumed the title as well. The *Register of the Freemen of Leicester* (courtesy of Wigston Library), however, records a 'Richard Walker Warren'. But he is down as the second son of John Warren, which he was. So I believe that 'Walker' is a mistranscription of 'Walter', especially since the date of his induction, 30 April 1886, also fits, in that he would then have been twenty-five years of age.

In June 1852 John married Mary Anne Hooke, a farmer's daughter from Anstey – a village just to the west of Leicester – and from the 1861 Census I can see that they set up home together a few miles further west at No.73, The Village, Desford, where they had five children. I have tried to locate exactly where their house was but have, so far, been unsuccessful. I am grateful to Dr. Pam Fisher of the Leicestershire Victoria County History Trust for clarifying why, though. Apparently 'The Village' was not the name of a street in Desford but simply referred to the village as a bloc, and No.73 would have been the seventy-third house visited by the enumerator during the Census. One day I may have a try at retracing the footsteps of the enumerator to see if it leads me to either the still-standing house or the site where it may have stood.

Then, just as now, of course, people changed jobs and, whilst in the late 1850s John was a Railway Inspector, in the early 1860s he became a Canal Inspector. Constructions of this kind were clearly 'his thing' and Desford was ideally situated for both the Ashby Canal and the Leicester and Swannington Railway. Unfortunately, in February 1866, something went terribly wrong, and John suddenly died somewhat far afield, in Lancaster. His death was notified to the Registrar by a Mary Hannah Edmondson who lived at 8, Ullswater Road, Lancaster (the address where John had died) and she declared that she had been present at his death. The cause reads: 'Disease of Brain. 10 days Convulsions Certified'. Since we all have to die, perhaps not the way most would choose. I cannot say for sure why he was in Lancaster and have no reason to believe that he had become estranged from his wife, but there is one possible explanation. At about this time a section of railway near to Lancaster was being connected to the Midland

Railway and he could have been working on that. In other words, 8, Ullswater Road could have been his digs and Mary Edmondson his landlady. I remain a little sceptical that there was nothing more to it than this though, not least because of the clear reference to Lancaster in the Leicester burial record which would seem to suggest a more permanent connection to the place than just working there at his time of death.

Even more curious is that John is recorded as the father of the second son born to his wife, Mary; William, who arrived just three weeks after John's death. For this record to be accurate, therefore, his relationship with his wife must still have been intimate during the summer of 1865. However, on the birth certificate there is no mention of John being deceased and it still gives his occupation as Canal Inspector when I know from both his death certificate and his will that, when he died, he was again working on the railways. Indeed, this would seem to suggest that Mary (his wife) may have been unaware of what John was doing or even, perhaps, where he was. So was Mary Edmondson just John's landlady, or could she have been the lover into whose arms he'd fallen following the failure of his marriage? Who can say? In any event, his body was brought back to Leicester and buried alongside his father, who had died just three months earlier.

After John's death his wife, Mary, goes on to marry a William Wilkinson, a French polisher, and they live together in Humberstone Gate which, although nowadays part pedestrianised, remains as it was then; a busy street in the heart of Leicester. Rather quaintly, however, Mary 'loses' three or four years of her age in the process. Comparing her two marriage certificates, when she married John, in June 1852, she gave her age as twenty-two, and must, therefore, have been born in either 1829 or 1830. But when it comes to her marriage to William in April 1869, she gives her age as only thirty-five when, on the basis of the first certificate, she would have been at least thirty-eight.

I think that this may well have been an attempt to conceal her real age since, at twenty-seven, William would have been some eleven or twelve years her junior and the deception may have been perpetuated to a degree as in the 1871 Census she is still at least a year or so younger than she would have been according to her record of marriage to John. By 1881, though, she appears to have 'come clean' as, at fifty-one, her age again matches the details recorded at her first wedding.

A further curiosity is that, in the 1871 Census, taken two years after Mary's remarriage, all John's children have been 'renamed Wilkinson' though in the census ten years later they are all Warrens again. This could well have been an attempt to salvage some consistency from what must have been an otherwise turbulent time for the family. Whatever, it is highly likely that this whole experience had a profound effect on my great-grandfather, Richard (only five years old when his father died), as well as on his brother and three sisters, all of whom were still in their most formative years. Not only was their natural father so tragically taken, but their names had been changed and they had been whisked from a quiet country village into the busy centre of a large town!

Richard, at least, seems to have emerged relatively unscathed, though, and records show that both William and Mary lived on well into ripe old age. By the time of the 1901 Census, they had moved to Cannock, Staffs., and by 1911 had moved again, this time to Small Heath in Birmingham. Although I have never obtained the relevant certificates, I believe that Mary died in late 1914, aged around eighty-five, and William in 1921, when he would have been around seventy-nine years of age, because I know that matching references exist to these effects for the Birmingham area.

*

The exact extent of Richard's education is not clear. His father's status as Freeman once entitled holders to send their sons to the Free Grammar School but no such privilege survived into the 1860s so, if any formal training took place at all, it is unlikely to have been anything other than to the basic elementary level, achieved by the vast majority of the day. In any case, due to the financial strain on most families at that time, there would have been pressure on Richard to start earning money as soon as possible. My guess is that he would have entered the world of work at the age of about nine or ten, probably during a period when he both worked and went to school, the Education Acts of the 1870s making (at least partial) attendance at school compulsory up to the age of fourteen. Initially Richard would have assisted his mother, and sister, Fanny, who 'took in hosiery'. A popular cottage industry at the time, it entailed making up (sewing up open ends of socks, seaming and attaching buttons, etc.), mending (faults due to machinery malfunctions or mistakes) or decorating the various garments with embroidery and the like. Mary had trained as a milliner (a maker of women's hats), but this type of work may well have been somewhat limited, the plentiful supply of work from the hosiery industry, on the other hand, being much more likely to provide her with a living wage. In any case, from decorating a hat to decorating hosiery probably does not require too great a leap of skill. Although not highly paid, this way of life was safer and certainly less dirty than the factory. Payment was based on piecework; per dozen garments or pairs of socks, etc. and, in harder times, perhaps even partly in kind, such as in candles rather than all as cash – even though payment in kind, or 'truck' as it was known, had been banned in the 1830s, in practice it had proved very difficult to eradicate.

The term 'hosiery' is not confined to the manufacture of socks and stockings, though it is fair to say that socks and stockings were then the backbone of the trade. The term applies to anything that is knitted as opposed to woven, in other words, produced by the interlinking of a single thread rather than through a warp and weft arrangement on a loom. Knitted items are more elastic and, therefore, better fitting and, as the process developed, it became possible to produce increasingly complex garments and styles.

Richard probably started by collecting the yarn, and unfinished items, from the factory and then returning the finished work. During this time, he would have become accustomed to the hot, oily smells of the works, the noise of the ever-running frames and the terms of the trade (both coarse and civil I expect).

Richard: "*A've cum fu mi mam.*"*

Counterman: "Well *sh'aint ere* lad."

R: "No, *me mam's* sent me… Mrs. Warren, er… Wilkinson, Mrs. Wilkinson… she *ses shi's dun* these and have *y'* got some more *for er*?"

As Richard watched his mother closely, he soon began to pick it up. Before long he would be let loose on a few simple pieces and soon became able to earn his keep. By now Mary was in her early forties and, unlike the 'life begins at forty' generations of today, forty then was when 'you began to feel it'. Poor diet, housing and sanitation began to compromise the body and with that, the onset of age came sooner. Straining to examine the stitching by candlelight or even gaslight on a dark winter's afternoon, shivering when the coal ran out before there was enough to buy more, and backache from the crouched position adopted when attending to detail, she must have thanked God for the help and company of her sons and daughters.

Although hand knitting is thought to date back at least to the Middle Ages, the invention of the first knitting machine is attributed to the Rev. William Lee of Calverton, Nottinghamshire during Elizabethan times. Somewhat fancifully, legend has it that he was driven to contrive the device through having to compete for his wife's attentions against her constant knitting. Quite how a country clergyman manages to knock up such a complex arrangement of needles, cams and levers in his 'garden shed' has been the subject of considerable debate down the ages but whatever the true circumstances, the knitting machine certainly appeared at about this time and William Lee was accredited with its invention. Although

---

* The Leicester accent is part of the East Midlands Group of dialects and is said to differ from that of the West Midlands due to the influence of the Danes during the so-called Danelaw. This was the period towards the end of the first millennium when a large swath of Eastern England was controlled by the Danes. Where the story suggests the strongest use of this accent, as with foreign and other heavily accented or emphasised words, I have put the text in italics.

refined considerably by the mid-nineteenth century, the industrial knitting frame was still a 'contraption' – basically a large wooden frame supporting the work while needles move in and out in sequence along the top looping more and more of the yarn and thus adding to the garment. As levers and pedals are pressed and released in a certain strict order the operator's whole body gyrates in time to the clunks, clatters and swishes as the yarn is linked. Not surprisingly, because of the effort required, frames were more often than not worked by men rather than women. Any slight departure from the order of play could result in a faulty garment that would either have to be repaired, completely unwound and redone or dumped. In time the movements of the operator become automatic (a bit like absent-minded driving), but you had to be fast and you had to be accurate.

As the process developed frames that could produce two or three garments at once began to appear and, although the application of power came late to the process, when it did, it revolutionised it.

Over the next few years Richard worked hard and, by acquiring a knitting frame of his own, could well have added another dimension to the enterprise. The availability of work varied, though: sometimes there was more than he could manage, and you could earn bonuses for fast turnarounds but other times were slow and you could barely earn enough to live on. During the harder times the only food consumed in the household may well have been just bread, honey and water. They got by, but only just – a sort of 'subsistence industry' I suppose.

Inevitably Richard soon found himself wanting to be free of his mother's apron strings. He wanted to go out to work and earn money he could truly call his own and, for a young man in that position, at that time, the factory was the only alternative. There was certainly no shortage of advertisements for trainee frame knitters in the local paper and so, at fifteen, Richard applied for one and was quickly accepted. At first, he enjoyed the independence, but the hours were long – twelve-hour days in the week: starting at six or seven in the morning, and a half a day on Saturday morning. Not long before, Saturday too would have been a full day, but the concession was aimed at reducing the incidence of 'keeping St. Monday'; a wry term for missing work on Mondays after overdoing Sunday's rest! In theory an hour and a half a day was allowed for meals but often less was taken and sometimes no breaks would have been taken at all. If you'd wanted anything you'd have taken a bottle of tea and a sandwich and drunk and eaten while working at the frame. The foremen would certainly have worked Richard a damn sight harder than his mother had. Each payday 12/6 of his 15 shillings a week was taken by his mother for board but the remaining 2/6 was all his own and in those days, it was enough for a bit of fun. A few pints of a Saturday night perhaps? Not always but more often when he was older. Or a variety show perhaps, or (if his money lasted) maybe a trip out of town on a Saturday afternoon.

*

The sixth of June 1881 was Whit Bank Holiday Monday so, despite it being early summer, it was probably raining, but this is the day that the twenty-year-old Richard Walter Warren stepped out to be married to Louisa Sidwell (she a year older) in the brick-built St. Andrew's Parish Church, which still stands today on the corner of Jarrom Street and (what was then) Asylum Street, a stone's throw from both their homes: Richard's in Laxton Street and Louisa's parents' house in Bonners Lane.

The 1881 Census gives Louisa's father Charles's occupation as 'FWK'. Not a rude word but short for 'Framework Knitter'. In other words, he was a hosiery worker too, so perhaps Richard and Charles worked together and this may well have been the mechanism through which Richard and Louisa met. In fact, Charles's father (also Charles) had been something of an entrepreneur in the industry. He is listed in the 1851 Census as living in Elbow Lane (somewhere near where the Highcross John Lewis car park currently stands) and a manufacturer of fancy hosiery employing no less than thirteen men. At the same time Charles Jr. is down as a fancy hosiery worker and I have little doubt, therefore, that he worked for his father at this time. It is interesting then to read in the next two subsequent Censuses that Charles Jr. is employed in the boot and shoe industry, only to have returned to the hosiery industry by 1881. Since Charles Sr. would have been sixty-four in 1851, I would venture that his enterprise was at its height just before he retired (or died) and, for whatever reason, the firm ceased to exist somewhere between 1851 and 1861. Charles Sr.'s business, though, could well have given his son's early life a bit of a boost and, if any legacy resulted, entitled him to something of a better standard of living than may have otherwise been possible.

I think that it is fair to say that marriage, in those days, was not so lightly entered into as in many cases today and Richard certainly seems to have been out to impress. On his marriage certificate he styles himself 'Richard Walter Ward Warren'. The 'Ward' bit can only have come from his grandfather – Richard Ward Warren, the well-to-do builder and, in addition of course, it makes the name sound a bit 'double-barrelled' – Ward-Warren? In reality, though, I can find no other record remotely suggesting the inclusion of 'Ward' in Richard's names. Moreover, he styles himself a 'hosier' – a term usually reserved for a hosiery firm owner or at least a manager, whereas I have no reason to believe that he was anything other than an ordinary, everyday frame knitter at this time.

It was an auspicious occasion for all concerned, though, and I can imagine Charles bristling with pride as he gave away his eldest daughter to be married that day. Already greying, a man in his mid-forties and, although distinguished, he would have seemed older than the same today. Undoubtedly, his wife, Caroline, would have fussed and wept at the enormity of the event.

As to whether Richard's mother, Mary, was there I cannot say, but I have no reason to believe that she would not have been, no doubt escorted by William Wilkinson. On the other hand, could Richard, by now, have gone his own way, renouncing his mother's and stepfather's attempts to create a 'new family' after the death of his true father? I do know that Richard was supported by his brother John because he is a witness and was, presumably, best man. Whatever the family circumstances, weddings of the day were always great events and, with the formalities over, a good deal of festivity often followed. The celebrations may well have run on well into the night and when, the following morning, back in Laxton Street, a still-weary Richard woke beside his new bride, he dearly wished that he did not have to turn out to work that day. It must have crossed his mind to send somebody to say he was sick, but he would have soon dismissed the notion because everybody there knew he was getting married – some were even there, for heaven's sake! So it would only have led to trouble. Resigned again to reality, Louisa still asleep, the boards would have creaked as Richard crept across the floor of the small bedroom. No water for a wash, he struggles with his clothes for a few minutes and is gone.

On the street it is the crack of dawn, a bright day with the usual crowd gathering outside each factory. Richard's factory was only a few streets away and, as he nears the gates, the usual jibes and innuendoes that follow the first nuptial night ring out. Richard smiles but doesn't react – it would just have made matters worse. Inside the factory it's hot and noisy – the machines rattling and banging as they knit along with the steaming molten metal used to make needle mounts. As Richard sets to work over his machine he dreams of a better life.

There's gorra be more to life than this, he thinks.

As the day passes, increasingly aware of his new circumstances, Richard resolves to improve his lot but for the time being at least, if he is to make ends meet, the twelve-hour daily drudge must continue.

*

Ten years earlier, in 1871, France had been defeated by the Prussians and then came the declaration in the Hall of Mirrors at Versailles of the unification of the German states. Bismarck and the Prussians had finally got their way and the German people were, at last, a single nation and a strong, confident and proud nation at that, with Prussia at the helm. By now the French knew only too well what that could lead to. Then Germany and Russia 'renew their vows' but just as France was beginning to feel yet more isolated, the old German Kaiser, Wilhelm I, dies. Just three months after that, Wilhelm's son and heir, Frederick, also dies, leaving the stage wide open for the hot-headed young Wilhelm II. At twenty-nine, like any young man in charge of a powerful machine, 'Billy' was impatient to make it 'roar'. As far as he was concerned, the formula that had served so well over the years, namely the various pacts with Russia, were unnecessary – especially when the Germanies were now united and powerful. Perhaps, above all, he envied Britain's mastery of the seas and made sure everyone knew that he wanted this glory for himself and Germany. In hindsight, of course, we now know the awful consequences of those ambitions but, at the time, the events did little more than raise a few eyebrows in London. After all, damn it, Britannia ruled the waves and always would!

There were changes afoot in Russia too. In 1894 Tsar Alexander III dies and is succeeded by Nicholas II. As the new Tsar, Nicholas was dismayed at his cousin's, the new Kaiser's, attitude towards his country and Nicholas decides instead to ally with France. This Dual Entente of 1895 meant that Germany now found herself living in between two neighbours, both hostile to her, and both prepared to react if she tried any funny business with either of them. Far from conciliatory, though, Germany's reaction was to strengthen her position by allying with Italy and her old consort Austria-Hungary.

In Britain minds were still elsewhere. Eyes looked to Empire not Europe. Europe had its problems, always had had, always would have – leave 'em to it. The Empire was Britain's concern, Britain's strength and Britain's future. Why… it was not only Britain that knew this, surely the whole world did! The idea that anybody would challenge the *status quo* was absurd… of course it was. And this 'Splendid Isolation' continued well into the early twentieth century before the penny began to drop. Europe was, indeed, very important, not least because it was next door. Anybody who has fallen out with a next-door neighbour knows this: you have to make an effort to get on with them even though you may not like them simply because you have to live beside them every day!

Slowly it began to dawn that Germany was getting too big for her boots. The old scores that Britain had had with Russia and France meant that Britain could easily be left out in the cold if Europe really did explode. And this anxiety was only to increase when Britain went to war with the Dutch settlers in South Africa, apparently on the pretext of protecting British interests (the recent discovery of diamonds and then large amounts of gold being just coincidences of course). The dissent from Europe was palpable and events began not only to affect Britain's security, but also, much more importantly, they were affecting its ability to trade, so, one way or another, something had to change.

*

Back in Laxton Street love blossomed and within six months of the marriage Louisa was pregnant. Also, Richard had been as good as his promise to himself, and that winter had landed a job in the factory warehouse. With the imminent birth of his first child in mind, away from the noisy, sweaty frames and now on 22/6 a week (almost a quarter more than his previous wage) Richard began to feel more secure and optimistic. What more could he possibly wish for? Things had been tough in the past right enough but that was the past and this was now. What could possibly go wrong?

In fact, things were going so well that Richard and Louisa started to enjoy themselves a little.

Approaching their first wedding anniversary, the streets were abuzz with the forthcoming visit of the Prince and Princess of Wales, who were to open the new Abbey Park. Leicester took great pride in this additional recreation from its inception and still does today. Situated north of the centre, as the name suggests, it was formerly the grounds to the twelfth-century abbey. Somewhere to walk, relax and get away from the grime for a few hours. There were to be trees, flower gardens and rustic bridges as well as a bandstand. The Prince of Wales – Prince Edward – later to become Edward VII, was already forty years old and, although anxious to 'take over the reins', was kept very much in the background by his controlling mother Victoria. Although he could not possibly have known for sure, but may well have suspected, he would have almost another twenty years to wait before inheriting the throne. Always keen to 'press the flesh' though, Edward would undertake many notable engagements including the opening of the Thames Embankment, the Mersey Tunnel, and Tower Bridge, but today it was Leicester's turn. So, on Whit Monday 1882, Richard, in straw boater, and the now obviously pregnant Louisa, in Sunday best, made their way across town to witness the spectacle for themselves. A bright late spring day, the problem was that everybody else had the same idea and the nearer they got to the park, the more populous the crowds became, to the extent that when the Prince and Princess arrived, there was little chance, if any, of seeing the royal couple at all. Louisa would claim to have glimpsed Alexandra's hat tails flapping in the breeze but that was as far as it went, and after half an hour or so spent trying to secure a more advantageous position, Louisa began to feel a bit dizzy and, worried that the excitement of the event could affect her pregnancy, they decided to slope back home.

Once safely home again, Louisa sat on the front doorstep taking in the late afternoon air. Now more comfortable, she watched Richard as he relaxed. Bottle of beer in one hand, fag in the other, he was making the absolute most of what remained of their day off.

As the pregnancy progressed, though, it began to dawn that the house in Laxton Street simply wasn't big enough for a family and, with more money to hand, Richard had got wind of a slightly bigger place for rent two or three streets away. 1B, Mill Street was not, in fact, that much bigger than 22, Laxton Street, but it did have two bedrooms and so, on the evening of Saturday 28 October 1882, on Richard's twenty-second birthday, and the night before Florence Helen was born, they moved in. It was a difficult time as Louisa could do little to help and what furniture there was had to be moved by hand – piece by piece. Although the nights were swiftly drawing in, it was unseasonably warm for the time of year, and, as Richard went backwards and forwards from one house to the other, he passed the usual Saturday-nighters (or, at least, the ones who hadn't blown all their drinking money the night before). Communities in those days were much closer than now and most knew Richard, if not well, then certainly by sight. Soon hands were lent; a chair here, a bench there. Two moved the small wooden kitchen table and another two or three the most important item – the bed. The bed was still downstairs and still only half-made when, exhausted, Richard and Louisa finally collapsed onto it.

Just before daybreak Louisa jumped bolt upright and screamed, 'It's coming… the baby's coming!' *It could have waited till we'd settled in*, Richard thought to himself, but it had been obvious by Louisa's size that the birth could not be far off. Jumping out of bed he dressed on the run and was soon out on the street and banging on the door of a small mid-terrace in Raglan Street.

The local midwife was Mrs. Flaherty. Nobody ever really knew her first name – she was always just called 'Mrs. Flaherty' or often just 'Flatty'; a sort of cross between 'Flaherty' and 'Fatty' and reflective of her shape. A short, round, red-faced Irish immigrant, she, the youngest of seven sisters, had fled the potato famine with her family thirty-five years earlier. If times were bad in Ireland, they did not, at first, find them much better in Leicester but at least there were labouring jobs to be had for her father – firstly on the local railway system then later building the new tram network, so they muddled through. Although a 'Mrs.' by title there was no Mr. Flaherty and she lived alone. Neither could it have been her maiden name, as her father was O'Connell. Rumour had it that she had become pregnant shortly after arriving in England (perhaps the father was called Flaherty – you never really got to the bottom of it), and when the time came for her to give birth, her parents were not only unable to afford the two shillings and sixpence for a midwife, but they did not see the need for one. Not a single child in the family had ever been delivered by a midwife. Sadly, the infant was lodged awkwardly and, despite an hour's clumsy struggling, strangled on its own cord or some such. On top of this Flatty was left with a severe infection and it was touch and go at one stage as to whether she, herself, would make it. Sadly, the infection damaged her so badly that she was unable to conceive again. Apparently, however, determined to do her best to prevent this sort of thing from happening to anybody else, the whole ordeal served some useful purpose in that it spurred her on to a life of midwifery. Her training had not exactly been a formal one, certainly not in the modern sense of the word anyway: consisting solely of assisting another midwife. It was certainly 'hands-on' though, and what a kerfuffle when soon she had to deal with two different mothers, while out on her own, both going into labour within half an hour of each other!

"Mrs. Flaherty can *y'ear mi. Y've gorra cum* quick. It's Louisa *shi's avin* the baby. Flatty please."

No sooner had he shouted than a scuffling sound came from the passageway. It had been a busy night and Flatty had only just got back from another delivery.

"*Bejabbers,* you'll be wakin' the dead so *y'* will and *oi* don't know what else."

"But she's started Flatty, she's started." And with more shuffling, this time in the direction of Mill Street, "Be along *wid yer* then laddy."

"*Oi've* never *larst* a single one of 'em *surr,*" she'd assure anxious fathers. Of course, this could not have been true, and everyone knew it. I'm sure, though, that Richard would have drawn comfort from these words that bright October Sunday morning when, on account of the bed still being downstairs, he was left pacing the street in front of his new house with the trepidation and anticipation that only a first-time father knows. He need not have worried; for a first birth, much to the relief of a weary Mrs Flaherty, it was to be an easy and uncomplicated affair.

"To be sure, you're halfway out already…" had been the last words Richard heard just after he had bundled the baggy old woman into the house. Though it would have seemed an age to Richard, less than twenty minutes after her unceremonious entrance Flatty was at the door again, and shouted across to Richard, "It's a wee girly – you've got a wee daughter, so 'tis."

Richard and Louisa soon got down to family life and seeing to baby Flo. But since infant deaths were an everyday event at the time, it was both an anxious as well as a joyous time for the new parents. In Flo's case, though, there was little need to worry as she was a healthy child and, with the attention and fuss so often heaped on the firstborn by doting parents, she thrived all the more.

By the autumn of 1883 Louisa found herself pregnant again, and with Flo now growing and the prospect of another baby to care for, 1B, Mill Street was beginning to feel a bit pokey too. Also, having now spent their first summer there, they had come to realise how bad the smell from the nearby refuse tip could get. One baby in the sink and another inside her, Louisa protested one morning, "I can't cater for two babies here and that stink – it's not healthy, Richard. Not good for babies at all!"

But Richard had no time to argue as he was already late for work. All he could do was to mutter under his breath, "*Ah s'all ata* see *wor ah* can do," as he dashed out the house.

19, York Street seemed to fit the bill. A bit across town but a little more room – a narrow structure but it had a third storey. Just across the street from the Mission Hall, and it was here that their first son was born at precisely midday on Saturday 22 March 1884. Mrs. Flaherty had been with the couple all night with one false alarm after another, but the little lad just did not want to come into the world. No real problems, it was just one of those things. In the end he had no choice. By no means as skilful as a modern midwife, Flatty was, nevertheless, fully aware of the dangers of letting things go on too long. Ever conscious of the young couple's inability to afford a doctor's fee, she should have sent for one long before, but in the end, with one invasive palm one side of the baby's head, one the other and one last firm tug, he was out. This birth was as noisy as Flo's was silent. As the infant's lungs burst into life the jabbering from Flatty's lips (that had gone from encouragements to curses as the delivery became more and more protracted) was lost and all were filled with a great sense of relief.

Drama over and nursing their newborn son, Louisa asked Richard, "What shall we call him?"

"John," said Richard. "After *me* dad."

"Not William, then?" replied Louisa.

R: "*Nar ee's me* stepdad, after *mi* real dad – John."

L: "What, just John, then?"

R: "*Yeh,* what's wrong *wi* it?"

L: "Well… it's just… er… a bit plain, that's all."

R: "It *waar mi* dad's name, *mi* real dad's name. I wish *me* dad could see 'im. I wished *ad know'd* 'im better."

L: "I know, Richard, I know," (comforting). "What about your brother, *as e* got a middle name?"

R: "*Aye*, Harry."

L: "Then what about John Harry?"

R: "*Arr*… John Harry it is, then."

All a bit academic really, as John would, more often than not, be referred to as 'Jack'.

*

Life continued every bit as good for Richard, Louisa and their two children as it could for a young working-class family anywhere in Britain at the time. The export of clothing, especially to the United States, and low costs, kept the hosiery industry profitable. Furthermore, the plentiful supply of labour meant that, although the pay had never been brilliant, it was regular and sufficient to cover the essentials. And, with enough overtime, there was even room for a few (what passed as) luxuries now and again; a bit of decent meat of a weekend, a bottle of beer or two of an evening and the occasional day trip by train – often into the countryside, or occasionally to visit Louisa's relations who kept a pub at Broughton Astley.

The back door from the kitchen of 19, York Street opened onto a rectangular area of blue paving bricks just behind the lounge window. Measuring just three yards by four the enclosed yard was just big enough for two people to sit side by side in deckchairs. Beyond rose the high wall of a long factory outhouse which, by early afternoon, robbed the yard of much of its light. Also, although the summer of 1884 was a dry and warm one, it was not one of the sunniest, some contemporary meteorologists attributing this to the eruption of Krakatoa the year before, which had thrown fine dust clouds high into the atmosphere and affected much of the world. Nevertheless, with Flo in a wicker basket and John Harry in his mother's arms, that humble setting afforded father, mother and infants alike some considerable joy throughout those balmy evenings. Richard still felt good; he was settled, and his troubles all evaporated when in the bosom of his family. Louisa, however, although content too, remained a little unsure of Richard, and had by now sensed that he was perhaps a more complex character than she'd first thought. Although hard to put her finger on exactly what the problem was, he would occasionally become a more secretive and distant Richard, seeming somehow to linger, if only for short periods, 'at a distance'. Whatever it was or wherever he was, though, never seemed to detain him long enough to cause real concern but he still worried her. As they sat there during that odd summer of 1884 little could they have foreseen the diversion through hell along which the rocky road of fate was about to take them.

*

Although hosiery production continues in Leicester today, many factors, not least world competition, have forced its decline over the years. In the nineteenth century it was the backbone of the city, at one time employing around a quarter of all the male workers in the area. If the hosiery industry struggled, Leicester struggled, and by the mid-1880s increased production on the Continent (particularly in Germany) began to hinder the market. Whereas the majority of the hosiery produced in Leicester was fairly plain and utilitarian, Continental garments tended to be fancier and so more attractive to buyers. At the same time protectionist measures, introduced in the United States through the imposition of import duties, began to destroy what was left of this previously very lucrative market. As with all recessions, pressure is soon brought to bear on spending, both private and industrial, and so, as more people 'make do and mend', markets regress even more – particularly those for clothing.

The effect was as fast as it was devastating, and on a cold, dark Friday evening during November 1884, Richard, after bustling in through the back door, stands leaning towards the open fire. As he peers down, wringing his hands, Louisa notices his anguished face, now betrayed in the glow of the fire. Skirts rustling, she runs to his side. "What is it?"

R: "*A've bin* laid off – *th'ain't ne werk*. Ellis *ses am* one o' the last in and that's *ow the'v dun* it."

L: "When, when from?"

R: "Now – *am te goo an* ask *agen* a *wik* Monday."

L: "A week – *w'ill* manage."

R: "*Irr'll be* more. Th'll be *nowt* a *wik* on Monday, *ah* know it."

L: "Can *y'* get in anywhere else?"

R: "Doubt it – *the're* all in the same boat – orders falling off everywhere. Even big *uns* – Corah's, Biggs, Collins."

L: "What's to 'appen, Richard?"

R: "*Dunno*... no idea... we'll *ata* cut *darn* though."

The mercifully mild winter of 1884–5 came and went. There was work for a few days, then days off, then half days, then nothing.

Saturday 2 May 1885, just as dawn breaks: BANG, BANG, BANG, BANG! Richard runs out of bed and looks down through the bedroom window onto the street in front, head held hard against the wall to the left of the window so as to prevent whoever was below looking up and seeing him. He knew full well who it was though. "It's that little bastard Brown *agin, cum for* 'is dad's rent. *Ah toad* 'im *ah ain't got note for 'im*." BANG, BANG, BANG, BANG again. Louisa goes to shout out, but Richard quickly interrupts and in a loud whisper, "*Shurrup*!"

"Richard, you there? Richard *wi'v gorr'ave* some money. If *y'* can't pay the rent *y'll ata goo*!"

Richard peers down again, Brown, book in hand, looks around. Six-thirty on a Saturday morning, banging on the door but no neighbour tries to find out what's going on. No need, they all know what it is about. Still in bed, sheets over heads. Will he press me today? Can't go on much longer. What's to become?

Brown strains through the letter box, then peers through the front window and then another, yet louder, BANG, BANG, BANG. Then nothing as, with a deep sigh, and beginning to realise the inevitability of again becoming the victim of his father's wrath after he tells him of yet another moonlight flit, Brown starts to walk away but the last staccato had woken the infants, and both now start to cry. On hearing this Brown is back and is off again, this time with renewed vigour. "Richard Warren *a* know *y'* in. *Y'aint ped me nuthink fu* six *wix* now. *Ah* want me *muneh* now *oh yer* out!"

Richard, face red with rage, slams the wall with his forearm, in his mind the bastard Brown lying pummelled at his feet like all landlords, like all bosses, like all bloody capitalists! Bastards, bastards, the lot of *'em*! Louisa, tears streaming down her cheeks, buries her head in her hands in frustration. Brown fires his parting shot.

"*Am gooin' na* Richard *bur am cumin'* back later *wi mi* dad."

Louisa, now frantic, "*Wi'v gorra do summat* Richard, *wi'v gorra do summat. Ah* can't go on like this!"

Her words go unregistered as Richard, now paralytic with despair, starts to slide down the wall. At this Louisa gets out of bed, gathers her clothes and creeps from the bedroom. After dressing downstairs, as soon as the coast is clear, she runs from the house, scooping John into her arms and grabbing Flo's tiny hand, almost dragging her past the Mission Hall and onto Albion Street. It begins to drizzle as she crosses the tramline on Welford Road. Down York Road and across Oxford Street onto Bonners Lane, only stopping at the threshold of number ten – the home of her childhood. The frantic rapping of the polished brass door knocker makes Louisa's mother, Caroline, jump.

Caroline (in nervous whisper), "What on earth?" Then, thinking all manner of things, shouts, "Who is it?"

"It's me, Mam, let me in."

Caroline rushes down and as she opens the door Louisa, with her baby and Flo, stumble in, as if on the run from some dreaded nimrod. There and then the tale of despair falls from Louisa's lips, the truth she has been keeping hidden for so long, in a breathless catharsis.

"*Ah'v ad* it Mam, *ah'v ad* enough. *Wi'v ad nu* food *fur a dount kn'ow* long, *un* now *wi* can't *pe* the rent. Clem Brown's just *bin* round bangin' and rattlin' at the door, *ah din't* realise it but Richard *ain't* paid 'im in *wix. Ee ses ee's cummin'* back *wi* 'is dad *unall te* chuck us out!"

C: "Well where's Richard?"

L: "*Ah'v* left 'im at home. *Ee's* terrible with it all. *Ah'm* frightened, Mam."

C: "Oh, love… don't worry so. We'll work something out, I'm sure."

Caroline turns to Louisa's young brother and sister, who are by now peering from behind the curtain that divides the front room from the back at the bottom of the stairs.

C (worriedly): "Ernie, Kate, go upstairs and play with your toys."

L: "That's not all, Mam."

C: "Why… whatever now?"

L: "Nothing 'appened last month."

C: "What again… already. *Y'd* think *ee* could control 'imself a bit better. Especially under the circumstances."

L: "Ow can we feed another mouth, Mam… when we can't even feed and clothe these? When we can't even feed and clothe ourselves? *Ah'v* 'eard old Mrs. Stanton… *ah'v* 'eard she might be able to do *summat, ye* know."

C: "*Yu'll der* no such thing! Where 'ave *y'eard* that?"

L: "When Ada Parker that time…"

C (drowning Louisa out): "No, it's wicked…" (and struggling to find another adjective that wouldn't scare the poor girl even more) "it's wicked. I'll not hear of it! And I hope God isn't listening either. It's a mortal sin. Oh my God." (Starts crying.)

"Your dad'll be home after one. For God's sake don't mention the other thing to him or he'll go up the flaming wall."

After a while Caroline calms down and, wiping her eyes, says, "Now then… come on… let's 'ave a cup of tea." And then turning to Flo, voice shaking at first, "And how are you, my little darling? Nanan's going to make a cake now you're here. Do you want to help?"

F (still upset): "Yes…"

C (in mild mirth): "Yes, and you can even lick the bowl out like before, if you want."

Charles Sidwell was always dependable and always predictable. If he said he was going to do something, he did it. The reverse was also true, though, and if he said he wasn't going to do something then hell would freeze over before such an event ever took place. At precisely twenty-five past one that afternoon the front door opened again, and Charles sauntered in, tossing his cap towards the line of pegs as he passed. He had done a good morning's work. Impressed with his swiftness and ability to rivet more shoe soles per day than the vast majority of his colleagues, Charles's foreman had promised him another two bob a week. Blissfully unaware of the catastrophe about to confront him, Charles walked into the dining room with the air of one about to settle down with the *Racing Times*.

L: "Hello, Dad." (Clearly upset.)

Ch: "Hello, Louie *me duck*. Is everything all right?"

L: "No, Dad, far from it. We're being kicked out!"

Ch (sitting down in front of her, hand outstretched in sympathy): "Kicked out, what *d'ya* mean?"

Listening with the intensity that only a loving father can, wincing sympathetically at each impassioned point, Charles, with breaking heart, sat through the whole sad and sorry affair. When Louisa had finished the room was silent. Slowly the kitchen door opened, and Caroline slid in. She had listened to every word behind the door, in the vain hope of more understanding, or a solution perhaps, the simple instant solution that she, Louisa and Richard had all missed. There was, of course, no simple solution, and as the afternoon passed, exhausted with it all, Louisa fell asleep in the comfort of her parents' high feather bed. Charles, eyes fixed on the clock above the mantelpiece (tick-tock, tick-tock, tick-tock), was left trying to make some sense of it all while Caroline 'kept busy' baking the cake, as planned, with Flo. Also in the warm kitchen, in a tin bath made acceptable by a liberal lining of blankets and cushions, baby John slept peacefully. For the first time in a long time, he had drunk undiluted milk and, although he'd have gone on drinking it for ever, left to his own devices, Caroline knew that enough was enough if the richness ordinarily denied him was not to make him ill.

*

The whole affair had upset poor old Charles to the extent that he was totally unable to sleep that night. Giving up the warmth of his marital bed to his dear daughter he had been cramped up on the sofa. Contorted and aching, by six o'clock he'd had enough. Up with the lark he tramped the length and breadth of the town that Sunday morning in the hope that he'd turn something up. Quite what, though, he didn't know. He'd have done anything to save them from the workhouse, even have had them stay at Bonners Lane if he could, but the house was small enough as it was, and he knew that there simply wasn't enough room there for them all.

Just as he was about to turn back, however, something caught his eye. A sign in bright red painted letters on a piece of plywood that hung from a door at the top of Outram Street:

FLAT FOR
CHEAP RENTAL
OR QUICK SALE
COLLIER
LONDON ROAD

Charles new Jack Collier of old. He was a wily character and as sharp as they come. They had been kids together and still bumped into each other from time to time as both drank in the Old Wagon & Horses on Granby Street. What's more, Charles had something on Jack – he knew something about Jack Collier that very few others knew, something quite acceptable today, but in those days, shameful and could get you into trouble with the police. Jack was a homosexual and once, when both had 'had a few', had got the wrong end of the stick and propositioned Charles. Charles was horrified and made it clear in no uncertain terms, but the cat was now out of the bag. In the cold light of day Jack had felt disgusted with himself. Not with the way he was – God knows he had come to terms with the way he was years before. But it had always been a secret – discreet, under cover, under control. It was just that he was angry with himself for having upset Charles. Deep down he knew Charles didn't share his ways. Why, oh why had he done it? He liked Charles, he respected this straight-laced, dependable man, even though he thought him a bit dull at times, he was still a friend, a good friend – one who would help him when he got into scrapes and, the chancer that he was, Jack did get into a few scrapes from time to time.

Never a bitter man and liking Jack too (but not in that way), Charles had shortly after reconciled with him and, in any case, would never have set out to blackmail Jack, but the health, welfare and future of his daughter and grandchildren were at stake here and, as a possible solution began to emerge in his mind, he set off at once for London Road.

"Mornin' Charlie, *ow y'* keepin'?" enquired Jack as he answered the purposeful rap on his front door.

"Not *sa* bad Jack, *yerself*?"

"Yes, okay. What brings you down this way of a Sunday morning?"

"I'll not beat about the bush, Jack. *Y've* got a property, Outram Street, cheap."

"Oh, your ship come in 'as it?"

"Hardly, I need a favour."

"*Oh ah*, what is it?"

"*Ah* want to rent it."

Jack (slowly and suspiciously): "What?"

"*Ah* need somewhere cheap!"

Jack (now sensing mischief): "What you up to then?"

"Oh, not what you'd think."

Jack: "And what would that be?"

"Oh I *dunno*, it's *fo me* daughter 'nd 'er 'usband."

"Your Ellen gettin' married then?" (Putting two and two together and making five.)

"No, Louie and Richard."

"What, I thought they 'ad 'ouse on York Street. Opposite the Mission." Then it dawned on Jack. "*Ee's* 'osiery worker *in't ee*?"

Charles's simple nod said it all.

"Half a crown a *wik un y' cun ay* it."

"Two bob."

"Mmm… done! When did they *wanna* move in?"

"Now."

"That bad, eh?"

"That bad…"

Charles borrowed a handcart and throughout that afternoon and evening he, Richard, Mary and Louisa moved everything the half-mile or so across town from York Street to Outram Street. Luckily the Browns never showed up, but they still wanted their money, so Richard was far from out of the woods but at least the wolf had been sent packing – for the time being anyway.

"*A'll mek* it up *te y'* Charlie, *ah* promise."

Ch (patting Richard's shoulder): "*Ah* know *y'* will lad, *ah* know."

*

Flat 2, Court B, Outram Street was a hovel, it was as simple as that; there was no other way to describe it and no doubt about it, it was a dump. To make matters worse, it stood almost opposite the same refuse tip by the canal bridge on Mill Street that they'd been so relieved to get away from only just over a year earlier. But, at two shillings a week (exactly Charles's recent pay rise), beggars can't be choosers. One room and a washroom, not a real home – not even a real house but a roof over their heads – shelter, of sorts, at least.

Few words were uttered between Richard and Louisa during the first days after the upheaval. The spring weather was fine, though, as they swept out the dust and flakes of lime wash that had built up inside the place during the three months that it had been unoccupied. As they set to, Charles dropped off some new lime wash and a brush he'd had lying about, and a neighbour or two, popping their heads around the door to greet the newcomers, made things feel a bit better. Swept out with newly lime-washed walls, by midweek the place slowly began to look a little more acceptable. The two troopers looked at each other and decided that to continue their self-imposed vows of silence would serve no further purpose.

"Did *y'* know I'm expectin' again?" Louisa said softly.

"*A'd* thought as much, aye," replied Richard.

It was a struggle, but life went on. Each day Richard set out at half-past five and made his way through the town, calling from one factory to another. Occasionally there'd be half a day's work, less occasionally, a full day. Once he managed to get a fortnight on the trot, through sheer luck when a foundry manager had 'bitten off more than he could chew'. A French firm had placed a large order for railway components and, although the firm had the capacity to make them, it had need of extra labourers to move things about from process to process. Although Richard had to wait the whole fortnight to be paid, he was in the end, and well paid too – a boiling of beef on the following Saturday night bore full witness to that.

As Louisa grew bigger, summer turned to autumn and the hovel began to feel cold in the evenings; a lot colder than York Street. By the beginning of October, it was no good, they would have to light a fire, but what with? Richard managed to cadge a few old, torn sacks from the Great Central Goods Yard, promising to return them repaired. They were large sacks too – made to hold two and a half hundredweight of corn (125kg in today's 'money'). Then, for several days on end, he would walk out into the countryside with a couple of these sacks and a small axe, filling them with as much kindling and wood as he could carry. Pretty soon one wall of the washroom was stacked to the ceiling. It was a good job as well, since, by mid-October, it had begun to snow and although starting out as just a light smattering, soon set in, until everywhere was completely blanketed over. On top of it all the pregnancy was not going to plan. A diet consisting almost entirely of milk, potatoes, bread and honey, although supplying the essentials, has its limits when it comes to healthy development and certainly lacks variety. Occasionally, however, late on a Saturday afternoon (especially on the weekend before a Bank Holiday Monday), if he was in the right place at the right time, Richard was able to get hold of a scrap of meat or fish that, in the absence of refrigeration, would not last until Monday, or perhaps a few 'specks'. These were overripe fruits and vegetables that would not last much longer, some would even be starting to rot. They were very cheap (tuppence a half dozen, say), or could sometimes even be had for free, if you 'laid it on with a trowel'. However, the competition for specs was keen, especially in winter, when every sort of fruit or vegetable was in short supply. To make things worse, it was a task often delegated to the older boys in the family who knew all the 'tricks of the trade'. As a result, Richard often found that somebody had got there before him.

"*Y' te* late this time, Richard, Johnson's lads 'ad 'em all. 'Ere's apple *te* be *gooin'* on wi', though."

In any event, as the recession tightened its grip, even the supply of specs began to dry up. No greengrocer could afford to have too much of anything left over at the end of the week if he was to avoid ruin.

Then, in early November, things got even worse when Louisa caught the flu. Richard was a proud man but was now at his wits' end. After making her as comfortable as possible he rushes round to her parents' house for help. As soon as Caroline opens the door Richard's angst spews out in a breathless, contorted rattle. Still with Richard in mid-flow Caroline interrupts, "C'mon, I'll get *me* coat." As she enters the hovel Caroline can hear Louisa's rasping breaths. "Why the hell did *y'* let 'er get this bad before tellin' us?"

R: "*A'v oney bin* gone twenty minutes, she *won't* this bad then."

C: "Well sh'is now. For God's sake go and get Sloane, go and get Dr. Sloane, now!"

R: "But..."

C (in exasperation): "Oh don't worry, *wi'll* pay 'im somehow."

Richard was back within half an hour but not with Dr. Sloane. Andrew Harwood was the latest addition to the practice – newly qualified from the Birmingham Medical School, it was his first day in his first job as a GP. Determined to look the part, however, he entered confidently, but, when face to face with Louisa, he caught his breath and began to fumble a little, hoping his inexperience would not show. Louisa's breathing was still loud, and the young doctor struggled to listen to the other workings of her chest through his stethoscope. Sitting on the side of the bed, he began to put his best bedside manner to the test.

"Not feeling too good then?"

L: "I'll be all right, just a bit tired."

H (looking up): "Er yes... she's very feverish. How long's she been like this?"

R: "Just today, Doctor. She 'ad 'eadache yesterday, that's all."

H: "Yes... I don't know. Yes..." (Thinks what best to do – *this place is a dump – no money.*) While taking Louisa's pulse, "When's the baby due?"

R: "Not sure... a month... five o' six weeks, *dunno...*"

H (mind now made up): "Okay, she'll have to be kept warm, keep that fire going." Turning to Caroline, "Are you her mother?"

C: "Yes, Doctor."

H: "Can you stay with her?"

C: "Yes, of course."

H: "Okay, two aspirin four times a day, plenty of water, but it must be clean, can you boil it?"

C: "Yes, at home. *Ah* could *tek* 'er 'ome."

H: "Good... but best not move her now – see how we go, eh? Oh, and whatever food you can get in her – soup, beef juice, nothing heavy." (As if.) "Better if she's not sick. I'll be round again tomorrow morning."

As Harwood rose to his feet, there was a brief moment of embarrassing silence – a clumsy novice way of inviting payment. Then, realising that none was forthcoming, with an almost imperceptible nervous cough he was gone.

"Can *y'* nip *te* Charlie's works Richard, and let 'im know what's 'appened? *Ee'll ata* pick up Kate and Ernie from Mrs. Harris's when *ee* comes out."

"Will do, Caroline."

With Richard gone, Caroline kneels by the bed and gently strokes her daughter's forehead.

"Oh my love, *y'v ad* a rough time of it lately there's no doubt."

L: "I'll be all right, Mam, don't worry so. It's just a bad cold that's all."

Richard looked in again later that afternoon, essentially to see to the fire, but he knew this was mother and daughter time, and in the evening went back to Bonners Lane to sleep on the couch.

Caroline undressed to her underwear and climbed in bed with Louisa. *God it's cold*, she thought as she tried to settle down. Still aware of Louisa's rasps well into the night, she was unable to sleep. It would take until after four in the morning for the weariness to win and she finally dropped off.

Caroline woke with a start and for a minute she was not quite sure where she was but then caught sight of the back of Louisa's head as a shaft of light filtering through the single tiny window reflected off her thick auburn hair. There was silence, oh God, no breathing – Caroline, fearing the worst, put out her hand to shake her daughter but Louisa turned. The rasping had stopped. She felt her forehead, no sweat, she was cooler. "Thank God! Thank God! The fever's gone, thank God."

Through the next week or two Louisa slowly recovered, but for days she was as weak as a kitten and totally unable to get out of bed.

The pregnancy continued, though, as normally as possible under the circumstances and on a dull Christmas Eve afternoon Mrs. Flaherty was again summoned. The birth was not complicated, but Flatty was shocked when she saw how thin Louisa had become.

"*Y'* all skin and bone, sure y'are."

If Louisa was skinny, then her baby certainly was. Weighing in at barely three pounds, Flatty had certainly seen better. He was alive, right enough, but he didn't cry, he barely moved, and he had the pale look about him; the look that Flatty called 'the shadow of death'. Of course, she didn't say anything to Richard and Louisa, but there was a nervous atmosphere, and it was clear to everybody that all was not quite as it should have been.

F: "*Ye'v* another wee boy."

L: "Is he all right?"

F: "He'll need a bit of looking after but I'm sure he'll be fine. Have *y'* thought of a name for him yet?"

R: "Richard, Richard Walter – same as me."

F: "Oh, *begorrah*, Richard Walter, is it? Sure, *me* own father was Walter, it's a fine name and no mistakin'."

(Flatty's father had had many names over the years…)

The winter of 1885–6 was one of the most severe on record and it snowed almost continuously; even in May, blizzards still blew. Richard had continued to get the odd job here and the odd week there and, with continued support from Louisa's parents, they managed to keep going. Louisa gave her new baby all the love and care that she could (and more) but he would not thrive. Her own body was so undernourished that her breasts were almost unable to produce milk. Not that baby Richard would take much anyway. Flatty arranged for another recent mother to act as wet nurse but it made no difference. The little lad remained emaciated and when his stomach became distended, again at Charles's expense, Louisa took him to see Dr. Sloane.

Sloane (feeling the infant's stomach): "Mmm… you'll have to keep trying to get him to take something – try little and often rather than set feeding times."

L: "I've tried everything, Doctor, it's a real struggle. I'm very worried."

Sloane knew the signs of malnutrition when he saw it. He saw it every day. He knew how it caused irreparable damage to the infant body and this baby had not only been undernourished from birth but from conception. *How his mother must have suffered throughout her term*, he thought.

"Try and stick with it, Mrs. Warren. One time soon we'll begin to see an improvement. It'll come all at once, you'll see."

But it didn't, and barely a year later, on another grey November's morning, when Louisa went to baby Richard in his cot, she found him cold and stiff. As she silently wept for her dead child, she thought to herself – *not much of a life, not much of an existence. But then what is? Do we who are spared have it any better? We seem to have been suffering so long and now this. Perhaps survival just means more suffering.* As a tear fell from her eye and ran across the baby's sallow forehead, *a final baptism*, Louisa thought, *in the arms of Jesus now. Night, night my lovely baby boy, my young Richard, night, night my son, God bless.*

Chapter 2

My Son, My Son

'...would God I had died for thee,
O Absalom, my son, my son!'
2 Samuel, 18:33

For hours Louisa lay by the bedside of her dead infant son, barely moving, barely conscious. It was a Monday morning and Richard, unaware of the tragedy, had left early in order to stand a better chance of being taken on if, indeed, there was any work at all to be had that week. As dawn broke, Flo and John began to stir on the small straw mattress in the corner of the floor on which they slept and slowly crawled out onto the cold, dismal scene. Flo looked first at her mother and then at her dead baby brother, at only four years of age she was no stranger to misery but she knew that something different had happened, something that had never happened before and far sadder than anything that had ever happened before. Baby Richard had never made much noise in his short life but now he wasn't making any noise at all. What's more he wasn't even moving. She clung to her mother but Louisa was so far gone that she didn't even realise the child was there. Even Flo's increasingly anxious cries didn't move her and this set John off as well. Along with her baby, it seemed that part of Louisa had also died; the maternal instinct, the part that makes a mother react automatically to the cries of her children, had deserted her.

It was early afternoon by the time Richard returned. It was always the same when he came home – footsteps a few yards away, getting louder and louder, and then the quick opening of the front door. Once inside he would go directly to the fireplace, warming his hands if there was a fire or, arms outstretched, hands holding onto the mantelpiece, he would stretch and lean against it, sometimes with a groan, as if ridding himself of the pressures of the day. Often Flo would come up to him and put her arm around his leg – proudly hugging it. Richard knew that it was Flo's special way of telling him how glad she was to see him home safe and he loved it. This time it was different though. Richard could see that there was something very wrong as soon as he turned from the door. Louisa, crouched beside the cot, lifted her head towards him and then the tear-soaked hair and the pain in her reddened eyes said it all. A howl, the like of which he had never made before, exploded from Richard's mouth and he sank to the floor as a mixture of agony, despair and anger overwhelmed him. His son, his son whom he dearly loved and had carried his name, was gone. In his heart, of course, he'd known that this would be the outcome all along, and so he couldn't really take in why he was still so shocked. He felt he was looking at the end – no work, the poverty, the hunger, the cold and now this. *If this is life you're better off out of it, son*, he thought to himself. Sobbing inconsolably, the pair crumpled into each other's arms.

For some time, no words were spoken, and it was only the two children, moving cautiously towards them and then snuggling up beside them, that seemed to bring them round. First Richard rolled over and stared up at the ceiling. The more he thought about it the angrier he became. The factory bosses who had sacked him, the landlord who had kicked him out on the street, every bloody creditor that had hounded him for money. In a flash he was on his feet and out of the house again.

"No, Richard, don't go, no, don't, not now." But Louisa might as well have saved her breath. He was gone and she had a good idea where. Despite the hardships Richard usually had the price of a drink on him and if he didn't, he knew where he could get it.

*

After gathering together what was left of herself, Louisa bathed her face in the bowl on the small dresser which stood at the foot of the bed. Still shaking, she dried herself slowly then went out onto the landing and knocked on the front door to Flat 1, which was virtually opposite her own. The occupant of Flat 1 was one Maud Tomlinson: a plain, thin, middle-aged but kindly woman who was originally from Redruth in Cornwall and still spoke in a strong West Country accent. Court B was a bit of a labyrinth of hovels and no door was very far from the next. At the time Maud lived alone, her husband, Stan, serving three years in Leicester Prison for receiving stolen goods; a stupid and hopeless attempt to pull himself and his wife out of poverty once and for all. Being far from the cleverest of criminals, he had tried to 'shift' some stolen gin in a nearby pub. Overhearing, the landlord, who had never liked him and who certainly wasn't going to have him competing with his own trade in his own pub, informed the police.

"Come in," Maud shouted, in almost immediate response to the knock.

As Louisa entered Maud could see that all was far from well. She knew that the family had been struggling and how sick the baby had been from many a long chinwag across the landing, so when Louisa poured her heart out she understood immediately.

M: "Are you sure *ee's* dead *moy* dear?"

L: "Yes, I'm sure. I wish I wasn't, Maud, but I'm sure."

M (now concerned): "You'll need Dr. Sloane, you'll need to fetch him anyway."

L: "Oh yes, of course, I'll…"

M (now realising that if Louisa went herself, it could make matters worse): "Don't worry, *moy* dear, I'll go, I'll go and get 'im now." And with that she left Louisa with a hot cup of tea and set out to fetch the doctor.

"Can the doctor come to Outram Street? It's Mrs. Warren, her baby's died."

Without responding the receptionist goes to tell Dr. Sloane. "He says he'll be over in half an hour, Mrs. Tomlinson."

Dr. Sloane didn't take long over the examination. He was all too familiar with the lot of the poor, unfortunate child. The same old skin swellings, distended belly and that grey, drawn look of malnutrition; there'd been others just the same the week before and there'd be more next week. He hated it but it had become his stock in trade. He wanted to cure the sick, not certify deaths all the time, but starvation was a difficult enemy that could not be prevented by vaccination or cured by pills or an operation. Only freedom from poverty could do that.

Sloane: "Take this to the Registrar, Louisa, when you feel a bit better."

Louisa: "I'll do it now."

S: "Next few days 'll do. You need to rest now."

L: "I'll do it now, I said."

S: "Yes… yes, all right. Just don't be too hard on yourself. You've had a big shock. Do you need anything else; something to calm you, to make you sleep perhaps?"

L: "No, I'm all right, really."

S: "Well, if you do, you know where I am. Are you sure you're okay?"

L (firm but stressed): "Yes, sure."

S (hesitant): "Of course… okay, well, good day to you then and… I'm so sorry." After pausing just a second or two, just in case – he then turned and left.

Not even thinking to ask Maud to look after Flo and John, and now resigned to the hard reality of it all, Louisa's face lost all expression, her movements, more instinctive than planned, seemed to take on an automatic air. In a matter of fact way she scooped up the tiny infant's body and wrapped him in a small blanket. Subconsciously, of course, she was starting the funeral process which would begin the end of the ordeal. Then, turning to Flo and John, "Mummy's got to go out and leave you for a few minutes. I won't be long, I promise. Be good and wait for Mummy, I'll be back in no time." Finally, glancing back at the fire, which was by now nearly out anyway, she added, "And don't go near the fire." With that she made for the door and, slamming it behind her, was gone.

Soon she was knocking on her parents' front door in Bonners Lane. When Caroline answered no words were necessary. Louisa, almost unable to walk, was helped in by her mother.

C: "Oh no, no my love, my love. Give him to me."

With that Caroline took the tiny corpse and placed it slowly and reverently on the front room sofa, tucking the blanket into the corner between the seat and backrest, as if putting the child to bed.

C: "How's Richard taken it?"

L: "Bad, Mam, bad. He's gone. I think he's going to get drunk."

C: "Well, what about Flo and little John?"

L: "They're all right, Mam, I've left 'em at 'ome."

C: "God, let's go and get them. Hurry up, we don't want worse to happen. Let's go and get 'em now!"

L: "One thing, Mam. I 'ave to call in at the Registrar's. I 'ave to do it on the way. This agony has gone on long enough. I want to start the ending… now!"

C: "Oh we can do that tomorrow, love, now come on."

L (in raised voice and eyes filled with tears): 'No, Mam! I want to do it now, I 'ave to do it now!"

C (now fearing for her daughter's sanity and what should happen if the delay were prolonged): "Okay then, go and do it then while I fetch 'em but 'urry love, I'm worried for *y'*."

Safely rescued, Caroline brought the two children back to Bonners Lane and gave them a glass of milk and a thick bread and dripping sandwich each. She then tenderly put them to bed in her own bed. Later Louisa returned but, saying nothing, went straight up to her parents' bedroom and cried herself to sleep next to Flo and John.

Awaiting Charles's return and knowing that he would be as punctual as ever, Caroline sat next to Richard's tiny body on the front room sofa. It was freezing. The front room was only ever used on high days and holidays – Christmas and perhaps the occasional party (but there had not been a great deal to celebrate in recent times). As punctual as ever, at exactly half-past seven Charles walked in. Looking first at Caroline and then the tiny bundle his eyes filled. God knows they'd had their share of bad luck and God knows he'd done his best to help but there was something… something evil working against them. *Whenever would they be free from it?* he thought, as he pulled up a chair beside the sofa and, head in hands, slowly sank into it.

Once more silence reigned as Charles continued to struggle to come to terms with things, and, only when he was sure he felt ready, "What happened?"

As Caroline explained, Charles bowed his head and nodded slightly at each significant juncture.

Ch: "Why on earth did she have to register the death today?"

C: "I don't know, she said she just had to. To start the end perhaps? She's not thinking straight, she left them poor kids on their own *unall.* Even though Mrs. Tomlinson was in next door. But then again, after all that's gone off need *y'* wonder at it?"

Ch: "I suppose not."

Charles was this time consigned to the dining room while Caroline slumped into the bedroom armchair next to her daughter and grandchildren. As he lay there he could not draw his thoughts from the dead baby Richard, cold and alone in the dreary, dark front room beyond the stairs.

"Let this be an end on it, for God's sake. God rest the poor child." As he closed his eyes he prayed, "God help us all."

*

The following morning the Sidwell household was in a dreadful state. Arrangements had to be made for the infant's burial and, with

Richard God knows where and in what state, Charles felt compelled to do something, if only to dull the pain of his aching heart on that freezing, foggy Tuesday morning. Grim-faced, already on the move, he pulled on his overcoat, pausing momentarily, half-bowing over his dead grandson then, twisting his cap into place over his balding head, a step or two more and he opened the front door upon which, to his shock, he was directly confronted by Richard.

Charles (startled): "God, you about gave me a heart attack lad!" Then, examining his son-in-law more closely, "You look bloody awful son, come in, come in before *y'* catch *yer* death o' cold."

Richard was clearly the worse for wear, his clothes and face filthy, as if he'd spent the night in the gutter, and still so affected by drink that he could hardly speak. As he walked in he removed his cap and, squeezing it tightly to his chest, stood silently over the settee, gazing down at his dead son. Unable to stop himself crying, his body jerked as the tears left clean streaks down his soiled cheeks.

"Caroline," Charles shouted, "Richard's 'ere, make 'im a cup of tea."

Richard slowly drew away from the sofa and made for the back room. Pulling a chair out from under the table (almost not far enough) he slowly squeezed his body down. With his head still bowed, Richard looked beaten and totally devoid of energy – it was quite clear to all that he was at the end of his tether.

Charles: "*Ah* was about to get something arranged."

Richard (in a very quiet, muffled but stern voice): "*Ah'll* see t' it."

Ch (knowing the answer): "Is… is there any insurance?"

R (voice now raised): "'Ow *d' y'* expect me, 'ow d' *y'* expect me to?"

Ch: "*Ah* know lad, *ah* know… don't worry, we'll work something out."

R: "*Ah* said, *ah'll* see to it!"

How? Charles wondered. Although words were now useless, his strained, quizzical expression said it all.

R (now getting up): "*Ah'll* see to it and that's the end *on* it!"

Richard turned and walked abruptly towards the front room, closely followed by Charles, who pulled the curtain at the foot of the stairs across behind him so as to separate them from his wife, in order to be more frank.

"Richard, just a minute, lad."

Richard stopped at the front door, right hand clutching the coat hook and head bowed against it. He then turned to Charles, his manner now more doleful and resigned.

"*Ah'm* sorry, Charley. *Y've* done so much for us. It's just that *ah* must do this *miself. Ah* must, for 'im" – looking back towards the sofa. "It's all as *ah* can do for 'im now. Give me till Thursday morning." With that Richard's body seemed to jump back to life again, and, swinging the door open, he was gone; disappeared into the fog.

Caroline, emerging from the closed curtain and standing in front of the sofa, gazed first down at the infant and then up at her husband. "Oh, what a mess, what an awful mess..." she said. Charles slowly regained himself and, without another word, he too was gone into the fog.

As Caroline knelt by the sofa she whispered, as if to the infant's spirit, "C'mon, let me wash you, my darling baby boy," and with that, she brought in a bowl of water, some carbolic soap and a towel and slowly and reverently bathed the now doll-like, still, stiff corpse. After drying him she wrapped him tightly in a fine silk and lace tablecloth, once her mother's, and laid him back onto the sofa seat, which she had covered with a clean white sheet.

In those days you knew exactly when there had been a death in the household and deaths in early childhood were, sadly, all too common. Drawn curtains, often with a simple black panel in the middle of the window, fraught expressions and, of course, neighbours were much more likely to speak to each other back then. It was quite usual and indeed, almost obligatory to visit and pay one's last respects. With an infant, of course, there were no great lifetime achievements to mull over but nevertheless a visit from family, friends or neighbours was support; support which, at such a time, would have meant so much to any grieving family.

*

As Thursday approached Charles, Caroline and Louisa began to get more and more anxious. Though he did not say as much, Charles, in particular, had his doubts; serious doubts. *What the hell is he doing?* he thought to himself. *Has he worked something out by now, or is he back in some gutter, or worse, has he gone and done something stupid? Oh God, I hope not. Surely we've had enough pain and misery!* One part of him wanted to trust Richard but the other wanted to get on with the arrangements and not prolong the agony a moment longer than necessary. Richard had made it quite clear that he would see to things, though, and whatever Richard was, and however he behaved, normally, like his father-in-law, if he said he would do something, barring catastrophe, he would do it. Also Charles knew that Richard had a temper, especially when he was under pressure, and if Charles were to act when Richard had already taken care of things (as he'd promised) he shuddered to think what might happen. Above all he wanted to avoid any more unpleasantness but at the same time, nobody had called as yet regarding any arrangements, and he knew that Richard had little or no money. What on earth should he do?

Eventually Thursday morning dawned but there was still no sign of Richard or any word as to the arrangements. By this time Charles's frustration was palpable and there was an air of tension in the Sidwell household as they went through the routine of getting up, lighting the fire, having a wash and preparing breakfast. Every act was undertaken in silence with only the occasional nod, sometimes followed by a grunt or other monosyllabic sound – so as to prevent any welled-up emotion from spilling out. All were close to tears and the simplest of inconveniences could well have brought each to despair.

By mid-morning they had run out of things to do. All the adults were dressed in black, the house had been cleaned from top to bottom and the table had been laid. There was not a great deal awaiting those who would return to the house after the ceremony but some degree of hospitality was always expected at such occasions and, in this case, the budget had run to some currant bread and butter and a barrel of beer. Charles and Caroline still had two relatively young children in Kate and Ernest and some of their old clothes came in handy for Flo and John: Flo had on one of Kate's old Sunday best dresses and John some of Ernest's old clothes. The outfits were complemented, as was often then the way, by white sashes for Kate and Flo and white ties for Ernest and John, which Caroline had made from an old bed sheet. So, in this state they all sat uneasily in the parlour waiting for something to happen – long periods of silence when only breathing and the occasional sound of horses' hooves and a cart or carriage in the street could be heard. Each long quarter, on the quarter, the mantle clock registering the passage of time. Eventually and inevitably, on the last chime of the clock striking twelve noon Charles drew a long breath and rose abruptly to his feet. "That's it, *ah've* 'ad enough. *Am gooin'* down Welford Road t' explain, *wi'v gorra* do *summat*." Quickly donning his cap in his customary 'twisting it around his head' style, Charles was up and ready to go. Both Caroline and Louisa instinctively edged forward as if to stop him but then, just as soon, slowed and looked to the floor in the realisation that there was nothing else for it – they must all move on before the whole thing destroyed them. But then, as Charles pulled the door open with the swiftness and purpose of one who now meant business, he suddenly jumped back in surprise. Just as before, bold as brass, in an old black suit (a little frayed but still smart and clean) there again stood Richard. As Charles struggled to regain his composure his eyes rose towards Richard's face. Even paler than before, his complexion now almost grey, his eyes still bloodshot, staring and lifeless, were indeed the windows to his soul that day.

"Richard! We wondered where on earth... what on earth 'ad 'appened *te y'* lad."

"*Ah* said *ah'd* be 'ere didn't *ah*?" came the muffled reply as Richard bent towards the pavement in front of the house to pick something up. As he slowly rose it became clear that the object was a child's coffin; a small, white-painted deal coffin. Charles's eyes darted to the casket, then back to Richard's face; fearful of what was to come next, and still breathless from the shock, the words slipped from his lips, "Aye *y'* did that lad. But just the same, we were worried *te* death!"

"Well *ah'm* 'ere now," replied Richard, now standing with the box in his arms.

Just exactly how long had he been standing there? thought Charles but then, just as soon, dismissed the matter. *I suppose we're all acting a bit strangely at the moment*, he thought, *and after all, who wouldn't in the circumstances?*

Richard walked in, moved slowly over to where his dead child lay and placed the coffin slowly and respectfully on the floor in front of the sofa.

"I'd like a few moments alone with *me* son," said Richard, in the soft but purposeful tone of one determined to move a painful but necessary matter forward. With this Charles and the two women, who by now were at the foot of the stairs in the far corner of the room, withdrew and after what seemed like an hour but was probably only ten minutes or so, with not a word from Richard, they heard the front door slam. Charles rushed through and opened the front door again just in time to see Richard disappear around the corner at the end of the street, the small white coffin on his shoulder. Running back to the house, he called out, "Come on everybody, come on, let's go, it's all right now."

As was the tradition, Caroline fumbled to stop the clock, hurriedly drew a drape over the mirror and then drew the front curtains before they all moved out after Richard. So as to keep Richard in sight, Charles found himself half running and half walking on ahead and then returning periodically to reassure the others that all was as hoped. *Of course, he must be going to the cemetery*, he thought to himself, but he also knew Richard well enough by now to have his doubts.

Sure enough, though, onto Grange Lane, past Infirmary Square, down Infirmary Road, across the tramlines and onto Welford Road, Richard maintained a steady purposeful tread. Pausing only once at the saw mills in order to change shoulders, then over the railway bridge and through the cemetery gates. A formal church service of any sort would have been out of the question but as the party followed up the hill towards the common graves, they could see the spectral form of the Reverend Lewis set against the leaden sky of a cold winter's afternoon. Robes billowing in the wind, he was talking to Maud Tomlinson, who had obviously been informed of the arrangements. Mrs. Flaherty and Charles and Caroline's immediate neighbours, Mrs. Norton and Mrs. Colery (who had herself been only recently widowed), were also there.

Richard strode up to the side of the tiny grave and gazed into it; only about four feet deep, the coffin below covered with a thin layer of soil by the gravedigger so as to preserve as much dignity as possible within the means of such affairs. From his pocket Richard took two lengths of cord and, attaching each through the coffin handles, lowered his son into the earth with a grace appropriate to one sacrificing to God. Staring down, eyes welling with tears, for a moment he was still and then, as if a soldier on parade, took two paces back and looked up at the priest. Taking this as his cue the minister began his obsequies apace.

> *"I am the resurrection and the life sayeth the Lord. Whosoever believeth in me, though they die, will live, and everyone who liveth and believeth in me shall never die."*

Richard's mind wandered to thoughts of his son, how he was to be himself reborn; a better version of himself, a successful version. One who'd be able to provide for his family – somebody to look up to – something good. But sadly this could no longer be.

> *"Since we believe that Jesus died and rose again..."*

"I can't believe that it can never be," Richard kept repeating to himself.

"We brought nothing into the world..."

Why, oh why?

Then, as Richard looked skywards in despair he again became aware of the vicar's words.

"God so loved the world that he gave his only Son..."

Never quite sure whether he believed in God or not, Richard took brief comfort in the thought that if He were looking down then He, above all, would know how unbearable this pain was.

The rest of the service passed without Richard really hearing much more of it.

"... ashes to ashes, dust to dust, in sure and certain hope of the resurrection..."

In the end the small congregation came forward, one by one, each sprinkling a handful of soil into the grave. Charles was close to bursting and Louisa and Caroline inconsolable but Richard did not move, not even to comfort his wife. Such was his state of mind that if the grave had been big enough, he would have simply leaned forwards and dropped into it himself. Even when the rest of the party slowly began to move away, Richard neither moved nor spoke, and by now Louisa was beginning to realise that, even by Richard's standards, his behaviour was becoming increasingly worrying.

Charles, on the other hand, could not help some feeling of relief that the matter was now concluded as he moved back down towards the cemetery gates. "C'mon Carrie," he whispered, placing his arm around his wife. "We'd best get back ready for the guests. C'mon Louie love, Richard 'll be along soon."

Louisa (now beginning to regain herself somewhat), "No Dad, I'll wait for 'im. *Ah* must wait for 'im."

"But it's freezin'. You'll catch *yer* death."

"Yes, come on my love," added Caroline.

"No Mam, take the kids, *ah* need to speak to 'im alone. *Ee's* fallin' apart, I 'adn't realised. *Ah've bin* too wound up in *me* own grief *te* realise. Leave me, we'll come back together."

Charles (with the inflection of a father's concern clearly in his voice), "Okay love, *bur ah'm cumin'* back fo' *y'* if *yer* not there in *arf* an hour."

Louisa watched them all move off, out of the gate, over the railway and back towards the centre of town, and when they had all but disappeared her eyes rested on Richard; still statuesque, still with head bowed, staring down into the grave. If it were not for the fact that there were no memorials in this part of the cemetery, he could easily have been mistaken for a monument himself.

I don't think that 'depression' was regarded in the same way then as it is now but in modern terms Richard would have been beyond it. In his heart, however, he still knew that such a state, however it was described, held no future, so when Louisa slowly placed her arm around his back she broke the spell and, for the moment at least, Richard was almost back to his normal self.

Slowly and quietly, they made their way back to Bonners Lane and, by the time they arrived, both had realised that they still loved each other deeply. Although Richard Walter Jr. had gone, they were not. And more than this, they were still together. This understanding had not been achieved by any spoken word though, only touches; tender touches that made words unnecessary. The next few days, next few months, next few years even, would be difficult, they knew that. But they also knew that, somehow, they would get through them. Maybe it was for a reason, or maybe it was some sort of divine plan – of a sort that men cannot understand. Whatever, the questioning was now becoming futile, and that afternoon, surrounded by friends and family, at long last they began to sense a sort of renaissance in the air, a kind of regeneration that would steel them to move on.

*

Family rumour has always had it that Louisa gave birth to eleven boys in all – 'a football team' – along with two girls, making a total of thirteen children. And that there were, in total, three boys in this family that died during infancy. Search as I have, though, I must confess that I have been totally unable to find out anything about the other two unfortunate brothers. It could well be that I have missed their details, of course, or it could be that they were stillbirths. In any event, to withstand the loss of one child is devastating enough, but to have to go through it three times, to me, is unimaginable.

*

Just short of eight years after Richard Walter Jr. was laid to rest, another son was born to another poor family, this time in the Bosnian village of Obljaj, west of Sarajevo, in the Grahovo Valley, near to the Croatian border. His name: Gavrilo Princip. The exact date of Gavrilo's birth is a source of some confusion and indeed, this confusion was to serve some years later in saving him from the firing squad. Given the choice, though, as we shall see later, martyrdom may well have been what he would have chosen.

What is known is that Gavrilo first saw the light of day sometime in June or July 1894, the son of a postman, Petar, and his wife, Marija. As with the Warren family, the humble nature of the Princips' existence had led to poor health. In their case, very poor health as, out of a total of nine siblings, only Gavrilo and two others would survive infancy, with Gavrilo himself being dogged, from a very early age, by repeated bouts of tuberculosis. He was, nevertheless, a keen student of politics and as a young man is said to have pored over historic and patriotic literature. His education was certainly varied. In his early teens he attended the Military School in Sarajevo, however, seeming to change his mind, he later transferred to a Merchant's School, presumably with a view to pursuing a career in business. But three years later, when he entered the High School in Tuzla, he is said to have professed a desire to become a poet.

Something must have changed yet again, because shortly afterwards Gavrilo became obsessed with militant revolution, and it did not take long for his obsession to get him into trouble when he was expelled from his school for supposedly taking part in demonstrations in Sarajevo.

Whether Gavrilo sought militant revolution because of his situation or simply for its own sake, he was certainly in the right place at the right time. The Balkans were where the Ottoman Empire and the Habsburg Austro-Hungarian Empire met. It formed a political 'fault line' between these two once great, but now unstable, 'tectonic plates' that had begun to heave and pull against one another.

Having governed Bosnia-Herzegovina since the fifteenth century, by the end of the nineteenth century the Ottoman Turks were beginning to struggle financially and were finding it harder and harder to maintain their influence, especially in their furthest outposts. The Habsburgs seized on this power vacuum and in 1878 annexed Bosnia which, by 1908, had led to full occupation. But this new hegemony, although appearing outwardly confident, was also strained. The humiliating defeat exacted by Prussia on Austria-Hungary during the Seven Weeks War of 1866 had cost the Habsburg Empire other vast tracts of Central Europe and with it, much of its influence. At the same time, 500 or so years of Ottoman rule had left many Orthodox Bosnian Serb peasants restless, feeling disenfranchised and at the mercy of their Muslim landlords. As a result, many groups emerged vowing to take whatever steps they could to prevent Austria-Hungary taking over where the Turks had left off. Predictably, this began to fuel the causes of various independence groups, including the Young Bosnia Movement – a body aimed loosely at a Slavic unification of the Balkans, of which Gavrilo was a member. In the fullness of time, however, it was to be the notorious 'Black Hand Gang' or, as it was also known, 'Unification or Death' that predominated. And it would be this faction that became the one from which the Habsburgs would have most to fear – a Serb organisation with a pathological hatred of the overbearing House of Habsburg and hell-bent on its downfall. It had demonstrated its credentials very well in 1903 when it organised the assassination and mutilation of Serbia's pro-Habsburg King Alexander and Queen Draga. Perhaps inevitably, then, it was into the 'Black Hand' that Gavrilo would be drawn in his late teens.

By 1913 a state of abject panic reigned throughout the Balkans – the short-lived First Balkan War in which Gavrilo took part as an 'irregular combatant' had been fomented in order to rid the Balkans of Turkish influence once and for all. In parallel, relations between Serbia and Austria-Hungary were so strained that war between them seemed inevitable. Amidst all this confusion Gavrilo's mind, weakened by disease but strengthened by conviction, became so affected that he resolved to give his all for his 'cause célèbre'. So, when it was announced that the heir to the Austro-Hungarian throne – the Archduke Franz Ferdinand – and his wife; the Duchess Sophie, were to make an official visit to Sarajevo he took it as his 'calling' and volunteered, along with at least five others, to try to assassinate them. So obsessed were they that they had all planned to poison themselves afterwards. It was indeed a suicide mission, mollified only slightly by the fact that none of the volunteers enjoyed the best of health and none was expected to live beyond a few years anyway.

The somewhat belligerent reason given for the Archduke's visit, to review Austro-Hungarian troops on manoeuvres in Sarajevo, sparked controversy from the start and the fact that previous attempts had already been made on both the Archduke and his uncle, the Emperor Franz Joseph, by Balkan militants meant that many had very real fears about what might happen. And, even though these fears were expressed unreservedly, the Archduke would have none of it. Even the date – only three days before his fourteenth wedding anniversary and, in the Serbian Julian calendar, it was Saint Vitus Day; the anniversary of the Battle of Kosovo in 1389 when the Ottoman Turk Sultan Murad I was said to have been killed by the Serbian legend Miloš Obilić. But even this was not enough to dissuade him.

The 28th of June 1914 was my grandfather's twentieth birthday, so it is perhaps a blessing that he could never have foreseen the full consequences the events of that bright, hot, sunny day in Sarajevo would hold, not least for him personally. The event is widely documented and although versions vary slightly in detail, the essential account of what happened goes something like this.

The royal train pulled into Sarajevo Station just before ten o'clock and the Archduke and Sophie stepped down to be greeted by General Oskar Potiorek, the Bosnian Governor. As the royal couple were to be whisked by car to the City Hall for the official reception, the conspirators had distributed themselves along the route in such a way that each could attempt the assassination should the opportunity arise. Very early into the journey, just as the convoy passed the central police station, Nedeljko Čabrinović was the first of the gang to have a go when he hurled a grenade at the Archduke's car. Instead of achieving its purpose, though, the grenade bounced off and exploded under the car behind, severely wounding its occupants. In the pandemonium that followed the Archduke's driver accelerated away and the rest of the journey was conducted at such a furious pace that none of the other conspirators (including Gavrilo) were able either to hurl grenades or fire at the car without serious risk of harming innocent bystanders. The royal dignitaries' safe arrival at the reception gave all an opportunity to collect themselves and when, at length, the Archduke enquired as to what had happened he was told of the serious injuries sustained by the occupants in the car behind. His adamant response was to insist on being taken to see them. Again fears were expressed about safety but, as before, they were dismissed and when, despite the suggestion that at least Sophie should not go, she vowed that she would not leave her husband's side, the frustration must have been palpable!

It seems that what happened next was much more the result of a chance conspiracy of events rather than planning. If anything had occurred differently or in a different sequence the outcome would have almost certainly been entirely different.

For security reasons it was decided to take a certain route but, unfortunately, nobody seemed to have informed the driver of this, and instead of driving straight along Appel Quay, as planned, he turned into Franz Joseph Street – the very street to which Gavrilo Princip had sloped following the earlier failed assassination attempt. Governor Potiorek immediately realised the mistake and ordered the car be turned round but, by this time, it was almost directly alongside Gavrilo. Once again panic ensued as the driver braked sharply and began a muddled reversing manoeuvre. Gavrilo saw his chance and seized it. Walking up to the car he levelled his gun at the Archduke and Duchess and shot them several times at point-blank range. There are several, so-called, eyewitness accounts of what happened next but essentially, both dignitaries were fatally wounded and bled to death at the scene. Apparently, the Archduke slumped back – hit in the neck, the bullet severing his jugular vein. Murmuring his last words he very quickly lost consciousness and died. Sophie was slumped forwards and also died shortly afterwards.

The deed done, Gavrilo began to turn the gun towards himself and would have undoubtedly committed suicide had a quick-thinking member of the public not grabbed it from him in time. The inevitable followed and, although saved from the mob, Gavrilo was grabbed and beaten half to death by the police who ran forward to arrest him.

The other conspirators were also arrested and robustly interrogated but only one of them, Danilo Ilić, confessed to the conspiracy. Gavrilo admitted deliberately aiming his gun at the Archduke and shooting him but claimed that he never intended to kill Sophie.

In custody Gavrilo tried, but failed, to poison himself. He was eventually charged with treason and murder but, throughout the trial, gave little away. As expected he was found guilty, along with seven others, and would normally have then been sentenced to death. However, as I mentioned earlier, there was some confusion as to whether he had been born just before or just after 28 June 1894. Whereas the former case would have made him over twenty years old at the time of the assassination and therefore eligible for execution, the latter made him under twenty and ineligible. In the event the court allowed him the benefit of the doubt but the sentence given was the maximum possible under such circumstances; twenty years in prison.

Gavrilo was sent to Theresienstadt Prison in Terezín, just thirty-five miles or so north of Prague in what is today the Czech Republic, but was then Bohemia – part of Austria-Hungary. (Theresienstadt is, of course, much more famous – or should I say infamous – for its period as a concentration camp run by the Nazis during the Second World War.)

Nowadays relatively easily treated with antibiotics, tuberculosis was then incurable and Gavrilo continued to suffer from it throughout his incarceration. He even had to have one of his arms amputated as a result. Eventually he died in captivity some six months before the Great War ended, thus never living to see the end of the Habsburg Empire whose demise he had so passionately sought.

Fearing that he may 'live on after death' as a political focus he was initially buried in a secret grave but one of the burial party is said to have kept a record of the location and this enabled his subsequent exhumation and re-interment beneath the chapel in St. Marks Cemetery in Sarajevo, which had been built as a permanent monument to Serb heroes. In a similar vein, Gavrilo Princip's place in history was to be later trumpeted by Tito in order to unite the so-called Southern Slavs into the 'artificial' state of Yugoslavia. All under the watchful eye, of course, of the most powerful Slavic nation – Russia and the then Soviet Union. Unsurprisingly, after Tito's death in 1980 his conglomeration of Balkan states collapsed and descended into civil war. As, by this time, Russia was struggling with her finances and the Soviet Union was becoming increasingly unstable too, much to the relief of many, there was little she could do to 'aid her cousins' on this occasion.

In today's Bosnia-Herzegovina, perhaps with more recent atrocities in mind, the modern perception of Gavrilo and what he did have come full circle and he and his confederates are again regarded as terrorists. As a result, St. Marks has become neglected and visitors are discouraged. But, what goes round comes round I suppose, so until, or indeed if ever, the seemingly never-ending flux that the Balkans seems to be finally crystallises, who knows how the future may judge him.

I do not know whether or not his parents outlived him. In fact some even believe that the man known as Gavrilo Princip was not the son of Petar and Marija at all – there will always be controversy. But he must, nevertheless, have been somebody's son. So, if his parents had still been alive when their son died, I suspect that they would have mourned him every bit as much as Richard and Louisa had mourned their son.

Often cited as 'the man responsible for starting the First World War', as such Gavrilo must have been taunted incessantly over its devastating toll during his time in prison. And, although it is fair to say that his actions certainly went a long way towards justifying Austria-Hungary's excuse for declaring war on Serbia, and all knew full well that it wouldn't end there, the powder keg had essentially been in place and fused for some time before the assassination. In reality all that was needed was that 'vital spark' in order to blow everything to Kingdom Come! By his actions Gavrilo clearly provided that spark but, had he failed, there can surely be little doubt that somebody or something else would have provided another such spark before too much longer.

As a postscript, this account would be incomplete without reference to another strange twist in the story. Another coincidence, an omen, a monumental irony? Call it what you will, but there was definitely something a bit creepy about that car in which the Archduke and his wife took their last ride that day. The 1910, open-topped Gräf & Stift is said to have born the registration number 'A111 118'. Was this simply a jumble of letters and figures denoting registration details or an adumbration of 'Armistice 11/11/18'? Weird or what?!

*

Back in Outram Street, Christmas 1886 was a grim affair. Richard had, by now, been out of regular employment for two years, and with trying to bring up three children in squalor and with the taste of death still in their mouths, nobody felt much like celebrating. Christmas Day that year was much like any other Saturday to them. It did not even affect Richard's search for work, which continued through rain or shine. By now, however, the strain was beginning to tell, and he was finding it increasingly difficult to get out of bed of a morning or, once up, to drag himself from the house. When he did have breakfast it would merely consist of a stale crust or a glass of milk or even just a raw carrot. Anything, in fact, left over after the kids had eaten the best of what little there was. Sometimes – often on a Monday morning, when the weather was good and he felt as though a new era was about to dawn – Richard would call on as many as twenty different firms before midday. Other times he would just sit and quietly stare into space. If it was a warm summer's day he would sit in the open – Victoria Park, Abbey Park or on a town bench. If it were cold he would shelter in London Road Station or the town hall library or even the museum – anywhere where it was warm (or warmer). These sessions could last anything from twenty minutes or so to several hours. On occasions he would 'come round' and find it difficult to believe how much time had slipped by. More often than not his thoughts would drift to a warm comfortable home: he in an armchair, beside a blazing fire, with the smell of cooking in the air. Flo sat in front of the hearth, stroking a pet dog and John knelt nearby playing with a train set. Louisa calls from the kitchen, "Another bottle of beer before dinner, Richard?" There would be enough money (not great wealth – just enough to make life easy), no despair and above all, no illness. At times he could even smell the food and taste the beer. Another day he might find himself by the sea or even abroad, in a hot country – relaxing under the sun, being waited on, being powerful and in control. Perhaps a boat trip that afternoon? Nobody to ask favours of, no responsibility, only contentment. *Could that day ever dawn?* he would wonder.

These trance-like states served to give Richard some degree of freedom from his fears and anxieties, when his jaw did not ache through the constant grinding of his teeth, when his brain did not spin with his constant quest, when he was briefly relieved of his yoke. But eventually and inevitably, he would return to reality: "Three 'ours, no can't be. Mus' be *gooin'* mad!"

In a way he may well have been right; whereas today, we would call it depression or nervous breakdown or something along those lines, then, it was seen as weakness or 'lack of moral fibre'; a disruptive device of the Devil that could lead to dubious thoughts, crime or gambling, perhaps, even immoral distraction. Yet thankfully, although it must have been a struggle, Richard did manage to retain his grip on reality. Put simply, he had no choice because he knew that, without his continued determination, the family unit would not survive and Louisa, Flo and John would have had no option but to throw themselves upon the mercy of the Corporation. As it was, Richard's efforts continued to bring in a few bob every now and then: a day's labouring here or a day's sweeping up there. Throughout the winter Richard continued, at least a couple of days a week, to wander out into the surrounding countryside in order to collect as much firewood as he could carry. Not only did this provide enough fuel to keep his own household reasonably warm but, as word got round, he built up a small but regular group of customers to whom he was able to sell any surpluses. Although it only made a few coppers, it was better than nothing. Another godsend was the newly formed Leicester and Leicestershire Amalgamated Hosiery Union, which Richard had joined shortly before losing his job. Through his contacts with them he was able to receive the occasional discretionary payment. Again these were minimal but had 'saved the day' on more than one occasion. Above all, though, Charles Sidwell continued to keep a caring and watchful eye on his daughter's plight and would press the occasional half-crown into her hand when he could see that, without it, things would have been too awful to contemplate. Although she had never trained for any occupation, Louisa herself was not without resources and was able to supplement the income in her own right from time to time with a bit of charring at the houses of the local 'better-off'. This fitted in well because she could often take Flo and John along with her where they would play in some corner until the work was done.

So in this eclectic way and by managing to renegotiate the rent (with the promise of payback when times were better) the family, by the skin of their teeth, just managed to carry on. Half-starved, constantly unwell and bumping along the bottom, the longer it went on the lower their expectations sank, until all must have felt that things would probably never change; this was how it would be for the rest of their lives (what little they may be left with). And thus death became less of a thing to be feared, in fact, on occasions it may almost have seemed something to look forward to. Not only would it release them from grind and poverty but, hopefully, elevate them to God's house, to live with Him and the angels in heaven for ever whilst all the tyrants and bosses and landlords and capitalists burned in hell!

Then, one Thursday morning, quite out of the blue, everything changed. It was one of those ordinary days where Richard was neither enthusiastic nor lethargic, just perfunctory – eyes glazed, the ninth or tenth enquiry of the day, expecting the usual brush-off, he almost did not recognise that so rare of responses.

Richard: "*Ay y'* got *oat* in the way o' *wuk* [work] *fur a'* experienced hand?"

Foreman: "Might 'ave."

R (instinctively turning to leave, stops in his tracks): "Really, what?"

F: "You're Richard Warren, *ain't y'*?"

R: "*Ahr ah'm.*"

F: "As used *te werk fu* Grindrod's on th' counter?"

R: "Yes."

F: "Charley, what's 'is name, *Sid'le*… Sidwell's son-in-law?"

R (now beginning to recognise his correspondent): "Yes, and you're Harry… Harry Topham. I remember now, you 'ad a frame at Grindrod's. You managed *te* keep *gooin'* then?"

F: "Skin o' *me* teeth, Richard, skin o' *me* teeth. 'Avin' *bin* wi' Grindrod's for nearly twenty years I got a foreman's job just after they laid you lot off. I don't know whether you knew Bob Fowler but it were 'is job as saved me. He dropped dead there and then on the factory floor. One minute tellin' some poor bugger off *fur* 'oldin' a fag *te* near 'is work, the next on the bloody floor jerkin' about. After a bit *ee* just stopped movin'. A couple o' lads loaded 'im onto a cart and wheeled 'im round to Dr. Sloane's *bur* it wer' no good, *ee* were dead. A bit after *ah* were passin' 'ere just as this job were *pur* up and *as ah* were fed up at Grindrod's *ah* went in about it *un ah gorrit* there and then."

R: "Right 'Arry… *ah* remember Bob *bur ah din't* know 'im well."

F: "The point is Richard, like I *wor*, *yer* in the right place at the right time, lad. We need a counterman. Old Wheeler is on 'is last legs an' *ain't bin in fu thray wiks. Ah* can't see 'im *cumin'* back. Boss's son, young Pratt, 'as the final say *bur*, if truth be know, *ee's* still a bit wet be'ind the ears. If I say *yer* right *fo* the job *un y' doon't* muck it up when *y'* see 'im, *ah* reckon as *y'll ay* it."

R: "Well 'Arry if it's *gooin' ah* certainly want it. I'd be lyin' if *ah sed ah won't* desperate."

F: "Tell *y'* what Richard, scribble *y'* address on this and I'll 'ave a word wi' the little… this afternoon and see as we can't start things off. Then I'll pop round and see *y'*."

R (now flushed with renewed enthusiasm at the prospect): "Would *y'* 'Arry, would *y'*?"

Richard scribbled down his address on the back of Harry's packet of Players and, on handing it to him with an expectant grin, turned sharply on his heels. Then, with a spring in his step that had not seen the light of day for some considerable time, tripped down the factory steps. Right arm raised, with crossed fingers in the air, "See *y'* later then 'Arry!"

Reading the scribbled note, Harry Topham muttered under his breath, '2, Court B, Outram Street, God, is that where I think it is? If things are that bad I hope this works. If I've got the poor bugger's 'opes up an' it don't, *ee'll* never forgive me."

Harry wasn't the only one having second thoughts. At first Richard's elation made him feel like celebrating. This was the break he had waited for, for so long. Back home with a jug of four ale perhaps – he had sixpence halfpenny in his pocket. *What about threepence each way in the bookies? No, perhaps not – too soon – never count your chickens,* he thought. As Richard walked along he began to ruminate even more and all the negative possibilities began to gather in his mind. He began to ask himself how many times he had been here before. This was different though; somebody he knew, somebody who knew his father-in-law too, it was almost in the bag, he had been promised. But then, promised, oh yes... he'd been promised before all right – the job at Fabricated Yarns – *bloody time-wasting idiot,* he thought. *Just a joke to 'im but my whole life to me, idiot!* But then his mood lifted again as he thought of Harry Topham. *This is not the same, Harry wouldn't do that, he's a good man; a gentleman. Well, we'll see, only time'll tell I suppose, meanwhile best carry on as before.*

Pratt Jr. was a lanky, sallow youth with thick, wavy, fair hair, the red pock-markings of acne on his face contrasting sharply with the paleness of the rest of his skin; a result of his constant picking at the spots. Not yet a year out of school he was still learning, but he was far from 'the brightest button' and it was proving a slow process. His father's wealth had enabled the boy to attend a minor public school and to stay on into the sixth form where, as a prefect, he had been able, with some degree of autonomy, to make the lives of those junior pupils who dared cross him a complete misery. On transitioning from school to work he had assumed that this 'power' would somehow transfer seamlessly and automatically to the workmen and women of Pratt & Piggott and was still having difficulty understanding why it had not. Like the time an old hand named Jim Blaney had been so wound up by the little squirt that, out of sight, Jim had grabbed him by the throat and snarled in his face, "Speak to me like that again and I'll 'ave *y'* by the bollocks *y'* little bastard!" Luckily for Blaney, although severely shaken, out of embarrassment Pratt Jr. found himself unable to tell even his father about this and the matter passed.

As was usually the case, Pratt Jr. made his first appearance of the day just before one o'clock. The fact that one o'clock signalled the end of the lunch break was no coincidence and meant that he could check that everybody was back at their work on time. In practice, though, it was rarely, if ever, the case that anybody was late back. Harry Topham saw to that, because he knew that young Pratt would no longer challenge any of the workers directly. No, it would be down to him – he would be for the high jump. Although Pratt Jr. had convinced himself that it was beneath his station to talk directly to the staff, Topham knew that he was really too scared to. The truth was that, after the Blaney affair, everybody had realised that he was only who he was because of his father and sadly, he was by no means his father's equal when it came to man management.

"Afternoon, Mr. Colin," said Topham, as Pratt Jr. strolled in. (Perhaps because it gave the address a certain air of beholden, senior managers and owners of firms in the area often liked to be addressed as 'Mr.' followed by their first name.)

"Good afternoon, Topham," replied Pratt Jr. in his usual officious, half-singing, semi-broken voice. "All's well I trust."

"No problems, sir," replied Topham. And rarely were there any; Topham was a good foreman – a diplomat, a listener and what's more, intelligent, much sought-after qualities in a junior manager.

"There is just one thing."

"*Yeeess*," squeaked Pratt Jr., looking up from a pattern book that he was pretending to read.

H.T.: "Well, it's just that they're struggling to do the counter work now that Bert Wheeler's gone."

P.J.: "*Whooo* said *ee* was gone? He's off sick, isn't *ee*?"

H.T.: "Fact is, sir, *ee* can hardly stand, *ee's* sixty-three and *ee* looks eighty-three. It's not a case of a week to get over the flu. I can't see 'im ever comin' back *un* even if *ee* does *ee* can't cut it. The counter's been struggling for some time, sir, and a lot of what we make still passes over it."

This last phrase made Pratt Jr. think for a minute (as Harry knew it would). Could it be possible that the wages being saved were less than the profit being lost?

P.J.: "Do you know for a fact that Wheeler's not coming back?"

H.T.: "Pretty sure."

P.J.: "*Ah* see. Have you anybody in mind then, or should we advertise, what do you think?"

H.T.: "Well, as it happens, sir, I do know somebody – Richard Warren. I used to work with 'im at Grindrod's. He's a good *un*."

P.J.: "Mmm… If *ee's* experienced *ee'll* want more money, if *ee's* not *ee'll* be no good!"

H.T.: "*Ee's* a good counterman but *ee's* been out o' work a while – *ee's* not greedy. Perhaps I should discuss it with Mr. Pratt Sr.?"

P.J. (anxious not to have his authority circumnavigated): "No, no agreed. If *ee* can start Monday it's five pence an hour."

God! thought Harry, *I thought slavery had been abolished!* But he knew better than to argue at this stage. He could see that Richard was desperate and he didn't want to spoil things for the chap. After all, he'd led him to believe it was in the bag. Hopefully, when he'd been in the job a year or so the Pratts would see he was a good worker and give him some more money. Hopefully…

That night Harry called on Richard and Louisa as promised and gave them the good news. "Start Monday – told *y'* it were in the bag."

"Oh, thanks, 'Arry, thanks a lot, mate," said Richard, while vigorously shaking his hand.

"Oh, thank you so much," said Louisa, tears in her eyes. "Will *y'* stop and 'ave something to eat?" Harry declined; looking around the four bare walls he wondered what manner of fare they could possibly offer. "Must get back, wife and kids and that…" Then, looking towards Richard, "Monday seven sharp mind, see *y'* then."

"Oh, I'll be there, 'Arry, I'll be there," replied Richard. "Cheerio and oh, er, thanks again."

"My pleasure mate, cheerio."

When Harry had gone Richard slumped, head back, legs outstretched, into the threadbare armchair, at the same time a tremendous sigh exploding through his lips. Louisa, kneeling at his side, was still crying tears of joy.

"A new start, Richard, we can start getting ourselves back on our feet now."

"Yes," replied Richard, "a new start."

Chapter 3

Kith and Kin

'One would be in less danger
From the wiles of a stranger
If one's own kin and kith
Were more fun to be with.'
'Family Court' – Ogden Nash

All that weekend Richard and Louisa could think of nothing else but the prospect of the better life that would come with Richard's new job. And, although they did not understand exactly why, Flo and John had sensed this brighter outlook in their parents and begun to feel the benefit of it too. Richard was up bright and early that Monday. By five o'clock he was washed, dressed and set for work. Louisa had sorted out his last decent pair of trousers and shirt over the weekend and, after a few mends here and there and a couple of buttons sewn on, they had been duly washed, ironed and ready to wear. Richard had blackened his boots and bought a new razor. There were a few holes in his underwear and socks but who would see those? He did not possess a necktie, which was as well, since he had neither collars nor a stud for his shirt. Instead, Louisa had made him a muffler – a kind of small scarf made from a square of old silk material that went around the neck inside the shirt and made a sort of decorative bulge beneath the undone top button of his shirt. Richard brushed down his jacket and with it on, donned his cap. He looked quite smart… from a distance.

"Your dinner," Louisa told him, as she pressed a couple of butterine sandwiches wrapped in newspaper into his hand. "Tell me 'ow it all went when you get 'ome tonight."

"Will do. Bye Flo, bye John, give Dad a kiss." After embracing both children tenderly Richard looked up at Louisa and, with a half-smiling, half-anxious expression, said, "I 'ope I can do this okay, I'm a bit out of practice after all this time."

"You'll be fine, now get on," she replied, wafting him away with both arms. And with that he smiled, turned and went. As Louisa watched him disappear around the corner, she too had her doubts, but she believed in her husband enough to know that he would try hard to make the best of this opportunity. Above all, she knew how determined he could be and to her mind, that made it as good as won.

Being the middle of March, it was just getting light on a fine spring morning and even with only a jacket over his shirt and vest, Richard was not cold. Neither was he tired – his mouth was no longer gaping yawns of hopelessness. For once in a very long while he had a clear purpose; this would not be another hopeless day, not another day set to end in failure, this was to be the first of the many good days to come – his anguish was at an end, he could get back to enjoying life a bit more and get back on his feet.

'PRATT & PIGGOTT HOSIERY MANUFACTURERS' read the sign arched above the gate.

By now it was ten to seven and queues of workers were pouring into the factory. *Better find Harry Topham*, Richard thought to himself, but Harry, expecting Richard to be early, had been waiting for him. "*Oy* Richard," he shouted. "C'mon, I'll show you the ropes."

Once inside, it all came flooding back; the shuffling rhythm of the frames, the smell of hot metal and oil, the feeling of belonging once again, of being something, somebody, again. They walked down a narrow corridor with brick walls, painted down the ages with layer on layer of glossy enamel paint. Even by day the passage was so dark in some parts that it had to be lit by candles. Through the door marked 'STORE' was a tall-ceilinged room some eighty by thirty feet filled with rows of shelving. Between each row was a gap just wide enough for a man to walk up and down and deposit or collect stock, the boards creaking and clattering in reply to the hobnails of their boots as they went. The shelves were packed with all manner of garments – socks, stockings, vests, long johns, jumpers: some white, some coloured, some patterned and some plain. In here the smell was less hot metal and oil and more new wool and polished wood, a redolence formerly so familiar to Richard, but one, he now realised, that had been temporarily lost to the back of his mind. *On familiar ground again*, he thought to himself.

Harry: "Ere we are then, Richard. It all works pretty well the same as at Grindrod's. *Y'* need to know where each type of garment is stacked o' course and all the rates, but yo'll soon get the 'ang *on* it." In amongst the shelving stood two men in brown coats – one sorting garments and the other, notebook and pencil in hand, noting the locations.

"Alec! Don!" shouted Harry. "This is Richard; *ee'll* be workin' *wi' y'*."

The men shook hands and exchanged greetings.

"Where *yow* from then, Richard?" asked Alec.

"*Bin art o'* work *fur* over two year now, used *te* work at Grindrod's," replied Richard. Both Alec and Don knew the all too familiar story, looking down at the floor and shaking their heads while sucking in air through clenched teeth in commiseration.

"Got kids?" asked Don.

"*Ahr* two," replied Richard.

"'Ard *innit*," said Alec. "*Ah* were out *me sel* nearly six months from last Christmas *te* last summer – enough *te breck* a man!"

"Can *y'* make sure Richard knows what is doin' lads, please?" said Harry.

Alec and Don both nodded and turned back to their work. "Will do, boss," added Alec. "See *y'* in a bit, Rich lad," he added.

Harry went on, "Counter's through 'ere."

Richard followed Harry through a door in the corner of the storeroom which led to the rear of a solid oak counter of some fifteen feet by four. In front of the counter the room extended another thirty feet or so. It was a cold place with a floor of stained, polished board, whitewashed walls and a tall ceiling that made the room seem even bigger than it actually was. There were benches placed against the walls all around the room and, to the right of the counter, a series of large windows almost the length of the room. These were frosted over to just above head height so that staff could neither see out, nor the public see in. Above the frosting, the windows were clear glass, in order to let in as much natural light as possible. In fact, the frosting did not really interfere too much with the ingress of light, as the windows faced a narrow street, across which was another factory, so that the only source of natural light came directly from above. After the large windows, in the far right-hand corner was the main entrance, where customers and outworkers would come to collect garments and yarn, etc., and deposit finished or semi-finished items. Outside, the entrance door was raised some two feet above pavement level, and it was necessary to ascend three high concrete steps in order to enter the building. From time to time, horses and carts clattered by and people would walk down the street, their boots clicking on the pavement with each step, sometimes in conversation with others and sometimes not. Despite the background noise of the factory, on moments not drowned out by the business of the day, a muffled version of this street hubbub could always be heard from within the counter room – the volume of the passing traffic being raised a pitch or two between four and half-past in the afternoon when the chatter, shouts and occasional screams of children leaving the nearby school filled the air.

"*Y'll* need *te* get *yerself* a couple o' ware'ouse coats but *y'* can wear this *un* 'o Bert's *fur* now." Richard put it on. Bert had obviously been a shorter, fatter man as, although there was plenty of room in the coat when buttoned up, the hem fell some eight inches above Richard's knees.

"Not exactly the perfect fit," said Harry, "*bur* it'll do *fur nar*."

Richard stood behind the counter, with arms held widely either side and palms spread flat onto the counter surface. He was back in his proper world – back at work, back to the job he knew well, back after what had seemed so long.

Harry (noticing the euphoria): "*Doown't* get too excited, *ah ant* told *y'* the wages yet."

R: "Oh *yeh*, 'ow much is it?"

H: "Five pence an hour."

Although he had anticipated something along these lines, Richard was still a bit disappointed, but he did not show it. What would have been the point? He knew that he was in no position to argue. It was a case of take it or leave it and there was no way that he was going to leave it.

H: "Seven *te* six Monday *te* Friday with an hour fo' *y'* dinner and seven *te* midday on Saturday – 55 *ahrs* – it's well *uver* a quid a week *un ah* reckon after *y've bin* 'ere a bit…"

R (interrupting): "'Arry, I *ant cum* 'ere today *te* turn it *daarn*."

And with that the door tinkled open and a tall, middle-aged woman entered. Body bent slightly forward as one having spent many years crouching, she was draped in a black shawl and was carrying a basket full of socks that she had 'ended'.

H: "*Ah'll* be back a bit later *te* show *y'* round the rest o' the place, Richard, but for now, looks like *yer* in business."

R: "*Ahr*, 'Arry, looks like I am."

With the help of Alec and Don, as the day went on, Richard soon began to get the hang of things and at about 1.30pm Harry Topham returned with Pratt Jr. in tow.

H: "Mr. Colin, this is Richard Warren, the man I told you about last week – the new counterman. Richard, this is Mr. Colin Pratt, one of the directors."

Although he had not been told as much, Richard guessed immediately that 'Mr. Colin' was the boss's son – *Pratt by name and prat by nature,* he thought to himself, but he was not about to upset the apple cart at this early stage.

"Good afternoon, sir," said Richard.

"Oh afternoon," squeaked Pratt Jr. "*Yoou* come 'ighly recommended, I 'ope you can manage. Mr. Topham and I will keep in touch about you, while you are settling in and that."

The thinly veiled threat in these words did not escape Richard. It was obvious that Pratt Jr. was regularly going to press Harry for any sign of inadequacy as well as watching him closely himself as he crept about the place. Pratt Jr. had become so brainwashed by his father's rantings that he was virtually incapable of making the slightest decision for himself. Almost daily around the tea table the old man rattled on, "It is my considered opinion that the British worker is a lazy, idle beast at heart. The only way to stop 'im robbin' a business blind is by watchin' 'im like a 'awk... like a 'awk mind! I've never come across one as does a good job without bein' pushed, *bur ah'v* seen a lot as does *nowt...*"

"I hope you'll find me okay," said Richard. "I've always done my best."

"*Yeess* I '*ope* so *to-oo*," creaked Pratt.

At six o'clock the factory whistle blew, precipitating the mass exodus that poured out onto the street. Richard was in no hurry, though, and waited until the crowd died down. Thinking that he must get a better fitting one, he removed his brown coat and hung it up on one of the pegs at the rear of the counter. Well, he had survived the first day, but he could not get over how tired he felt. *I'm out of practice*, he thought, as he walked out through the factory gate into the sunshine of that spring evening.

"Fancy a pint, Richard?" shouted a voice. It was Harry.

"Love to, Harry, *me* old mate, but... first day and all that... after two and half years, *y'* know..."

"Quite understand, mate, quite understand," replied Harry. "See *y' tomorra*."

As he wandered home, Richard began to think about his future again. His first priority, now that he had a permanent job, would be to get himself, his wife and kids as far away from the hovel that was Outram Street as soon as possible. As he turned the corner and looked along the road towards the slum, he imagined the day when they could move out. He even imagined himself tearing it down, brick by brick and spitting on the resulting heap of rubble. It was not going to be easy, but he was going to get away from this place, come what may.

For the time being though, he had little choice; it was going to be business as usual. But then, as he climbed the communal staircase and walked through the front door, the delicious aroma of boiled beef instantly eclipsed his mood. Charlie had given Louisa two bob to buy the joint, in order to celebrate the start of Richard's new job. After boiling it up and starting off roasting it in the range at Bonners Lane, she had then brought it home to finish off. There were carrots, peas and potatoes as well and a couple of bottles of beer to wash it all down. Just as well because, as it turned out, there was to be more to the celebration than just a new job.

"Come in, come in and sit *y'* self down, duck," cried Louisa.

"Hello Daddy," Flo and John shouted in unison, both trying to climb on his knee at the same time.

Richard (almost overwhelmed): "God, what's all this then?"

"Now then, Richard, no blaspheming, and especially not in front of the children. I don't know, one day back at work and you're swearing again."

'Sorry, Mother," said Richard. "It's just… all this…"

The timing was perfect and within a few minutes the meal was on the table. All ravenous, they ate like they had never eaten before, the only sound that of cutlery clattering against plates, until Louisa had eaten her fill, Richard had finally mopped up the last drop of gravy with a piece of bread and both children's plates had been licked clean.

Richard knew where the money for the celebration had come from. "*Y'* dad?" he asked as he sat back in his armchair.

"Yes," replied Louisa. "Good on 'im then," said Richard.

Afterwards Richard took the pots outside and washed up while Louisa laid the children to bed on their mattress in the corner of the bedroom. When she came back Richard was half-asleep. He stirred back to life, though, as Louisa knelt down beside his chair and laid her head on his lap.

"There's something else, Richard, something I need to tell you."

"Go on then," said Richard.

"I've been meaning to say for a bit, now, but I wasn't sure about it, and I wasn't sure as to how you'd take it."

Richard already had half an idea though. "You're expectin' *agen*?"

"Yes, do you mind?"

"How could I mind? Today of all days. It's wonderful news, Louie. We've 'ad so much good luck of late that I'm waiting for the next thing to *gu* wrong now, that's all."

As the evening wore on, they spoke quietly of what they would do, now that things were on the up, eventually turning in around ten o'clock. Although they would continue to bask in the reflection of their sudden change of fortune for some time to come, if truth be known, for the moment, both were still a bit bemused by it all.

*

1887 saw Queen Victoria's Golden Jubilee and, with the usual meteorological uncertainties that accompany such occasions, a summer that started out hot turned very unsettled and many of the planned celebrations of June and July that year were marred by bursts of torrential rain. Sunday 21 August saw more tears shed at Flat 2, Outram Street; this time, though, they were tears of joy as it was the day that Louisa gave birth to another boy. Unlike Richard Walter, Richard Archibald, although slightly underweight, was a bouncing, healthy baby.

"Sure, he was in a hurry *te* come into the world and I can't think *fer* the life o' me whatever for," exclaimed Mrs. Flaherty, her words almost lost as the screaming infant literally skidded from the womb.

Richard was delighted, and had been determined that, if it were a boy, he would name him after himself again, but he dared not tempt fate by also repeating the middle name. I do not know where 'Archibald' came from, it certainly does not seem to appear anywhere else in the Warren line. Perhaps it came from one of Louisa's relatives or perhaps it was chosen for some other reason, but it seemed to stick, as Richard was always known to my father simply as 'Arch'.

That evening, with Flo and John asleep on their mattress in the corner of the room and baby Richard asleep in Louisa's arms, Richard sat on the side of the bed next to his wife. The birth had somehow added to his increasing sense of security and, folding his arms and cocking his head back, he began to take stock.

"*Ah* reckon as we're becoming a real family *agen*. What wi' Flo now nearly five, John three and now young Richard."

Louisa didn't reply but simply nuzzled the baby's head and smiled. It was clear to her too that the uncomplicated nature of the birth had brought tremendous relief to all concerned because, although Richard's abilities had now been fully recognised at work and his wages had risen to something approaching an acceptable level, the possibility that the new baby could have been born weak, like little Richard Walter, had been hanging over their heads for months. As the candle flickered beside the bed, although she knew that the trials which faced all working-class Victorian children still lay ahead, he was, she thought, at least over the first hurdle.

Christmas 1887 was the first Christmas for some time where it was seen fit to permit some degree of cheer. Although the size of the room did not allow for the erection of a tree, Richard had been out the weekend before to one of the places where he used to collect firewood when he had been out of work – the period he now called his 'dark days'. In the woods he had managed to find a small fir sapling which he split down the middle of the trunk to make two half trees. He gave one half to Mrs. Tomlinson next door and, with the aid of a few nails and some string, suspended his half in a corner of the room. Louisa, helped by Flo and John, then proceeded to decorate the branches, using rolled-up strips of newspaper tied into bows, lengths of string and baubles made from sealing wax and everything else that was to hand. When they had finished, all agreed that it wasn't half bad. Both children had given the project their hearts and souls because their father had told them that, although Father Christmas had been unable to give them much in previous years, this time he'd won 'the Great Reindeer Race', and so was in a position to give every boy and girl extra presents this year. In their imagination, Flo and John could see Father Christmas in full flight, zooming past a winning post suspended in a moonlit night sky. Predictably they accepted every impossibility at face value and, as he had suspected, Richard was not called upon for any clarifications.

After eating their Christmas dinner the presents were opened; for Flo and John, among a few other more individual gifts, there was an apple, an orange, a bag of nuts, a few coins and a small toy each. As the children played quietly and with baby Richard (Arch) fast asleep in his cot, Richard, pint of four ale in hand, and Louisa with a glass of sherry, relaxed in front of the fire.

"*Ah'v* made a New Year's Resolution," said Richard.

"What?" Louisa asked (as if she didn't know).

"*Te ger* out of 'ere," replied Richard. "*Te* get a better 'ouse. *Ah'v* tried *te* pay *y'* dad back some o' the money I owe 'im *bur ee'll* not *ay* it, *ee'll* not *ay* a penny *on it*. So *ah'v* put it aside and we may as well use it for *summat*."

"Oh, I wish we could, Richard, *wi'v bin* through so much lately, surely, if we can afford it we owe it to ourselves..."

Richard (after thought): "We do *un* all, we do, love... we'll get there!"

And get there they did, as by the same time the following year the family had moved to 26, Middle Street. Although still a small, terraced dwelling, and only a couple of blocks away, it was a house not a flat, and although not much further from the dump, since there were now several other houses in between, you were not so aware that the dump was there. There was still a bit of a smell, it had to be said, but it was not quite so bad, as the houses shielded some of this, too.

Neither Middle Street nor Outram Street still exist in modern Leicester, as both now lie beneath the campus of De Montfort University, but in the day the house in Middle Street was to remain the humble abode of the Warren family for some ten years. During this period, Louisa gave birth to another four boys: Frederick Arthur (1889), Frank William (1892), Albert George (my grandfather) (1894) and Walter Sydney (1896). All, thankfully, were healthy and would survive childhood, but there were already signs that what lay ahead for them might not be anything like as peaceable. There were 'rumblings', low and distant at first but rumblings that would not go away. Rumblings that would only get louder with time and, before long, would be so loud that they could no longer be ignored. Then the rumblings would turn to thunder, a thunder that would have to be confronted if the world were to remain free, and it would be down to the likes of these boys to confront it.

*

The Habsburgs were yet another family with many children (both corporal and territorial). They took their name (also spelt 'Hapsburg') from their twelfth-century Habsburg Castle near Zurich, set in a region now in modern day Switzerland but back then part of Swabia (in German: *Schwaben*) – one of the many 'stem duchies' of Germany that existed at the time. Through various allegiances the Habsburgs began to acquire feudal rights across what is today's Austria and, by the mid-fifteenth century, Frederick III had become Holy Roman Emperor, thus making Austria the most important state in the Holy Roman Empire. In all, the Habsburgs would go on to produce Holy Roman Emperors for almost 300 years, and then, only after a brief hiatus in the mid-eighteenth century, continue to do so as the House of Habsburg-Lorraine, for another forty years; until, in fact, Napoleon abolished the whole institution.

The Habsburgs extended their dominion to the Low Countries when, in 1477, Maximilian I (later to become Emperor) married

Mary, Duchess of Burgundy. This effectively marked the start of the Habsburg Empire proper, since, for the first time, it controlled land outside Austria. Next came most of Spain, when Maximilian's son, Phillip, married Joanne of Castile. Then their son, Charles V (Charles I of Spain), inherited all this as well as Southern Italy. With Charles in Spain, it rather shifted the focus of the Holy Roman Empire that way and Austria was left to Charles's younger brother, Ferdinand I, to oversee. But in 1556, Charles, dogged by ill health, abdicated, leaving Ferdinand with both the Austrian Empire (by now reinforced through the addition of Bosnia, Serbia and parts of Hungary) and the title of Holy Roman Emperor whilst Charles's son, Phillip II, was left Spain and the Spanish Netherlands. Thus was the way that the foundations of the Austro-Hungarian Empire that emerged at the start of the nineteenth century were laid.

Along the way the Habsburgs, like the Warrens and indeed, like all families, encountered issues from time to time. And although some problems were down to marriages between too closely related couples, others resulted from the fact that they were not related closely enough! As inbreeding weakened the family line the Germanic races from one side of the Empire could not get on with the Slavic races on the other, and the seventeenth century was marred by almost constant infighting. Inbreeding was almost certainly the cause of the infertility that left no heirs to the Spanish Habsburgs when Charles II died in 1700, and when Charles VI on the Austrian side died in 1740, with no male heir, the succession of his daughter, Marie Theresa, led to the renowned War of the Austrian Succession. In the event, Marie Theresa was able to continue the dynasty by ruling jointly alongside her husband, Francis, Duke of Lorraine (Franz Stephen), under the umbrella House of Habsburg-Lorraine. (Both Marie Theresa and Francis being grandchildren, albeit by different grandmothers, of the former emperor Ferdinand III).

The dynasty survived in this form for some sixty years, but when Napoleon I became Emperor of France, there were scores to be settled with his old enemy Austria. In 1805 he dealt her two crippling blows: firstly at Ulm, and then at Austerlitz, and in the following year, after trouncing the Prussians at Jena, he finally pulled the rug from beneath the Habsburgs by abolishing the Holy Roman Empire. The last Habsburg Holy Roman Emperor, Francis II, having seen this coming, though, had already preserved his power by declaring himself Emperor of Austria. And probably the best thing to come out of it all would be that Austria's conflicts with France had automatically allied her with Britain, Prussia and Russia and it was, indeed, this Quadruple Alliance, with particular thanks to the Prussians, which finally saw off Napoleon at Waterloo in 1815.

With Napoleon gone, Austria was able to regain much of the lands that she had lost to him. These 'sons and daughters', though, remained many, varied and far-flung, each with an individual culture and, in many cases, an individual language: Italians, Magyars, Romanians, Ukrainians, and Poles, etc. It was perhaps inevitable then that, with time, they began to feel like second-class citizens when the Germanic peoples were being treated more favourably, simply because the Habsburgs themselves were Germanic. Here the Quadruple Alliance came in handy again in dealing with the resultant pockets of rebellion but, as the nineteenth century progressed, the cracks grew wider, and the Empire found itself struggling to maintain its integrity. At the same time, real fears arose about the growing desire for German unification. Although Austria held sway over the various small German states on or near her borders, the spectre of them combining into one large powerful state under Prussia began to loom large, and there was absolutely nothing that she could do about it.

Austria's predicament was compounded when in 1835 the Emperor Francis II died and was succeeded by his son Ferdinand I (not to be confused with Ferdinand I, Holy Roman Emperor, referred to earlier) who lost overall control of Hungary, Bohemia and the small Italian states. Seeing the vulnerability and weakness in Austria that these losses had exposed, many of the German states became more determined than ever to stand up to her. Ferdinand's credibility had been so damaged that in 1848 he decided to abdicate in favour of his son, Franz Joseph. Not that this made a lot of difference to Austria's stability as the Hungarian and Bohemian troubles continued whilst the Italian states were finally lost for good under the unification of Italy during the 1850s and '60s. Nevertheless, although an increasing number of German states were becoming determined to unify under Prussian domination, some remained loyal to Austria and these tensions eventually led to war in 1866. It took only seven weeks for Prussia to trounce Austria and the North German Confederation was created (later the German Empire) from which Austria was excluded. Now deprived of any influence at all over the German states, Franz Joseph turned his attention to consolidating the other parts of his Empire.

By 1867 the threat of the complete secession of Hungary had become so great that, embarrassing though it was for the once mighty Austria, a compromise became the only way to avoid it. A sort of devolution occurred whereby Hungary became semi-independent. Franz Joseph was to remain king and foreign affairs remained a joint matter, but Hungary was allowed her own government to deal with internal affairs. Thus, the state became known officially as Austria-Hungary.

Elsewhere, though, 'family squabbles' continued, largely on racial issues, and when the wresting of Bosnia-Herzegovina from the Ottomans in 1878 drew Russian threats as to the treatment of her 'southern cousins', Austria was forced into the pact that would commit the now united Germany to defend Austria in the event of war.

*

The familial origins of the Turkish Ottoman Dynasty are sketchy, but it is said to have sprung from within a small state in Northern Anatolia under its chieftain Ertuğrul during the thirteenth century (Anatolia being roughly the Asian part of modern Turkey). When Ertuğrul died towards the end of the century, his son, Osman Ghazi (Sultan Osman I), with an eye on the Byzantine Empire to the west, began to dominate and absorb various other surrounding states. The name 'Ottoman' is an eponym of 'Osman' which is said to mean 'ruler', and indeed, the 'Osama' in Osama Bin Laden is also thought to be another derivative of this; perhaps to evoke reminders of a powerful Islamic past. Similarly, 'Ghazi' is said to mean 'Muslim warrior' – quite in keeping with the reputation of many of the inhabitants of Anatolia at the time.

The once immensely powerful Roman Byzantine Empire had been crippled by the sacking of its capital Constantinople (modern day Istanbul) by the Fourth Crusade in 1204. This left other Byzantine towns vulnerable in that, although they were heavily fortified, if surrounded, they could easily be besieged and forced into submission as there were insufficient resources to come to their aid in time. On the other hand, the Ottomans had plenty of soldiers, and it was in this way that they were able to take their first important Byzantine town – Bursa – in 1326. Osman died during the course of this campaign, but his remains were buried at Bursa, later to become the Ottoman capital.

Some sixty miles due north of Bursa lay Constantinople, a city that had grown rich over the years through its strategic position on the Bosporus – an essential trade route between the Aegean and Black Seas. It was perhaps no surprise, then, that it was in this direction that Ottoman expansion quickened throughout the fourteenth century under Osman's successors Orhan (or Orkhan) and then later, Murad I. During 1354 the Ottomans moved westwards across the Sea of Marmara and took the Gallipoli peninsula and, in so doing, began their conquests in Europe. Despite the Black Death, they continued north through Slavic Bulgaria and into the Balkans, at the same time squeezing Constantinople's western supply routes. Things came to a head in June 1389 near Pristina – then at the heart of the Serbian Empire, when the Ottomans under Sultan Murad faced the Serbs and their other Balkan and Bulgarian allies at the Battle of Kosovo Field (also known as the Battle of Blackbird Field; 'Kosovo' being said to allude to 'Blackbird' in Croatian). If the Ottomans had set out to carve this particular clash bitterly into the Serbian heart from then on, they could hardly have chosen a better day for it. The fifteenth of June held a particular significance for the Christian Serbs since, under the Julian Calendar still observed, it was the feast day of the Martyr Saint Vitus, said to have been tortured to death by the Romans in the fourth century A.D. for his refusal to renounce his Christianity.

The Turks prevailed and the Battle of Kosovo ended the medieval Serb Empire, but the cost was high. Both sides' armies were virtually annihilated and both sides lost their leaders.

Accounts of the thick of battle lend very readily to debate, not only because of the prevailing confusion, but also due to the natural tendency to use biased and rhetorical language under such circumstances. Such emotional factors mixed with the metamorphosis of time make the stuff of apocrypha and legend which, of course, the truth rarely hinders.

Not surprisingly then, accounts differ depending on whether you are an Ottoman or a Serb. The Serbian version hails their knight Miloš Obilić (pron: *Milosh Obilich)* as a hero for entering the Sultan's tent at the height of the battle and stabbing Murad to death. The Turks maintain, however, that the killing happened after the battle was over. Both accounts seem to agree that Obilić killed Murad and that Obilić himself was then killed by the Sultan's guards. The stuff of legends, each telling and retelling of this story down the ages, especially whenever tensions between Turkey and Serbia were heightened, would raise both the Ottomans' festerings over what they saw as murder and the Serbs' anger over the invasion of their sovereignty. Inevitably, then, when the structure of the Ottoman Empire began to crumble during the nineteenth century, encouraging militant Serbs to challenge the status quo, the old tale re-emerged as a quintessential tenet of Serbian patriotism as it remains so to this day.

It seems that Yıldırım Bayezid, Murad's younger son, certainly lived up to his name ('Thunderbolt' in Turkish) as it is said, on hearing of his father's death, he lured his elder brother Yakub into a fatal ambush in order to make himself heir to the throne. Whatever, despite the Battle of Kosovo briefly delaying their advances into Europe, the Ottomans were soon able to build a new powerful army. Serbia, on the other hand, had been subsumed and there was soon pressure on the Serb nobility to intermarry their heirs within prominent Ottoman families in order to consolidate the subjection. Bayezid's subsequent acquisition of Bulgaria would give him (or so he thought) the ability to turn up the heat on his 'jewel in the crown' – Constantinople – however, his game was about to be brought to an abrupt end by a 'storm from the East'. Timur, the self-styled Emir of the Timurid Empire, whose borders stretched from the shores of the Black Sea to the edge of China was, like Bayezid, an expansionist. Said to be descended from the fragmented Mongol hordes of Genghis Khan, after having invaded and destroyed Baghdad, he was drawn by the Ottoman harrying of disputed territories on the edge of Anatolia. Unsurprisingly he had little trouble in persuading the local emirs of these territories to assist him in an invasion as, being Muslims themselves, they were a bit peeved at being constantly attacked by fellow Muslims. As a result, Bayezid was trounced at the Battle of Ankara in 1402. Captured and humiliated, he died in custody later that year.

Timur's victory devastated the Ottoman Empire and reduced it to a mere fraction of its former self, with many of the small Turkish states as well as the Balkans regaining their autonomy. Bayezid's three sons fought over what was left with his youngest, Mehmed I, eventually prevailing in 1413. This precipitated an astonishing reversal of fortunes with Mehmed's son and heir, Murad II, retaking control of most of Western Anatolia, Serbia (through his marriage to the Serbian princess, Mara Branković) and much of Bulgaria. The re-expansion was, to some degree, frustrated by Polish and Hungarian forces attacking from the north, but these were finally dealt with at Varna in 1444.

For some strange reason, around this time Murad II decided to cede the throne to his twelve-year-old son, Mehmed, only to reclaim it again shortly afterwards, leaving Mehmed (as Mehmed II) only able to show his true mettle and earn the title 'Conqueror' after his father died in 1451. By Mehmed II's death in 1481, Athens and much of Greece, along with much of the Adriatic coast and Bosnia, had been added to the Empire and the northern extremity extended beyond the Black Sea. Perhaps of most importance politically, though, Mehmed succeeded where his great-grandfather, Bayezid, had failed – he took Constantinople.

In 1453, having just turned twenty-one, he laid siege to the Byzantine capital. He is said to have hatched a brilliant plot in which ships were slipped into the bay after being pulled overland by soldiers and cattle, and when the Byzantines realised what was going on it was all too late. At first, he offered the ruling emperor Constantine XI a deal – surrender and be spared or else. Constantine refused and a fierce assault on the famous great walls then ensued. Initially repulsed, the Turks finally broke through, flooded in and overwhelmed the Byzantines. Constantine was killed in the onslaught and, as was the way of the time, the Turks were able to consolidate their efforts while pillaging the spoils for days after.

The fall of Constantinople is held by many to mark the end of the Middle Ages. From then on it replaced Bursa as the Ottoman capital, having served the Byzantine Empire in that same office for over a thousand years. With time, however, 'Istanbul' would become its more popular name, though there are references to this name being used as far back as the tenth century. After its fall to the Ottomans, people would use either or even both names, but the use of Constantinople was frowned on by some Sultans on account of its Byzantine connotations. In something of a double irony, the matter was not finally settled until the Ottoman Empire had ceased to exist and the father of modern Turkey, Mustafa Kemal Atatürk (Father Turk), became its first president in the 1920s, officially renaming the city Istanbul in 1930. The origin of the name is somewhat controversial in that some hold that this comes from the Turkish *İslâm-bol* (plenty of Islam), others that it is an Arabianised version of Constantinople and yet others that the name comes from Greek – the language of

Byzantium for 800 years prior to its fall. *Stin póli* (στην πόλη) means 'to the city' – the theory being that Constantinople, being 'the big city', would simply be referred to as 'the city', so signs pointing to it would simply read 'to the city' and, over time, *stin póli* evolved into 'Istanbul'.

Mehmed II was generally a tolerant ruler, encouraging multiculturalism by welcoming Greeks and this attitude continued into the reign of his son, Bayezid II, with the welcoming of many Jewish refugees following their expulsion from Spain in 1492. By annexing Bosnia, however, Mehmed proliferated Islam in this particular part of the Balkans. This juxtaposition with Christianity, however, would inevitably contribute to recurrent discord in this part of the world down the ages and, of course, set the stage for Princip's assassination of the Archduke Franz Ferdinand in 1914 along with all its catastrophic consequences.

In 1494 Mehmed II's great-grandson Suleiman was born – the future Sultan who would come to be known as 'The Magnificent' and turn the Ottoman Empire into one of the richest and most powerful Empires that the world had ever seen. Suleiman I came to the throne in 1520 when the Ottoman Empire already extended from the Black Sea through much of Arabia to Egypt. But by the time of his death, in 1566, it stretched even further, dominating the Balkans and Hungary, challenging both Persia and Austria and extending its influence as far as Algiers. With its armies securing the land and its formidable navy dominating the surrounding seas, the Empire was able to hold sway over the considerable east-west trade traversing the area. Before long, this control became so strong that more and more traders were avoiding having to pass through, or even near, such a gatekeeper. Suleiman's reputation as a powerful overlord is legendary but he is also remembered as something of a poet and as the architect of great legal reforms. Tackling many of the criminal and civil matters apt to arise at the time, his legislation became the basis of 'Ottoman Law', vestiges of which still survive to this day.

The Golden Age was not to last forever, though, and when their navy was defeated off Lepanto (Naupactus or Nafpaktos in modern day Greece) at the hands of the Papal Alliance in 1571, it proved that the Great Ottoman Empire, although still mighty, was not invincible. Despite this setback the extent of the Empire continued to expand, reaching its zenith over the following twenty-five years after Sultan Murad III occupied the Caucasus. However, by 1603 the Ottomans were kicked out again. And as with other large, unwieldy edifices, such a level of extension had begun to expose structural failures which left the central government less and less able to maintain control, especially over the further flung regions to the extent that they began to act in a more and more independent way.

The next two hundred years saw almost constant internal and external conflict, during which the Empire lost all its possessions around the Black Sea and much of the Balkans. As Russian influence grew, the Turks were pressed to take Christian issues much more seriously, particularly regarding their treatment of Christians within their own territories. Sultan Selim III, who came to power in 1789, tried to make reforms, but by then, it was all a bit too late, and he was deposed by the Janissaries (elite soldiers) in 1807.

A desperate period followed when the fate of the Ottoman Empire hung by a thread. With control of North Africa lost and Greece now pressing for independence, it was clear that the party was over. By the mid-nineteenth century, noticing the weakness of her ancient adversary, Russia stirred. Tsar Nicholas I expressed outrage at what he saw as France's and the Roman Catholic Church's interference in the protection of Christians within the Ottoman Empire – a role which the Tsar had always regarded as his, and his alone. This tussle, known as the 'Quarrel of the Monks', in January 1853 prompted the Tsar to comment to the British Ambassador Sir George Hamilton Seymour (about Turkey):

> *"We have a sick man on our hands, a man gravely ill, it will be a great misfortune if one of these days he slips through our hands, especially before the necessary arrangements are made."*

Although Sir George did not disagree with the Tsar at the time, Britain had begun to harbour great suspicions that Russia's true ambitions lay in expansionism rather than therapy, particularly since domination over Turkey would give her a clear run from the Black Sea to the Mediterranean.

In gathering her troops in the Balkans in October 1853 Russia began to apply pressure towards Turkey from the north-west. Turkey's response was the summary declaration of war on Russia, completely ignoring the Metternich System of negotiation that had maintained stability in Europe since the Napoleonic wars. With the outbreak of what was to become known as the Crimean War, for the first time since 1815 two large European nations were again at war with each other.

At first the Turks made the running, defeating the Russians at Oltenița (Oltenitza) in Southern Romania, but the Russians soon showed that they meant business when Admiral Paval Nakhimov followed the Turkish fleet into its Southern Black Sea port of Sinope (Sinop) and summarily destroyed it within a matter of hours. The Turks, however, were able to whip up support through this by labelling it 'the Sinope Massacre' as several thousand Turks had been killed in the process, which was enough to draw a joint British and French fleet into the Black Sea and by April 1854 both Britain and France had also declared war on Russia.

In spite of this escalation, Russia remained confident that her alliance with Austria would yield support from that direction; Russia having, after all, supported Austria in the Hungarian Revolt only six years earlier. However, the increasing exclusion of Austria in German affairs had made her insecure and, in the event, she would remain staunchly neutral, as too would Prussia. Austria's neutrality was a bitter disappointment to Russia and would stretch her resources to the limit. As a result Russia lost her grip on the Balkans and, as if adding insult to injury, when the Russians withdrew, with no objections from the Turks, the Austrians took advantage of the situation and moved in to fill the vacuum. With this, the focus of the war now returned to the Black Sea and more specifically, to its north: the Crimean Peninsula.

The battles of Alma, Balaclava (with its famous Charge of the Light Brigade) and Inkerman as well as the Siege of Sevastopol (which, lasting almost a year, must have seemed interminable at the time) are all well documented, those of Alma and Inkerman being particularly imbued in the British psyche down the generations with the eponymous naming of many a street, avenue or lane. And how many men of the 'older generation' wore a 'balaclava' to school?

Eventually, with the fall of Sevastopol, Russia, under Tsar Alexander II, had no option but to cave in.

Although the Turks had effectively started the war, it soon became clear that it was essentially the alliance between Britain and France that had prevailed over Russia. Admitted, the efforts of Turkish (and Sardinian) forces were by no means insignificant but it was by now clear that the Ottoman Empire was no longer the formidable power it once was. The Paris Peace Treaty that concluded the war guaranteed Ottoman territories on condition that the Ottomans treat Muslims and Christians equally. This proved easier said than done, though, and in reality had the effect of increasing tensions between the two religious groups rather than relieving them – especially so in the more distant parts of the Empire where Christians were more numerous, such as in the Balkans and Greece. Meanwhile, as Russia licked her wounds, inside the determination grew to re-establish her influence and 'protection' within Europe, the obvious route being through her 'Slavic cousins' in the Balkans.

By the early 1870s crop failures in Turkey were putting severe constraints on food supplies throughout the Ottoman Empire and heavy taxes, imposed to counter this, were enough to spark revolution, as rumours of the massacres of thousands of Christians in Bulgaria began to spread like wildfire round the world. In Britain, in response to the sheer scale of public outrage, Disraeli's government was forced to abandon its guarantee over Ottoman territories. (Just another 'piece of paper'... read on.)

The next move came in 1876 when Serbia and Montenegro declared war on the Ottoman Empire, thus providing Russia with an element of legitimacy in another intervention in order to 'turn the tables' on the Turks. Especially since Britain, the country that had helped the Turks so recently, was now roundly condemning them. It was also enough to assuage Austrian anxiety and, now prepared to help Russia (short of fighting), her presence in the Balkans lent a further (and unanticipated) advantage. In short, Russia found herself ready, willing and able to pay the Turks back for her humiliation in the Crimea.

From this powerful position Russia, at first, sought a peaceful outcome, but after negotiation and renegotiation the Ottomans would have none of it. They simply continued to press their dismay at the breaking of the Paris Treaty whilst themselves being pressed over Balkan and Romanian autonomy and, in particular, their continued ill-treatment of Christians. Eventually, with absolutely no peaceful solution in sight, in April 1877, Russia finally declared war on Turkey, despite all the possible consequences.

The Russians' first move under General Schilder-Schuldner was to secure the Danube and cross south into Bulgaria, at the same time the Turks, under Osman Nuri Pasha, moved north and occupied the town of Pleven (Plevna) twenty miles south of the Danube. Both sides were roughly equally matched and when the Russians attacked, both took heavy casualties. By July it was clear that the Turks could not be dislodged, only besieged. Over the following few months, with the help of Romanian forces, the Russians were able to strangle all supplies into the town and the Turks had no option but to attempt to break out. They eventually did so on a cold December night by quietly moving westwards over the River Vit, but were soon confronted by the Russians hand-to-hand. This time the Turks were hopelessly outnumbered and, in panic, were forced back across the Vit. The next day Osman surrendered, many of his soldiers either subsequently slaughtered by the Bulgarians or perishing in the bitter winter that was to follow.

As if things were not bad enough for the Turks, at this point Serbia decided to enter the war and despite their many defiant efforts, the Turks were unable to apply more than nominal resistance against what was now a formidable alliance of adversaries. In January the Turks sued for peace and, under the terms of the San Stefano Treaty of 3 March 1878, which settled the issue, the Ottomans were forced to recognise the autonomy of Romania, Serbia, Montenegro and Bulgaria. Southern Bulgaria (Eastern Rumelia), however, remained under Ottoman control, largely as a result of fears over the increasing level of Russian influence in the area.

During the last twenty years of the nineteenth century the Ottoman Empire in Europe was confined principally to what are now Albania, Macedonia and Northern Greece. However, increased resistance to Ottoman rule (particularly in Bulgaria as a result of its partitioning) left the Empire somewhat frayed at its edges while internal economic pressures and levels of taxation remained high. Despite repeated assurances given under the Berlin Treaty of 1878, the persecutions in Romania continued, particularly in Rumelia where the Armenian minorities were targeted. There was a particularly unsavoury cavalry group, made up largely of Kurds and known as the 'Hamidiye', after the then Sultan Abdülhamid II. Merely on the basis that the Armenians were in a minority, this group seems to have been given free rein to 'deal with them'. Although later played down by the Turks, what resulted became known as the Hamidian massacres of the 1890s during which hundreds of thousands of Armenians were horrendously slaughtered. Europe's response, again horrified by this sort of thing, would further strengthen the polarisation of opinion against the Ottomans.

As the atrocities continued, and with even his own subjects getting more and more fed up with him, Abdülhamid II became known as 'The Bloody Sultan'. He was finally dislodged by the 'Young Turk Revolution' of 1908. Under the banner of modernisation he was put under house arrest and replaced by his half-brother Mehmed (or Muhammad) V. Whilst the Armenians must have taken some considerable comfort from the ousting of Abdülhamid, their relief was not to last as, unfortunately, the new regime took over where the Hamidiye had left off and would continue to harass the Armenians for some time to come.

Then, as if the levels of complication and confusion were not enough, in 1911 the Ottomans became bogged down in a war with Italy.

The following year the Balkan League was formed between the Christian states of Serbia, Montenegro, Bulgaria and Greece. It was an alliance originally formed to oppose Austro-Hungarian domination but, with a little intervention from the Russians, it became redirected against the Ottomans and, after the First Balkan War of October 1912, the League left the Ottomans with very little, if any, control at all within Europe. Not that that meant cohesion, though, and as soon as the following year, pre-alliance scores began to re-emerge when Bulgaria turned on the Serbs and in so doing, sparked the Second Balkan War.

The Balkans and the countries surrounding them had, by now, become so unstable that just about anything could have set things off and, when opposing alliances between the great powers began to emerge, the Ottomans really started to 'feel the heat' and began to realise that they, themselves, were now in need of more powerful allies.

Although Mehmed had wanted the Empire to remain neutral, his role had, by this time, become little more than symbolic. The politicians, now at the helm, knew that if they joined the right side, they stood a strong chance of regaining some sort of foothold in Europe but if they remained neutral there would be no chance of this. In fact, given the necessity to join one side or another, there was really no choice. Alliance with the Allies meant alliance with France, and France was allied to the old enemy Russia, so that would never do. At the same time Germany saw Turkey as a geographic link to Africa, the Middle East and Asia and thus the Ottoman Empire's alliance with the Central Powers was forged.

When it later became clear that Turkey had not joined the 'right side', however there were the inevitable recriminations and the effective overruling of the Sultan by the politicians would bring the legality of the Alliance into question. But at that point, of course, it was all a bit too late.

*

And what of the Mother Russia herself? Well, the story of the establishment of what is often seen as the stern dynasty of the Romanovs, it has to be said, is a somewhat strange, confusing and in parts, fatuous one. The cruel antics of the first Tsar, Ivan the Terrible, during the sixteenth century are legendary and, by the end of his tyranny, poverty, starvation and confusion were such that the issue of succession had become hotly contested. Ivan died in 1584 and, perhaps predictably, in questionable circumstances. On his deathbed he is said to have named a prominent boyar (aristocrat) – Boris Godunov – as his heir in place of his eldest son at the time, Feodor (or Fedor), whom he is said to have considered unfit to rule. I say 'eldest son at the time' because Feodor had had an elder brother (also called Ivan) who had been murdered by his father. (Beginning to see what I mean about a 'strange' story?) Officially Feodor became Tsar Feodor I but, on account of the alleged dying wish, Godunov got to pull all the strings. There was also, however, a younger son, Dmitry who, since Feodor was childless, became heir apparent. Dmitry was only a baby when his father died, and when Godunov swept into Moscow, presumably out of fear of the competition, he banished the infant. There then arose a rumour that Dmitry had been found dead with stab wounds, the improbable explanation at the time being that the boy had accidentally stabbed himself while playing with knives. However, since Godunov and Feodor were still vying for the throne, it was suggested, of course, that Dmitry may have been simply 'rubbed out' by followers of either one or the other. But was Dmitry really dead? Then, as now, Russian affairs are not always as they seem and Dmitry turns up again in Moscow towards the end of the 1590s or, at least, somebody purporting to be Dmitry. Apparently, he explained that he had fled following an attempt on his life and hidden in various monasteries in Russia before becoming a teacher in Poland. At this all manner of rumours surrounding Dmitry's fate began to circulate. The man claiming to be Dmitry was certainly well educated, being fluent in both Russian and Polish. Furthermore, many, who should have known otherwise, seemed to agree that he bore a remarkable resemblance to Dmitry. It seems that he even managed to convince Ivan's wife, Maria, that he was her son. Thus the 'return' of Dmitry began to be accepted at face value by enough boyars prepared to challenge Godunov on the issue. Godunov, however, denied them the opportunity by dying shortly afterwards, rather audaciously naming his son as his heir, Feodor. (Obviously not the Feodor that was Ivan's son who had died without an heir in 1598). I told you that it was confusing!

In the event it turned out that this 'Dmitry' was not really Dmitry at all, but an impostor thought to have been Grigory (or Yuri) Otrepyev, a nobleman and former friend of the Romanovs. But, because so many wanted to believe in him, his support continued to grow and eventually he managed to dispose of Feodor (Godunov's son that is) and become Tsar in his own right, often referred to nowadays as the 'False Dmitry I' or 'Dmitry I the False'. Once ensconced he was able to crush all opposition and became the first to style himself 'Emperor of Russia'. It was not to last, though, and his support began to dwindle just as fast as it had grown. When he married an unconverted Catholic, he was seen as promoting Catholicism over and above Orthodox Christianity. His popularity receded even further when rumours spread of sexual perversion. In the end, barely a year after his succession, he was shot dead during a revolt led by the boyar, Vasili Shuisky, who then claimed the throne for himself as Vasili IV in 1606.

Please bear in mind that, so far, the story has only been about one False Dmitry who, although the most convincing False Dmitry, was certainly not to be the last. Meet the second False Dmitry, whose true identity remains a mystery to this day. He turns up about a year later in the small town of Starodub, a few hundred miles south-west of Moscow, apparently ranting about being a Russian aristocrat but then 'confessing' to being Dmitry, at which point worried local officials arrest and interrogate him. But he stuck to his story and as a result began to gather support, particularly among certain disaffected groups including the Poles and Cossacks who had supported the first False Dmitry and seemed to be suggesting that, since the claim was maintained under duress, it must be true. Then, almost undoubtedly encouraged by her Polish family, the first False Dmitry's bride, Marina, meets the second False Dmitry and 'recognises' him! Even more strange since nobody else seems to have thought that there was any resemblance whatsoever...

As his popularity developed this (so-called) Dmitry was even able to go so far as setting up an administrative centre at Tushino, just north of Moscow and, through his strong support from the Poles, stir up a Polish invasion. Although managing to consolidate his strength in the north, though, the second False Dmitry was never quite able to make it to Moscow and in 1610, following Russia's defeat to the Poles at Klushino (or Kluszyn), he was shot dead, apparently by a guard that he had previously ordered flogged. It was to be the end of the road for Vasili, too, when he was arrested and sent to Poland, shortly after which, he died.

This of course left the position of False Dmitry vacant and yes, in 1611 at Ivangorod on the Estonian border, lo and behold, another one turns up; this time thought to have been a deacon by the name of Sidorka. You would have thought that by now this ruse would have become a bit transparent but yet another attempt was made, led largely by the Cossacks, to make him Tsar. This time, though, the plot failed to gather momentum and in 1612 the third False Dmitry was arrested by the authorities and executed.

According to various accounts, other False Dmitrys would keep popping out of the woodwork for some time to come but it was by now dawning that the whole affair was just a farce and, anyway, soon to be the least of Russia's problems, as she started to descend into chaos. Poor harvests had led to famine and the resulting unrest had cost the deaths of hundreds of thousands. Many factions, particularly the Cossacks, were marauding at will, the Polish Army controlled Moscow, and there was still no Tsar. It was very much the 'Time of Troubles'.

One prominent leader to emerge from the struggles, however, was Prince Dmitry Pozharsky. No, not yet another false Dmitry, this time a nobleman descended from a local dynasty who was determined to reintroduce some sort of stability. Encouraged by Russian popular support he took command of a volunteer army assisted by a wealthy merchant, Kuzma Minin. Progress was slow but, by August 1612, they had reached the gates of Moscow. As battle ensued the supplies to the city were intercepted by yet another Dmitry (Trubetskoy) and by October, the Poles were forced to surrender.

The reinstated Parliament or 'Zemsky Sobor' elected Michael Romanov as Tsar Michael I. Although a direct descendant of Ivan the Terrible, this posed a couple of slight problems. Firstly, Michael was only sixteen years of age and, secondly, he did not want to be Tsar at all. Legend has it that he was found hiding in a monastery and took quite a bit of persuading. Finally, though, in May 1613, he was crowned in Moscow and so the 'Romanov Dynasty', which would last for 300 years, was established.

The reigns of Michael and then his son and successor, Alexis, brought with them some degree of stability, but very little in the way of modernisation took place and Russia began to lag behind her European counterparts. It would take the birth of Peter in 1672 to Alexis and his second wife, Natalya, to change all that. Peter I – later to become 'Peter the Great' – was crowned Tsar in 1682. This, again, was a far from simple affair (as the reader will surely, by this time, have come to expect) as Peter had a surviving elder half-brother, Ivan. But Ivan had been initially overlooked (a situation far from discouraged by Peter's mother who, of course, was not Ivan's mother) as he was said to have struggled mentally ('was considered imbecilic' to use the language of the day). Subsequently, though, a compromise was reached with a joint reign in which Peter and Ivan ruled alongside each other. Also, because of Ivan's problems and Peter's age (only ten at the time), Sophia (Ivan's true sister – Peter's half-sister) was meant to oversee the joint sovereigns as Regent. However, when it turned out that she had ambitions to usurp power for herself, she was removed to a convent where she would remain for the rest of her life.

When Ivan died in 1696 Peter began to consolidate his power.

Already an accomplished student of warfare, instead of simply installing himself, he set off on what might nowadays be described as an extended 'gap year'; travelling and working around Europe during which he is said to have studied shipbuilding in both Holland and London. They say that travel broadens the mind, and it was essentially the knowledge that he accumulated on his travels that helped him to breathe new life into the state of Russia.

When Peter returned to Moscow Sophia yet again tried to overthrow him. Now skilled and much wiser, though, his solution was summary and bloody and put paid to Sophia once and for all. She was said to have been literally driven mad by the carnage!

Peter the Great died in 1725. Although not without his critics, he clearly understood how conflict can often be based on the ignorance or the misunderstanding of foreign ways. His legacy, therefore, was not only a greatly improved infrastructure but a much clearer understanding by Russia of her European neighbours.

Following Peter's death the Romanov Dynasty continued rather uneventfully with a series of relatively short reigns, that is, of course until Peter III fell out with his wife in the early 1760s. Peter III's predecessor, Elizabeth, had remained unmarried and childless and so Peter (her nephew) was her only hope of maintaining the Romanov Dynasty. German by birth, having been born in Kiel, Peter III gave rise to the Holstein-Gottorp-Romanov line – the line which would continue until the assassination of Nicholas II ended the Tsars in July 1918. Perhaps more sinned against than sinning, Peter was a sickly child, orphaned at the age of twelve and brought up very strictly. Not surprising then, that he turned out inattentive and immoral. He was also, like his grandfather Peter the Great (and this is where the comparison ends), a reluctant Tsar. This Peter not only disliked Russia, he had a pathological hatred of it and everything to do with it. At the start of his reign he flatly refused to pursue the Prussians who were about to surrender in the Seven Years War. This was presumably because his German origin divided his loyalties, but it infuriated his Army.

Peter III's wife was Sophie Friederike Auguste von Anhalt-Zerbst (also known as Catherine). Although she was German too, she was a completely different kettle of fish to Peter. So, when Peter's behaviour became even more bizarre, it occurred to many that Catherine might make a better alternative. As Catherine's lover, Count Grigory Orlov, and his brother, Alexei, began to press the issue, however, with the series of arrests that followed, Catherine began to lose her nerve. The insurrection had been so well contrived, though, that plans to counter any opposition were already afoot and on entering St. Petersburg (the new capital since Peter the Great's reign), she was greeted to cheers from both soldiers and public alike. It was clear to Peter that he was now history – in more ways than one as it turned out, because within a few days he was dead – ostensibly of 'haemorrhoidal colic' but nobody really believed that that was the real cause.

Catherine was, of course, Catherine II or Catherine the Great, who went on, for the most part of her life, to continue to reform Russia in the spirit of Peter the Great. In fact, as well as widely read, she turned out to be a remarkable diplomat and general all-rounder. No reference intended, I hasten to add, towards her sexual appetite, even though, in reality, this next bit is generally regarded as apocryphal. Some say that she met her end while attempting to have sex with a stallion. At sixty-seven, though, I think this unlikely and consider the alternative explanation that it was as a result of a stroke, while sitting on the toilet, the more probable one. Slightly more dignified perhaps, but not much.

On Catherine's death her son Paul (Pavlov) ascended the throne, although Catherine had suggested in her lifetime that Peter III, on account of his sterility, could not have been Paul's father. Despite this, though, there was a clear physical resemblance between the two men, and it is perhaps more likely that Catherine was simply trying to preclude the son of the man she had grown to hate from inheriting the throne. But inherit the throne he did, the principle of primogeniture counting strongly in his favour.

Sadly Paul, like his father, was also emotionally unstable, and became unpopular when he drew Russia into war with Napoleonic France, largely, it is thought, through personal prejudices and his fear of a similar revolution in Russia. His meddlings made him enemies, and only five years after his accession he was assassinated in St. Michael's Palace by a group of drunken conspirators after refusing to sign his abdication. It is not clear to what extent Paul's successor, his son, Alexander I, knew about the intentions of the conspirators. Alexander was said to have been in the Palace at the time of the murder and may have even let the conspirators in but it is supposed that he may not have wanted his father killed. Whatever, Alexander was to inherit not only the throne of Russia but the full force of the conflict with Napoleonic France – his reign was certainly not to be an uneventful one.

Alexander I's death is officially recorded as 1 December 1825, but some believe that he faked it and lived out the remainder of his years as a wandering monk. Nevertheless, he was succeeded by his youngest brother, Nicholas (Nicholas I), Alexander's other brother, Constantine (Konstantin), who was older than Nicholas, having renounced his entitlement. Despite high ideals Nicholas I's direct approach made him many enemies from the start and he found it increasingly difficult to enact his reforms. Eventually he drew Russia into the Crimean War and her humiliating defeat at the hands of the Turks and their Western Allies. Not that Nicholas experienced the bitter end, since he had died, apparently the result of a chill, the year before the war ended. It must, however, have been pretty clear by the time he died, that Russia would not prevail.

Nicholas's son, Alexander II, inherited the new mess that Russia had created for herself after winding up the Crimean War. Russia was left weak and humiliated, corruption became rife, and it was clear that reform was needed. Alexander began with the long overdue abolition of serfdom (a sort of agricultural slavery), the 'Emancipation of the Serfs' as it was to become known. He also overhauled the country's infrastructure and its military and legal systems. Alexander II was the Tsar who sold the territory of Alaska to the United States in 1867 and, under the guise of protecting the Balkan Slavs and Christianity in general within the Ottoman Empire, in 1877 would send Russia to war again with the Turks, this time winning. Such sweeping measures had their opponents, though, and throughout his life attempt after attempt was made to assassinate Alexander. Finally, in March 1881, he was blown up by a group of anarchists just as he was about to introduce the basis for an elected parliament. As a result, Russia was, once again, thrown back into turmoil.

Alexander III followed; the second son of Alexander II (the first having died suddenly in 1865) and the father of the ill-fated Tsar Nicholas II. Although by no means weak in character he became known as 'The Peacemaker' since Russia managed to avoid being drawn into any other major conflict during his reign. His attitude towards Germany was less cordial than that of his father, however, and matters deteriorated even further when Germany chose to ally herself to Austria, rather than Russia, in dealing with the future of Eastern Europe under the shadow of the increasingly unstable Ottoman Empire.

Above all, Alexander III believed in a 'Russian Russia' and, perhaps embittered by his father's assassination, began for some reason to believe that there had been a Jewish element involved. As a result, he introduced a raft of anti-Semitic legislation, measures that would precipitate the wave of pogroms during the late nineteenth century which largely instigated the mass emigration of Jews from Russia, principally to the United States.

Although subject to several assassination attempts (they usually went with the job of Tsar), at a relatively early age and after a relatively short reign, Alexander III died of a kidney infection, thought to have been a result of damaging one of his kidneys when involved in a train crash with his family some years earlier.

And so, in May 1896 the last Tsar – Nicholas II – was crowned, as was the tradition, in the Dormition Cathedral in Moscow, even though the imperial capital at the time was St. Petersburg. He was first cousin to both Prince George of Wales (later to become George V) and Kaiser Wilhelm II of Germany.

Although Russia was strong both militarily and industrially, things did not get off to a very good start for Nicholas, when rowdy behaviour during one of the coronation celebrations led to a stampede, during which, it was said, over 1,000 revellers were trampled to death and a similar number injured. Then, against both his better judgement and plain common sense, that evening the Tsar was persuaded to attend a celebratory ball. Naturally this was viewed as 'adding insult to injury' and his stupid decision would taint his reputation indelibly in the eyes of many a Russian.

The unrest and anti-Semitism continued and when Russia suffered a humiliating and costly defeat at the hands of Japan in 1905, after being drawn into war over Japanese expansionism, it led to revolution. This time his popularity took an even steeper dive after guards opened fire on peaceful demonstrators in St. Petersburg campaigning for improved working conditions. It left some 500 dead or injured and gave rise to the soubriquet 'Nicholas the Bloody'.

As his reign continued and Russia became one of the first countries to enter World War I, even going to the extent of changing the name of its then capital, St. Petersburg, to Petrograd – the former name being too German-sounding – Nicholas did manage to work with the government but the relationship was uneasy and, from time to time, a troubled one. His family life, too, became complicated, with the emergence of Rasputin, and people were beginning to wonder why this somewhat risible character seemed to hold so much sway over so much of the royal family's affairs. Inevitably this, along with all the associated rumours, began to bring the Tsar's judgement into question – all grist to the mill of the likes of Lenin and the Bolsheviks, of course. With such unrest at home and the descent of Europe into war, it was becoming clear that, in order to recoup any degree of stability, this Tsar would certainly have his work cut out. And the rest, as they say, is history. As part of the Russian Revolution, during the summer of 1918, the peace of the Tsar's retreat in the Ural Mountains was shattered when Bolshevik insurgents stormed in, and Nicholas and his family were all brutally murdered.

...Oh, those Russians...

*

As the twentieth century dawned, then, Europe stood a conjunction of politically polarised, chaotic states – most now with deep-seated anxieties and suspicions about domination, but some with ambitions to dominate. As these tensions mounted, each day-to-day event began to be seen as having some bearing on the outcome and it was becoming clear that things could not continue as they were for much longer. If Europe was going to avoid war, things would have to stabilise. Although to some this meant that war was inevitable, all but the most jingoistic hoped it would not come to that. Indeed, only very few, if any, could have foreseen the full extent of the dreadful payment that would in reality, have to be met; the monumental cost to be borne by all, from kings and the aristocracy, through politicians and the elite, down to the Atkins family, the Schmidts, the Ivanovs, the Doğuşes, the Le Grands and the Warrens alike.

Chapter 4

Our Daily Bread

'Give us this day our daily bread.
And forgive us our trespasses...'
The Lord's Prayer

From the end of the 1880s and throughout the 1890s the centre of gravity of Leicester moved slightly further north-west when a plan to develop the West End fields between the River Soar and an area known as Newfoundpool was enacted. The development, said to have given rise to the local saying, 'West End, best end', included new factories and schools but its mainstay was the provision of some 3,000 or so affordable modern homes fit for working-class families. Interestingly the former landowner, Isaac Harrison, left his mark on his Newfoundpool section by naming the streets so that they spelt out his name: Looking at the map, the streets start with Hawthorne Street to the west through all the other letters of his name (as the initial letter of each street) ending in Newport Street to the east. The Harrison family lived in the (then) grand mansion, Newfoundpool House, which later became the Empire Hotel. Fronting onto Fosse Road North and backing onto Newport Street, 'the Empire' would be familiar to anybody with any historical experience of Leicester. I say 'historical' experience as the Empire has now been demolished, as has the adjacent old Saint Augustine's Church, which had previously been vandalised and set fire to. A Lidl supermarket and Tesco Express (complete with petrol station) now stand on their former sites. Progress, I suppose, but to my dad, who lived in Newport Street as a boy and young man, these were focal points of his life and I'm sure that he would have been sad to see them go.

By 1899 Richard and his family had moved to Tewkesbury Street, a gently rising street of small, terraced houses, a little to the south-west of the Harrison project. First to No.56 and then, by 1902, just across the road to No.53. The area's layout is still, in essence, the same today as it was back then, and both these houses look very similar to me, so I have no idea as to the reason for the subsequent move. It may have been that No.53 was slightly roomier, since, in their time at No.56, Ernest had been born, taking the family total to ten. Even so, looking at the narrow 'two up two downs', it is extremely difficult to imagine how such a large family could have enjoyed any great comfort or privacy living in either of these houses. There would have been enough space for three separate bedrooms, however, the two purpose-built ones and the 'end room' (in the rear section, above the kitchen). But whereas the two custom-made bedrooms would likely have had fires in them, it is unlikely that the end room would have. Situated above the kitchen, though, it would no doubt have benefited from the heat generated below on the occasions that the copper was lit.

Later, as the provision of indoor toilet facilities became more and more *de rigueur* down the years, the end rooms in larger proportioned properties of this design would often allow for the accommodation of both a modern bathroom and a small third bedroom.

Moving into a new, modern house must have been like a breath of fresh air to the family. Although Middle Street had served its purpose, it was old, and had become more damp and dilapidated with each passing year. Despite bitter complaints to the landlord, very little had been forthcoming in the way of improvements. As a result, when

Richard first heard of the proposed new development, he followed its progress closely in the hope that he might one day be able to secure one of the new houses for his family and, more importantly, be able to cover the rent. So, when the opportunity arose, he was well prepared and was one of the first to apply. Although the rent did turn out to be quite a bit more than they were currently paying, the two eldest children, Flo and John, had by this time left school and were both working in one of the many boot and shoe factories now established in Leicester. This meant that, with a bit of scrimping, there was just about enough money coming in each week to make it work.

On that first day, walking down those new cobbled streets with their straight building lines and raised pavements of flagstones bordered by kerb stones, the kids were ecstatic. Then, arriving at the front door (painted a sort of dark blue, as were all the others in the street) and walking through it into their new house. That smell of fresh mortar, sawn wood and new paint; a world away from the musty, fusty, dark dwelling that Middle Street was. In the parlour (front room) there was a modern, clean fireplace and even though everybody knew that it would only ever be used on 'high days and holidays', it was still a thrill just to know that it was there. Beyond, through doors at the bottom of the stairs, was the rear parlour (living/dining room) in which they would spend most of their waking hours in the house. This was a much more spacious living area than they were used to and had a modern cooking range gleaming with black lead polish, on which hung a trivet. Beyond the lounge was the kitchen with running mains water, a sink and a copper. Out the back was a yard paved with blue bricks, giving clear access to the brick toilet and 'coalhole' lean-tos which stood side by side behind the kitchen. At the end of the yard was a small garden, one side of which was soil for a small flower garden or vegetable patch and the other turf, so as to form a small lawn. It was paradise in comparison to the dingy backyard paved with cracked and disintegrating flagstones that lay behind 26, Middle Street.

Through a door in the corner of the parlour, the stairs, set in a space between the parlour and the living room, led to the bedrooms.

At the top of the stairs one door led to the larger front bedroom, opposite which was a short corridor or landing with one door off to the second (smaller) bedroom and another door, at the end, leading to the end room. Ostensibly the end room would have been a storage room for clothes, spares and the tin bath, etc. but in this case it had already been earmarked as a third bedroom. Flo, for the first time in her life, would have the privacy of her own room. Although a screen had divided her from the boys in the past, being the only girl, the arrangement was becoming increasingly inappropriate, especially as she was now a young woman. The fact that she had to share with a heap of clutter did not worry her in the slightest and it soon became clear to all concerned that anyone other than she would cross the threshold to this sanctum at their peril.

With Flo finally in her own room, the state of affairs at the start of 1901 saw Richard and Louisa occupying the rear bedroom with Ernest (Ernie), who at eighteen months old, was still in a cot. The front bedroom was shared by the other six boys: Walter (Syd, then aged four), Albert (six), and Frank (nine) in one double bed, Fred (twelve), and Richard (Arch, thirteen) in another double and John (Jack, seventeen) in his own single bed. Needless to say, there was not much space between them.

As 56, Tewkesbury Street had been brand new when the Warrens moved in, an exciting novelty and, in the case of the boys at least, a source of controversy, was the agreement that the family could choose the wallpaper. Flo had chosen a bold rose design for her room and, as Richard was not really interested, Louisa had chosen a small, warm floral design for her and Richard's bedroom, a sort of large, white fern leaf pattern on grey background for the stairs and landing, and a light, floral design for downstairs. When the boys did finally reach a consensus they went for a busy spiral design, sadly not really in keeping, as it made their already overcrowded bedroom seem even smaller. Overall, though, the scheme worked well, and the light downstairs pattern gave both the parlour and living room an airy feel in contrast to the cosier ambiance of the darker patterns in the bedrooms.

Sometime around 1898, when the day came to leave 26, Middle Street for good, most of the effects were carried by hand across town. No mean feat, it being some half a mile as the crow flies (nearer three-quarters via the streets) from Middle Street to Tewkesbury Street. Richard had a wheelbarrow and had borrowed two more. He had also been allowed the use of a hand trolley from work. Normally used for moving machinery and large quantities of stock around the factory, it was a sturdy wooden structure with small iron wheels, but the bearings had worn so badly that none of the four wheels stood upright. It weighed two or three hundredweight even empty and, when in motion along the cobbled streets, made a thunderous noise. Thankfully the route was a fairly level and even one, and since the trolley could be piled high with light things, Richard was able to move all the linen, clothes, lino and rugs, etc. in just two passes. Louisa had one of the wheelbarrows whilst Flo, ably assisted by Arch, had another, and John, ably assisted by Fred and Frank, had the third one. Albert and baby Syd had been taken to Bonners Lane to be looked after by their grandparents for the duration of the move.

When it came to the old oak dining table that had served them well for years, the beds, the dresser, the sofa and the armchairs (such as they were), a good friend of Richard's came to the rescue. Rex West had a milk delivery round and, by early afternoon, when he had finished his deliveries and the horse had been fed, these heavy items were loaded onto the cart and taken round to the new house on the promise of a pint or two when he and Richard were next in the Black Bull together.

Down to Goswell Street, onto Asylum Street, then Newarke opposite the Trinity Hospital Almshouses, over the new canal bridge, under the new viaduct and over the old river bridge onto New Parks Street. Right at Coventry Street and along Tudor Road to Tewkesbury Street on the left. There was not a great deal to move really and by mid-afternoon everything had been relocated. Flo and the boys had left their two borrowed wheelbarrows stacked on the trolley outside their old home in Middle Street for Richard to return them and, without any further adieu, had headed back to Tewkesbury Street, each having been rewarded for their efforts with a bag of sweets from the corner shop.

Before following on, Richard and Louisa were left gazing around inside the empty shell that had been their home for some ten years. As they did, the memories flooded back; some good, some not so. Yes, there had been problems, arguments and dramas all right. Like just after when Syd was born. With nine mouths to feed, things were becoming fraught, and Richard had done one of his 'disappearing acts' again. For three days he did not come home and only then at around midnight on Sunday, drunk. The house was in uproar the following morning as Louisa tried to force him from his bed.

"Get *te* work or we'll lose the 'ouse *un* all!"

With no money, in desperation Louisa had had to pawn her only coat in order to put food on the table. But, in all fairness, Richard had managed to redeem it within the month, once he had regained his senses.

On the other hand, four more boys had been born happily and healthily in Middle Street, they had seen ten Christmases and something like sixty birthdays – a lot to remember and be thankful for.

Suddenly both began to feel something of a sense of loss.

R: "Look, we've left that old stool behind the door there. I'll carry it back with me."

L: "No, leave it, it's half broken anyway."

R: "Come in for firewood."

L: "No leave it; leave a bit of us with this house. For all its problems it's not been a totally bad 'ouse and we've had some happy times here. Leave it something."

R: "Whoever comes next '*ull* only *bun* (burn) it."

L: "Then let 'em. Let 'em warm the house on us. It deserves it."

R: "Okay, come on then *luv*, let's go home… to our new home."

*

Although the winter of 1900 was generally mild, one particular Monday morning in January 1901 was exceptionally bitter, and when the house cracked and creaked against the frost, at half-past five in the morning Jack (as John was, by now, almost always called) stirred in his bed. As he poked his head out from under the blankets the silent freezing air hit his face. Through the gap in the thick curtains, he could make out the pattern of the ice that had formed on the inside of the bedroom window and that confirmed it; this start to the week was going to be a cold one.

Jack's bed was set along the back wall of the front bedroom, next to the door, with the two double beds containing five of his brothers set between him and the window. Before long the tin can alarm clock rang out and the incumbents of these other beds also began to stir. Soon bedsprings twanged and the sounds of these, along with groans and stretching noises, filled the room.

Jack and Arch had their jobs to go to, Fred, Frank and Albert had school, but Syd, who had not yet started school, had no such worries.

Jack had left school almost four years earlier, at the tender age of thirteen, and managed to get a job at the same boot and shoe factory where his sister Flo worked; earlier situated in Red Cross Street, nearer the town centre, but now operating from a brand-new factory on Tudor Road – literally only a few hundred yards from the new family home.

Monday, as tradition had it, was washday and Louisa was already up and about. Having lit the fire below the copper she was waiting for it to catch enough to make toast by. Everybody had toast made from the copper's fire for breakfast on washdays.

On such cold mornings the thing was to get dressed while getting out of bed in a continuous sort of way. Firstly, keeping as much blanket around you as possible, sit up, then remove pyjama top and replace it with vest and shirt. Next put socks and underpants or long johns on under the blankets and then very quickly swing sideways and put feet into trousers (braces already attached), pull them up, do them up, arms in braces and jumper on. The first one up (almost always Jack and hardly ever, if ever, Syd) to light the oil lamp next to the chimney breast. Lastly, find the warmest source of heat immediately, in this case, the copper.

Before long Jack was thumping down the stairs closely followed by Arch, then the younger boys. Syd would probably not have stirred at all were it not for the smell of fresh toast creeping up the stairs from the kitchen.

Shortly afterwards Richard is heard trudging slowly down the stairs, scratching his head and yawning at the same time. Half-dressed, straggly-haired and unshaven, he then stands at the sink in the kitchen for a few minutes, shaving into the broken piece of mirror kept there for just that purpose. Meanwhile the kids take it in turns to toast slices of bread on a long fork, poking them towards the fire through the small door under the copper. Nobody would say much on account of the cold; if you did start to speak, all that came out was a shivery noise that was difficult to understand and, of course, cost valuable heat to produce.

After shaving in ice-cold water Richard scoops a jugful from the copper, which was by now lukewarm, pours it into the sink and soaks his flannel with it. After rubbing the flannel on a large bar of coal tar soap he then proceeds to wipe his face, ears and neck with it. After rinsing the flannel, and wiping his face, ears and neck again, he would always throw it down into the sink and quickly bury his head in the towel to dry himself, making a sort of vibrating noise with his mouth as he did so – a sort of expression of relief on the completion of this uncomfortable but necessary process. Next, he would usually walk into the living room and sit down in the large armchair that was always parked directly in front of the fire. But on washdays the fire would generally be very low by now, in order to save on coal, what with the copper being alight as well. This was Richard's place, though, and Richard's alone, at least that is, when he was at home. As, although other members of the family had been known to sit on it when he was out, there would have been hell to pay had they not immediately relinquished it on his return. And it was always here that Richard ate his toast and drank his tea of a morning;

usually without milk on a Monday unless the milkman came early, because the milk from the weekend had, more often than not, all been drunk or what was left had gone off. After he had finished his breakfast the boots that had stood in front of the range all Sunday day and night would be pulled on and Richard would stand, straighten his shirt on rising, then don his coat and cap and, with a mumbled "See *y'* later," leave the house.

Flo would usually appear at around half-past six, fully dressed but still brushing her long curly hair. "Any toast left, Mum?" was followed by Louisa shouting across, "Do a piece for your sister, Syd." Not regarding the request as at all fair, Syd began to complain but, after the "Oh…", he thought better of it and did as he was told. It is fair to say, however, that other similar requests had not always been carried out with such good grace, particularly when his father wasn't around.

As the fire beneath the copper took hold and began to heat the kitchen and then percolate into the living room, it would brighten spirits and a bit more conversation would spring up across the two rooms about one current thing or another. Soon, however, it would be time for everybody to start thinking about leaving.

Richard gone, Jack, Arch and Flo all turned out together into the cold, foggy, damp half-light. In the winter these three all started work at the same time; eight o'clock, Arch, having only left school relatively recently, had been offered a full-time job as an errand boy at Eckersley's grocer's shop where he had previously worked after school and on Saturdays. The men (for that was what Arch was now that he had left school and was working) all carried small bags tied across their shoulders containing a bottle of tea and a couple of sandwiches (more often than not, just bread and butterine, but sometimes butter and jam or honey, and very occasionally egg or bully beef or even proper meat, but only if left over from some special meal or other). Flo had similar fare but carried hers in what she called her 'handbag' but was in reality, a sort of miniature suitcase which also contained various other paraphernalia including a mirror, powder and various items of make-up, etc.

As they walked others left their houses in a common purpose. On to busy Tudor Road they grunted their goodbyes through steaming mouths. Flo and Jack did not have far to go, as their new factory was only just up the road on the left, but Arch, who had another half-mile or so to go to the shop where he worked on Beatrice Road, ran on ahead and was out of sight by the time Flo and Jack got to work.

Jostling through the factory gate with the rest of the work force they would grab their time cards from the rack, queue up at the clocking-in machine and, when their turn came, place the card in the slot at the bottom of the machine and: *clunk!*, as they pressed hard down on the lever that stamped the card with their exact time of arrival. A few minutes late and you could lose a quarter of an hour's wages – do that more than once in a blue moon and you could be sacked.

Flo worked in what was known as the 'Closing Room': a large room, packed with machines, the purpose of which was to 'joint' the various pieces of leather that had been cut to shape or 'clicked' from hides of leather to form uppers. As newly cut edges tend to be uneven or too thick to be joined neatly, this is where Flo and her fellow 'skivers' came in. Not the old army term for avoiding work, but working a machine that, through pressing a pedal and manipulating the leather edge between rollers and against a blade, fashioned the edges to be joined into neat bevels. Sitting at the machine for hours on end, with just enough elbow room between you and the next worker, the task was repetitive and monotonous.

Jack, however, was a heel builder – basically self-explanatory and perhaps more of a skilled job than skiving, as it is more to do with the finishing of a shoe than its preparation. The heel is built by stacking and joining thicknesses of heel leather or 'lifts' to the height dictated by the design. Again, you are hunched over a machine all day and, apart from moving on from one design to the next, this process would have been rather repetitive too.

Thus went the working day for Flo and Jack, either side of an hour off for lunch sometime between noon and 2pm, depending on workflow and deadlines. But whatever, the machinery would clunk and rattle incessantly. How glad they must have been then to hear that siren sound at the end of the working day. What relief they must have felt, clocking off and walking out to freedom – especially on a summer's evening, but even the cold, rainy night that met them at the end of that particular shift would have been enough. The day's work was done and there was no more work for twelve hours. Thank God!

*

Before the 1890s, as with hosiery, a good deal of boot and shoe making, particularly skiving and closing, was done in homes or small workshops. In these times, of course, the quality of the work depended to a great degree on the skill, resources and dependability of the outworker. Also, like the hosiery industry, the boot and shoe industry became increasingly affected by the general recession of the time as more and more products, formerly manufactured domestically, were now being imported; the main source of these being the United States, where better quality goods could be produced more cheaply.

The natural economic reaction had been to consolidate all aspects of production into one place: the factory. With all the machinery together, it could be more easily and quickly maintained, the workforce was regularised and controlled, and the production process could be supervised throughout. Initially, at least, wages were improved too, but when recession set in and demand fell sharply, wages declined again as workers were put on part-time or, if things did not improve, laid off, sometimes for weeks on end. It would be these sorts of issues, along with all the other industrial disputes that arose between management and the labour force, which eventually led to the creation and development of the trade unions on the one side and the manufacturers' organisations on the other.

Things came to a head in the mid-1890s when, worried by rapidly increasing union membership and the ever-increasing number of (what management considered to be) unreasonable demands made by the unions, the National Boot and Shoe Manufacturers'

Federation issued their own list of demands. Known as 'The Seven Commandments' and presumably an allusion to the strictures of the Seven Commandments of Noah in the Old Testament, later the term would be used by George Orwell for another list of tenets in his parody of Communism: *Animal Farm*.

These seven proposals were a fairly indelicate attempt by the Federation to rationalise the situation and were basically concerned with two main aspects of the industry: pay (effectively frozen for two years) and the absolute right of management to manage.

The unions were outraged by the proposals and rejected them outright as unworkable, however, they did suggest negotiations under the fairly well-established arbitration system in place at the time. But the Federation rejected this and there was deadlock. And as both the headquarters of the Federation and those of the National Union of Boot and Shoe Operatives (NUBSO) were in Leicester, it was Leicester that would become the focus of the events that followed.

It soon became clear, to the unions at least, that the only option left was to go on strike, and so a strike fund was duly set up in preparation. In addition, fresh demands were made for pay increases but these, perhaps inevitably, were met with indifference and so the strike began. The 'knee-jerk reaction' of the employers to this was to lock the workers out.

The standoff dragged on for several long weeks, during which time meetings were held, marches organised, stirring speeches made and rousing socialist songs sung. Throughout, the mood in both camps was generally one of calm determination but eventually, what the employers had counted on happened – the unions simply ran out of money and were unable to afford to continue to fund the soaring cost of strike pay. In April 1895 a wishy-washy 'Terms of Settlement' was signed by both sides, which merely described piecework as 'undesirable' and required that the arbitration scheme be revised. Nevertheless, the period between 1895 and 1901 would see a return to relative stability and, although increases in the price of leather didn't help, the purchase and use of more and more American machinery and the increased adoption of American systems improved both the economics and quality of production. The industry was still not without its problems, though, and isolated pockets of unrest continued. As the demand for footwear fluctuated markedly from season to season, periods of reduced hours and layoffs inevitably continued, and it tended to be wintertime (when a decent wage was essential) that things were slackest. If you could hang on in work until Easter, when things usually picked up again, you could pretty well be assured of continued employment throughout the summer. But it was often touch and go and nothing could be taken for granted.

*

After some ten years at Pratt & Piggott Richard had found a better job at another hosiery manufacturer. The job was better paid but he was still, after all these years, a counterman. Furthermore, many, including the family, had thought that it had been a bit of a risky move to change jobs simply for better pay, especially in view of the recession and everything.

It was around this time, though, that some 'talk' arose about Richard, that he had been 'carrying on' with another woman, but Jack only got to hear about it that cold Monday evening in January. After leaving work he had spent some time walking about chatting with friends and finally said his goodbyes outside the home of one of his workmates on Southgate Street, which was quite near to Applegate Street where Richard's secret assignations were rumoured to be taking place. It was a fairly busy evening, and shortly afterwards Jack was jostled by a short, fat, ruddy-faced man who had bustled past him in order to speak to the tall, thin man who was walking behind him. The interloper apologised and when he raised his head to do so Jack could see that he was riled. Jack knew him vaguely but, for a minute, could not quite place him. Then he had it; he ran a nearby sweet shop – Lucas, Plucas or something – Blucas, that's him! 'E. Blucas Hard Confectioner' read the sign above the shop window. As Jack was only yards in front, he could clearly make out their conversation, not least because Blucas's voice was raised, both with emotion and the breathlessness that followed his rush to catch up with his friend. His exact words that night were very much in the vernacular, but the conversation broadly went as follows.

Blucas: "I knew it. I knew there was *summat gooin'* on. As I told *y'* before. She's been carrying on, I'm sure *on* it now and I know who with too."

Tall, thin man (TTM): "Hold on, Enoch. What do you know and 'ow?"

Blucas: "When I got back to the house tonight, she were out. No tea on the table, no lights on, no fire in the hearth, nothing. The house as cold as the grave. Well, what could I do? The Red Lion's more of *a* 'ome to me now and 'as *bin* these last six months. But as I were coming out the house, that Spanish woman from across the road – Peronso, or whatever 'er name is – came over." (In mocking Spanish accent): "'*Yourr* wife, I see 'er, she go out with a man about four o'clock. I see 'er, she gone!' Honestly Ray that woman *allus* 'as *bin* trouble but I were stunned… stunned! I just said aye I know. I don't know why. How could I know she'd gone out? I had no idea. And then she says, 'Oh then you know she go with Mr. Warren.' Well, I were dumbstruck! That woman knows full well what's been *gooin'* on and 'as done all along. She must think as I'm a bloody idiot."

At first Jack had been listening with intrigue as Blucas poured out his heart but, at the mention of his own surname, his mind seemed to shut everything else out. His face changed from a grin of amusement at the man's plight to a frown of serious contemplation. Who could it be? He knew several Warrens, many of whom were relations. Could it be one of them who had been 'carrying on' with Blucas's wife?

Ray (TTM): "Enoch, look, I don't know quite how to tell you but I know. I know all about it."

Blucas: "What do you mean, you know all about it? God knows I've got few friends these days, but I thought I could count on you, Ray. I thought, at least as *ah* could rely on you."

As they passed under a street lamp Jack was shocked by the wild expression on Blucas's face, especially the bulging eyes. *God, the offender, whoever he was, was clearly treading on dangerous ground*, he thought.

Ray: "Look Enoch, you can count on me, but I daren't have said for fear of being wrong."

Blucas: "Well, come on then, who is it? I'll bloody kill the bastard! And 'er, I'll bloody kill 'er *un* all!"

At just this moment a couple passed in the opposite direction and were clearly shocked by the outburst, which made Ray even more uneasy. "Look Enoch, this is exactly why I never said anything before. I know what you can be like. I expect she's been a bit bored lately, you out until all hours and that."

Blucas: "Bored! I'll give 'er bored."

Ray (in half whisper): "Now calm down, Enoch, or I'm off. We'll both be in trouble if you don't keep it down."

Blucas (face still contorted with rage, in a sort of strangulated growl): "That woman never wanted for anything. I've worked 'ard to keep that business going. God knows it *ain't bin* easy at times what with the recession and the strikes *un* all that, *bur ah* kept *gooin'*. And now look what's 'appened. This is the soddin' thanks *y'* get – face rubbed in the shit!"

At that very moment who should appear from around the corner but PC Collins pounding his beat. He knew Enoch Blucas of old but only as a shopkeeper; Blucas was no criminal. Collins knew that he had a quick temper, though, but he also knew that his bark was worse than his bite and had referred to him on more than one occasion as 'all piss and wind'. In the past Blucas had threatened all manner of things but rarely, if ever, carried any of his threats out. He had also heard the rumours about Blucas's wife and, putting two and two together, had realised what it was all about.

PC Collins: "Evening, everything all right here? If you could just keep the lid on it a bit, lads…"

Blucas: "Oh yes, yes… sorry Herbert, I'm just a bit upset, that's all."

Then, as the policeman continued on his beat, to Jack's dismay, Blucas and Ray started to speak in much more hushed tones. Still totally engrossed in the discourse, though, he casually pulled as close to them as he could without (he hoped) them noticing. Even then it was hard to hear what was being said. And what's more, Blucas's head was now bowed, his anger having turned more to melancholy. Ray's head was also bowed, part in empathy with his friend and part in an attempt to keep the conversation private.

Blucas (in a resigned tone): "Okay Ray, tell me the worst, who is it? Who is Warren?"

Ray: "Look Enoch, I *ain't* really sure to be honest, but before I say any more you've got to promise that you'll not do anything daft."

Blucas: "Mmm... Okay, what would be the point anyway Ray? What good *u'd* it do? What's done's done, I can't change that whatever I do, can I?"

Ray: "All right Enoch, but you've given me your word now... as I said, I can't be entirely sure, but I reckon as it might be a bloke called Dick Warren. If it is, well... he's a bit of a dark horse, or at least used to be, and people like that don't *genly* change. As I remember nobody knows a great deal about him apart from working in the 'osiery trade."

Blucas: "How did you come to know 'im then, Ray?"

Ray: "Well, as I said, I'm not entirely sure, I only think it could be 'im. But never mind how I know. I've told you now and now you know as much as I do."

The fact of the matter was that Ray had been passing the sweet shop one evening about a fortnight before, at a time when he knew his friend Blucas was away in Northampton buying stock. Blucas always stopped over on these visits and was wined and dined by his wholesaler who knew a good customer when he saw one. For all his faults, Enoch Blucas always placed a good order, and was always a good payer. In short, he was a good businessman, but sadly, like many a good businessman, he did not often put himself in other's shoes and, if the truth be known, had been totally blind to his wife's indifference for some time.

As it happened, though, Ray had been walking nearby with a drinking mate, Don Harris, on the same evening that Blucas was in Northampton. It was the same Don Harris who had worked with Richard at Pratt & Piggott some years before. It was very dark and just as they had crossed West Bridge and turned into Applegate Street, they had run directly into a couple walking the other way. After exchanging hasty apologies, Mrs. Blucas's eyes met Ray's but were just as soon nervously drawn away when she recognised him as one of her husband's friends.

Before anybody could say any more and realising that there was something more to this than just a 'bumping into strangers', her escort swept Mrs. Blucas away, heads bowed, the clicking of their heels on the pavement getting faster the further down the street they went. Then silence. As Ray and Don strained to look down the street, they could see the woman fumbling for the key to the entrance of the flat above the sweet shop, while the man stared up at the street light, hands in pockets, breath steaming from his mouth.

As Ray and Don continued to their destination Ray started talking, as if to himself: "Bloody hell… bloody hell!"

Don: "What?"

Ray: "That was Mrs. Blucas, with another bloke."

Don: "Who's Mrs. Blucas?"

Ray: "You know, the sweet shop back there, Enoch Blucas's wife. You know Enoch – he comes in the pub."

Don: "His wife, eh? Well, I can't be sure, but I think I know who the bloke is too."

Ray: "Who?"

Don: "I think *as* it may be a chap called Dick Warren. At any rate I used to work with a bloke by that name who looked just like him. It *wor* a few years back in the 'osiery."

Ray: "Is he married *un* all then?"

Don: "To tell the truth, I don't know much about him, I don't think so – never said anything about a wife and family in all the years I knew him. But we were never really that close. He sort of kept himself to himself, if you know what I mean. Can't think of any real close friends he had. I certainly never went round to his house or anything so I suppose he could be. Don't really know."

Because of the huddling Jack had not been able to catch everything that Blucas and Ray had said, but he thought he had heard the name 'Dick' and the word 'hosiery' mentioned, but it couldn't be. Surely not his dad. No… they could have been talking about anybody really, they must have been talking about somebody else. Did I hear 'Dick Warren' or just 'Dick' and was it 'hosiery'? Even if it was, well, there were so many hosiery and associated factories in the town. *Perhaps I'm putting two and two together and making five*, he thought. It could just as well be about anyone or anything really… and even if it was 'Dick Warren' well, there were lots of Dick Warrens in Leicester… and beyond for that matter. But what if it was his dad! Come to think of it, he didn't spend a great deal of time at home these days. And, when Jack called on his mates: Chris Sadler, Alf Lewis, Colin Mitchell – their fathers always seemed to be at home after work, but he was lucky to see his dad at home for two weekday evenings out of five. And more often than not he would not see him all day on a Saturday. For some strange reason he was always there on Sunday mornings, though.

Jack struggled with these thoughts all the way home, swaying from being convinced that he was jumping to conclusions one minute, to thinking, *it's bloody obviously him*, the next. Then another emotion; anger, took over. If it is true old Blucas won't have to kill him, I'll do it myself! After all his mother had been through – nothing to eat for years, no money, the awful death of his baby brother and the rest! How could he?

As he arrived back home Jack let himself in via the front door. It had only just gone eight o'clock. He could see that the light was on in the parlour, as it shone through a crack in the dividing door, and as he approached the bottom of the stairs, he could hear Flo and his mother chatting. Just then, the dividing door swung open, and Louisa appeared, having heard the front door open and close.

Louisa: "Hello love. I did some potatoes for tea, there's one or two left but they're a bit cold now or else I can make you a sandwich – cheese or something." Although the events of that evening had led Jack to think the worst of his father, if truth be known, he was very like his dad in many ways. One being, ironically, that he did not tend to keep regular hours himself. So, along with Richard, Louisa had, for some time now, given up on either of them being home at teatime and she often put some food aside for both of them, for when they came in.

Jack: "A cheese sandwich, thanks Mum." (Nods to Flo and sits down in Richard's chair). "Dad not back then yet?"

Louisa: "No, he came in about half an hour ago, said he had to meet somebody – something about an allotment."

Jack: "What?"

Louisa (shouts from kitchen): "An allotment – you know, a plot for growing veg and that – cheap food."

One way of putting it, thought Jack.

Jack: "Did he say when he'd be back?"

Louisa (handing Jack his sandwich on a plate): "Said not to wait up, as usual."

As he sat vacantly staring into the fire and chewing his sandwich, Jack's immediate thought was to ask his mother outright why she thought his dad stayed out so much, but then he thought better of it. He sorely wanted to go out again and walk up to Applegate Street to see if he could see for himself whether his dad was with Mrs. Blucas. The night was becoming bitterly cold, though, and the fireside was so warm. Perhaps he'd go tomorrow night if his dad was out again.

After an hour or so Flo stood up and announced that she was going to bed. "Night Mam, night Jack."

"I'll be up myself now," Louisa responded, completing her work in the kitchen by neatly folding a tea towel over the draining board. "Put the fire guard round before you come up, Jack, there's a love," she said, as she swept past him on her way up. And then Jack was alone.

Soon, slouched before the fire, Jack began to drift off, but then – bang! Jack awoke with a start at the sound of the front door being slammed. He could hear the sounds of his dad taking off his cap, scarf and coat, and putting them on the pegs the other side of the dividing door. Then the sound of Richard's boots making for the stairs. Jack instinctively got up and moved towards the door to the front room but, by the time he had opened it, Richard had cleared both the stairs and the landing, and all that Jack heard was the closing of the bedroom door. *What would have been the point?* he asked himself, *what would I have said?* Richard had never been, and never would be, a great conversationalist and Jack took very much after him in that respect also, so it was unlikely that they would have resolved whatever was going on in any case. Returning to put the guard in front of the fire, Jack noticed the time by the clock above the mantelpiece – two-thirty! What on earth had his dad been doing until then if not 'carrying on' with Mrs. Blucas?

But whatever, thought Jack, *can't do much now and if I'm not in bed soon I'll not be up for work tomorrow. The whole business will just have to keep till another time.*

*

One of the 'delights' of the age was surely having to go to the toilet (or '*gooin' lavy*') in the middle of the night. Even in a modern house of the time the process was an inconvenience (no pun intended) because the toilet was out in the backyard. Not number ones, you understand, as there was always a pot in the bedroom to receive liquid waste – a *guzunder*, so named as it *guzunder* the bed. No, you would only make your way out in the middle of the night to answer a most urgent of nature's number twos. Under normal circumstances you would have seen to it that no such calls arose by going in the evening before you went up to bed. But sometimes things were not normal; some foods, especially overripe fruit and vegetables, which were cheap, 'loosened things up a bit' and sometimes, of course, you simply forgot.

When waking in the dead of night and it dawned that the whole ordeal may have to be enacted, the mind turned to balancing the consequences of the operation against those of 'holding it in'. *Perhaps if I roll over… can I ignore it? Can I keep going until morning? Oh, it's no good, I'm just going to have to go through with it!*

It was very important not to disturb any of your bedfellows, as doing so could seriously damage your health and, in such a delicate state, ran the risk of significantly complicating matters, if you see what I mean. The only way was to creep out as gingerly and as quietly as possible, grab your boots and the old thick coat hung on the inside of the bedroom door for this very eventuality. Always either too big or too small, depending on your age, nevertheless it was essential attire if you were to avoid freezing to death. Closing the bedroom door behind you as silently as possible, only then donning the coat and boots, on the landing. Quietly down the stairs and through the rear parlour. The fire, if still aglow, would provide some warmth and light by which you could light an oil lamp. Out of the back door and onto the cold yard bricks. If the wind blew the lamp out, as it sometimes did, you were left in the pitch black. Along the yard and round to the toilet. Sometimes the door would be frozen shut and if the lamp were still alight, you would have to hold the top of it under the latch for a short while in order to thaw it out. If the lamp had gone out, of course, you may well have had to go back inside and relight it. Then, when you did get to press hard on the latch it would snap open, the sound echoing round the yard. It seemed as though the colder and darker it was, the more the hinges on the door creaked. Once inside, the glow from the moving handheld lamp made your shadow and those of the cistern, pipes and toilet dance around you. If frozen over, the surface of the water in the toilet would soon melt as it met with the body heat inevitably lost with your waste. If you weren't shivering before this loss, then you almost certainly would be afterwards.

The requisite cleansing that followed would do little to restore any comfort either. Bought toilet paper of the time was as that of today, as chalk is to cheese. Made from a strong but translucent paper, shiny on one side and slightly rough on the other – a design really that could only ever have been improved upon. Although not expensive, it was too much of an extravagance for most when all you were going to do was wipe your bottom on it and then throw it down the toilet. Arguably even harsher on the posterior but already bought, paid for and having served its primary purpose, the local newspaper was cut into bundles of roughly eight inches by twelve, one corner being pierced with the point of a pair of scissors. The bundle was then threaded with string and hung from a nail on the wall. Anybody having had the privilege to use such material in this way would, I'm sure, vouch for how unforgiving it can be, especially when very cold. The wretchedness of the whole affair meant that it was always undertaken at a brisk pace. Re-attired and chain pulled, the unfortunate victim would be back inside the kitchen long before the sound of the cistern refilling abated. A quick rinse of the hands in the sink (well… sometimes), back past the fire and then quickly up the stairs, removing the coat on the hoof, boots off at the door and back in bed. It's hard at first not to cause further disturbance, still shivering and with an overwhelming tendency to huddle. Eventually, though, the body warms enough to allow for some relaxation and, in a while, sleep resumes. But then, after what may seem only a few minutes: 'trinnnggg…' the sudden rude, strident sound of that old 'tin can' alarm again.

*

As per six days a week, except for holidays, which were few and far between, it was time to get up. Jack did the 'getting dressed under the bedclothes drill' but the late night before had made him a bit fractious and, as the other boys showed little or no sign of movement, each got a crack on the leg from Jack's arm as he passed to light the lamp. "Bugger off, Jack!" shouted Arch, as he felt the full force of the blow.

"Get up then," Jack shouted back, "and less of that language as well or you'll get another."

"Sod off," replied Arch (but, this time, under his breath). Despite all the protestations, though, it was still time to get up and, before long, they were all toasting again, this time by the fire on the range in the back parlour. Same routine, though: Richard thumps down the stairs, shaves and washes in the sink, everybody else washes, gets ready and chats. Just as the day before, Richard, Flo, Jack and Arch leave the house together, go their separate ways at the end of the street, arrive at work and get back to the graft.

"*Yer* late lad!" shouts Mr. Eckersley as the bell on the grocery shop door rings and a breathless Arch stumbles in. 'Sorry Mr. Eckersley, it was the clock at home, it's a few minutes slow."

Eckersley: "Is there only one clock in your 'ouse, then?"

Arch (not really understanding the full significance of this rhetoric): "Er… yes."

Eckersley: "Any more o' that cheek and I'll fetch thee one, lad. Now get up *te* t' stockroom and sort out them deliveries. Oh, and there's a load o' crates on the floor that need opening and the stuff putting on t' shelves."

Sam Eckersley was a broad Yorkshireman, born and raised in Bradford. Initially in the wool trade, he had met his wife of thirty-five years, Susan, on a day trip to Cleethorpes. She was the only child of the former shopkeeper who had been widowed some years before. Sam and Susan had hit it off immediately and after they returned from the trip, had started writing to each other. Before long, Sam would come down to Leicester on the train every now and again, and they would take a walk in the park or visit a show or just simply spend time together. Then, when Susan's father suddenly collapsed and died, Sam had immediately set off for Leicester in order to help and comfort her. Initially it was simply about keeping the business going but, perhaps inevitably, as time went on they grew much closer and, after marrying, now ran the shop together full-time. Despite his somewhat abrupt Yorkshire approach and, make no mistake about it, he was capable of raising 'merry hell' if he felt he'd been poorly used, he thought a lot of Arch and knew the lad was a good worker. At the same time, though, he always had and always would harbour an undying obsession against being taken for a fool by anybody and

Arch knew that if he were to put his foot in it too often, especially while some other matter might be on Eckersley's mind, there was a very real chance that he could lose his job.

After sorting the deliveries Arch refilled the shelves behind the counter so that all the most popular products were to hand when customers came in: cans of meat and veg, packets of tea and sugar, butter, margarine, biscuits, soap and starch, etc. Throughout the day there would be a constant in and out of customers – often housewives, but also kids with their mothers' purses containing both the money and a written list of what they needed.

Eckersley (hunched, elbows on counter, screwing his eyes to look inside the purse while sorting the contents with his extended index finger): "She's not given *y'* enough 'ere. *Yer* mam, she's not given *y'* enough."

If a boy, this usually met with silence, if a girl, some sort of defence such as: "Well… me mam said what was in there should cover it."

Eckersley: "Well it doesn't. Look, you'll 'ave to come back for the lard. I'll write it on the back of this list. Here, *tek* this to *y'* mam and tell 'er there weren't quite enough."

Presented with this sort of problem, Eckersley's reaction wasn't always the same, though. He knew who could well afford to pay their way, who could only just afford to pay (the above being a case in point) and those who really were in dire straits. He had to, after all, business is business, it was all part of the grocery trade of the time. Occasionally (and it was occasionally) he would 'forget' the odd penny or even, at times, two, but he would never admit it. It remained a 'mistake' on his part and no customer (barring the most scrupulously honest) would ever see any need to take it up with him. Of course, he realised that he couldn't do this sort of thing too often, even if he had wanted to, because in his words, if he were to 'break his leg' then he would not be able to help anybody else 'up the stairs'.

Arch did not have the use of a traditional errand boy's bike with its large basket on the front and frame panel advertising the shop; his deliveries were generally undertaken by handcart. These carts varied widely in shape and size from small (almost sack barrow affairs), through trailed trolleys to larger, heavier barrow carts that could carry a great deal at a time and required some strength to propel, especially when going uphill. Some had been made by professional cart makers and these tended to be strong, with free-moving, ball-bearinged wheels, designed to reduce the discomfort of pushing them. Even with these, though, Arch was little more than a child at the time and so would have been less able to lean over the handles and use gravity as an aid to thrust. Other carts were simply 'knocked up' and ranged from manageable conveyances to virtually immoveable objects that demanded great effort to push. As Eckersley was, by no means, a 'slave driver', Arch's trolley was well-made and not so large as to be cumbersome, but that's not to say that he never had to struggle with the thing.

When he had replenished the shelves behind the counter, it was time for him to start on the orders to be delivered. Generally, customers made a list in a notebook and Arch collected the items from the stockroom accordingly. Finally, Eckersley wrote the price next to each item on the list and totalled the bill at the bottom of the page. As cardboard boxes were only just becoming widely used, the groceries were mainly packed into small crates which were either purpose-made or cut from plywood tea chests. Regular customers would keep these and either hand them back in at the shop with their payment or Arch would collect them when he made a subsequent delivery.

Once the cart was loaded to the extent that Eckersley thought appropriate, Arch was off. He had soon acquired a mental map of the area and learned how to load the cart so that the first delivery was on top and the last at the very bottom, so that nothing (or very little) had to be moved out the way to get at any one particular crate along the route.

Rat-tat-tat... a face would appear at the window. To which Arch would mouth, "Groceries." The door would then open, and a crate be handed over, sometimes in exchange for an empty one. The order book would be in with the groceries and Eckersley would call personally on anybody who had not dropped into the shop and paid within three days or so.

Sometimes Arch would return to the shop, having made all the deliveries on the cart, and have to go out again to fulfil subsequent orders. Otherwise, it would be cleaning, sweeping up and tidying, etc. until his working day finished at seven o'clock (his hours being 'eight while seven' as Eckersley put it). All this earned him the princely sum of six bob a week, six shillings for sixty hours' work; a shilling a day or just over one old penny (0.4 of today's pennies) an hour. Obviously, a pound in those days went a great deal further than it does now, but his wage was still probably only the equivalent of something like £35 or £40 a week in real terms today and it seems a pitiful amount for such a job. Having said this, though, exact monetary comparisons with the past are difficult to make for various reasons. Firstly, the same things available today were not necessarily priced in direct proportion and secondly, the extent of supply and demand now differ since there was really nothing like the choice and variety of goods on offer back then. Also, people's expectations were different – if you hadn't enough money at the end of the week then you went without, it was as simple as that.

Occasionally (very occasionally) there might be a tip – a farthing here or there and even in Arch's early career, a ha'penny or indeed, a penny, had been known, but generally almost everybody was far too short of money to tip him on a regular basis.

The day's work done, Arch would run home. If it were payday, as with Flo and Jack, he would pass his unopened pay packet to his mother who would give each of them a little back for themselves. In Arch's case, a shilling, all the rest going into the housekeeping tin that would keep the family fed, clothed and sheltered for another week.

*

When Jack next finished work at the Boot and Shoe that Tuesday he made straight for Applegate Street again. Being the middle of winter, it was already dark; made even darker on account of the new moon.

In fact, it would have been very difficult indeed to identify anybody precisely by the illumination of the dim gas lights alone. Jack walked up and down Applegate Street a few times from the old West Gates to the corner of St. Nicholas Square and back again. Past Blucas's shop, which was closed and where there was absolutely no sign of life. As he paused at a railing opposite the shop, lit a 'Woody' and drew on it, he watched as a train thundered along the nearby bridge over the River Soar on its way into the new Central Station just a few streets down. The evening was not getting any warmer and it was starting to sleet, so Jack decided to make his way to the station for a bit of warmth. He bought a platform ticket, a cup of tea and a sandwich and sat down in the waiting room. Warmed by the large coal-burning stove in the centre of the room, his thoughts again turned to his dad and the possible combinations, permutations and interpretations of what he had heard.

Leaving the station three-quarters of an hour later, he returned to Applegate Street. Again, no sign of his dad nor anybody really, it being now half-past eight on a cold, rainy winter's night and everyone with any sense was at home by the fireside. Past Blucas's shop again: still closed, blacked-out and showing absolutely no signs of life. Jack hung about for another quarter of an hour. He thought of going back for another sandwich and a cup of tea but only had one and threepence ha'penny left in his pocket and that needed to last until, at least, Thursday. Still determined, though, he decided to spread his net a bit wider and, turning his coat collar up against the driving weather, headed along Red Cross Street, behind St. Martin's church, past the Opera House and up to the Clock Tower. Another 'Woody' and then back down High Street to Applegate Street again, but still no sign. Round the whole thing again, kicking his heels, loitering in doorways, staring into shopfronts and then round again, more slowly this time, just for good measure. Then, just as he was re-entering Applegate Street, a door slammed and the keys turned in the lock but then, silence again. He ran to the front of the shop to see if it was the source of the noise but when he got there it was still closed, still black and still lifeless. He walked in circles on the pavement near the shop for a few minutes, looking up and down the street, looking at the other houses. Did the noise come from here or there or even somewhere completely different? After having walked up and down another few times he was still no wiser. Jack glanced at his watch. "Ten past eleven!" he gasped under his breath. "This is a waste of bloody time! I've had enough." Then, turning for home, he thought, *I'll have to come another night, when the weather's a bit better. Or, perhaps I'll leave it, what good would it do anyway? Only cause trouble if I did find out that there were* summat gooin' *on.*

*

When Jack got back to Tewkesbury Street all the houses there were black and lifeless too. When he got in all the family had gone to bed. He didn't know whether his father had come home and gone to bed or not and, by that time, he didn't much care. As the fire was still in, he went through and sat down in his dad's place, rubbing his hands before turning his palms towards the fire, in order to gather its warmth. As he began to regain the feeling in his limbs, he reached for the opened copy of the *Leicester Daily Mercury* spread out on the sofa next to him.

THE QUEEN

DYING.

[It read at the top of the column, then:]

The following was sent this afternoon –
Osborne [House] 4pm.
The Queen is slowly sinking.

[Signed below by the Queen's physicians]

It had been known for some time that Queen Victoria was not enjoying the best of health. Perhaps unsurprisingly, in view of her great age, but after over sixty-three years on the throne, few people living could remember any different. There were also anxieties about the succession – Albert Edward, Prince of Wales, was, by now, 'getting on' himself and had lived something of a colourful life to date, to say the least.

As Jack read on, though, it became clear to him that the life of the only monarch he had ever known was drawing to a close:

EIGHT O'CLOCK BULLETIN.

DIMINISHING STRENGTH.

[The article noted that there had been a 'slight improvement' in the morning, but members of the Royal Family were already starting to gather at Victoria's bedside.]

The end of an era, thought Jack. *I only hope it's not the same for us.*
In reality, of course, the Queen had passed away earlier that very evening.

Chapter 5

Yesterday, Today and Tomorrow

'... yesterday is but a dream
And tomorrow is only a vision;
And today well-lived, makes
Yesterday a dream of happiness
And every tomorrow a dream of hope.'

'Look to this Day' – Kālidāsa
(Ancient Sanskrit Poem)

In order to react to anything, one must, of course, first receive the news, and in the absence of television or even domestic radio in those days, that task fell primarily to the newspapers. But there were moving pictures. (You can watch Queen Victoria's funeral on YouTube.) Filming, however, was still very much in its infancy and, of course, there were no soundtracks. In any event the first cinema did not arrive in Leicester until 1910 but with the new technology of wireless telegraphy, newspapers were beginning to report matters much more quickly.

In addition to the 'nationals', Leicester, as elsewhere, had its local press: *The Chronicle*, *The Daily Post*, *The Herald*, *The Journal* and so on, as well as the *Leicester Daily Mercury* (as it was at this time; later the *Leicester Mercury*). Known in local parlance as *The Merc[u]reh* (the 'u' sound all but omitted) this publication has probably been and probably still is the most popular 'local'. Still going after over 145 years it is certainly the most enduring and now, as then, it still appeals to many with its comprehensive coverage of both local and national matters, views, current affairs, and advertising, etc. I, for one, have found its archives a very useful source of the news of the time while writing this book.

When it came out on Wednesday 23 January 1901, the *Daily Mercury* reported the death of Victoria the previous day as follows:

DEATH OF THE QUEEN

It is with feelings of the profoundest sorrow and regret that we have to record the death of Her Majesty Queen Victoria which took place at half past six o'clock on Tuesday evening, at Osborne House, Isle of Wight. Since Saturday last the melancholy event had been anticipated: the whole Empire, grief-stricken, has watched in spirit by the sick chamber. Her Majesty had not enjoyed her wonted health for several months. The infirmities of age, added to great anxieties caused by personal affliction, and troubles of State, had crept on slowly but surely, undermining a naturally strong constitution. Last November it was observed at Balmoral that she was unable to walk from her carriage to the railway train to travel south. That is said to have been the beginning of her indisposition, and gradually she became weaker and weaker. Nevertheless, on Monday week she commanded an interview with Lord Roberts and on Wednesday morning Her Majesty was able to take exercise in her donkey chaise in the grounds of Osborne House. In the afternoon of that day, however, she countermanded the order for the usual drive. The carriage only drove up to be sent back again. The "Court Circular" personally supervised by the Queen, did not make its appearance one day subsequently, and on Friday the country was informed that the beloved and venerable sovereign had broken down. At first the full significance of the announcement was not realised but a bulletin issued by Sir Jas. Bird and Sir Douglas Powell on Saturday awakened popular sympathy and concern. The official intimations that followed did not allay the national anxiety, and throughout Sunday gloomy anticipations were forced upon the people.

During that night the Queen passed through a most critical time. It was feared the end was approaching and all the members of the Royal Family then in the Isle of Wight were summoned to the bedside. The Prince of Wales was absent, having gone to London to meet the Kaiser, who hurried from Berlin as soon as he had news of the grave condition of his grandmother. The ominous symptoms were allayed for the time, and the bulletin which greeted the Prince of Wales and the German Emperor on their arrival at Osborne on Monday told of a slight improvement. There had been some refreshing sleep and more nourishment had been taken. Throughout the day the improvement was maintained, but there was no vital change, as was clear from the statement of the doctors issued at midnight on Monday. The medical men in attendance then included Sir Thos. Barlow. He is an authority on cerebral disorders, and it had been critically stated that there was a local obstruction of the brain circulation – a blood clot on the brain. The next bulletin disappointed any faint hopes that Monday's intimation may have aroused. It was then evident that her Majesty was hovering between life and death, and a few hours later came the fateful words – the Queen is sinking, leading up to the final notification that the honoured and beloved Monarch of sixty-four years, the faithful wife, the revered mother, and the good woman had passed away from us for ever.

THE CLOSING SCENES

The Queen's end came peacefully, and, perhaps painlessly, for she passed away in her sleep. The special correspondent of the "Standard" of Cowes on Tuesday night says: –

A restless night has been succeeded by twelve hours of alternating hope and fear. At half-past three in the afternoon hope was banished, and it was admitted that the end had come. All the members of the Royal Family were summoned and entered the death chamber. The Bishop of Winchester was already kneeling at the bedside of his Royal mistress, and the attendants had withdrawn to a corner of the apartment. The Prince of Wales and the German Emperor walked side by side and were followed by the other members of the family, the Princess of Wales, the Duke and Duchess of Connaught, the Duke of York, Princess Henry of Battenberg, the Duchess of Saxe-Coburg, Princess Christian, the Grand Duchess Elisabeth of Hesse, and the Duchess of Argyll.

During the three hours of intense emotion that followed Her Majesty had occasional and short returns to consciousness. It was evident that she recognised her children and grandchildren, though the recognition was not as clear as in the morning. Then only was the Queen able to manifest her pleasure at the presence of her sons and daughters, and to indicate her especial gratification at the filial devotion of her grandson, the Emperor William, whose presence will ever be held in grateful memory by the Anglo-Saxon race.

As the day passed, and the grey, cold light of winter faded into darkness, other members of the family joined the group in the chamber of the dying monarch. The Duchess of York, the children of the Duke of Connaught, the Duke of Argyll, and Prince and Princess Louis of Battenberg came in time to take a last leave. The Lord Chamberlain whose presence on these mournful occasions is a necessity of State, was also in attendance. Prince Christian, however, was too late; while Mr. Balfour, First Lord of the Treasury, who came in place of the Prime Minister [Lord Salisbury] did not enter the room. The Duchess of Albany and her son, the Duke of Saxe-Coburg had not reached Osborne.

> The people of Cowes were conscious that their Sovereign and neighbour was dying. Many of them walked up the broad avenue to the gates of Osborne House and stood for hours in silence. To them the announcement was given by Mr. Fraser, Chief of the Queen's Police on instructions from Sir John McNeill, Her Majesty's Equerry. He came to the gates of the lodge and said, "Gentlemen, I am sorry to say that the Queen passed away at half-past six o'clock [pm] in the presence of her children and grandchildren."

The sheer devastation gushing out from these lines of copy reflect just how much Britain and indeed the British Empire despaired at the loss of their much-loved monarch of sixty-four years. In a time when life expectancy was not much more than half that of today, very few had ever lived under any other sovereign and of those that had, most would have been either too old or not old enough at the time, to have been able to recall clearly their lives under William (or, even more so, under George).

The report also brings home the (often very) close familial relationship between the royal families of Europe at the time, not least in that Kaiser Wilhelm II of Germany was Victoria's grandson. And, as those who continue to hold the traditional view of primogeniture delight in reminding us, under the new laws of succession, where the eldest offspring inherits the line irrespective of gender, the Kaiser would have likely ascended the British throne in late 1901. This would have been because he was the eldest child of Victoria's firstborn, known as Vicky; the Princess Royal, who had married Kaiser Friedrich III of Germany. Although already terminally ill when Queen Victoria died, Vicky would have been the rightful heir on Victoria's death in early 1901 so, later that year, when she too died, her son, the Kaiser Wilhelm II, would logically have succeeded her.

The law of unintended consequences comes to mind as, when Vicky and Friedrich married in 1858, Britain and Germany were very much friends and allies and few, if any, could have foreseen how things would turn out over forty years later. If they had known, I suspect that the marriage would not have received anything like the blessing that it did.

As well as the Kaiser being Victoria's grandson, Leopold II of the Belgians was her first cousin and Tsar Nicholas II of Russia was married to one of her granddaughters but from then on it gets a little more intricate. The various royal houses have intermarried (often several times) down the ages but by way of example, the royals of Scandinavia were related through the House of Oldenburg, those of Portugal through the Saxe-Coburg-Gothas (Prince Albert's line), the Romanian royal family were related through the House of Hohenzollern (the Kaiser's family) and so on. Though connections to the Austrian House of Habsburg exist, they are, it has to be said, even more tenuous. Just to give one example, though: Leopold II (mentioned above) was initially married to Marie Henriette of Austria.

*

The fact of the matter was that, as inevitably happens to all who survive life's vicissitudes, the Queen's great age had finally caught up on her. Her deterioration and confusion, noticed a few months earlier, had probably been signs of an impending stroke which, by mid-January, had sealed her fate. And of course, it was obvious, given the circumstances, that something like this was going to happen before too much longer, on account of her age – eighty-one – a great age then, if not now. Nevertheless, there followed devastation. Not only throughout Britain and its Empire, vast as it then was, but throughout the world. I can only think that it must have been something like the air of depression that descended when Diana, Princess of Wales, died. Although Victoria and Diana were very different as far as royals go; one very old, the other in her prime; one a queen for most of her life, the other never to be so, both were widely admired royals whose existence had, to some degree, been taken for granted and then suddenly lost! I remember the feeling of desolation evoked by the sombre press releases and the sight of the quivering Tony Blair.

And then, on the day of Diana's funeral, the gloom and the deserted streets as millions gazed at the morbid spectacle on TV. The laments and eulogies: 'Goodbye England's Rose…' and all that. I can only assume that this is something of what it must have felt like for those last 'Victorians' as reality dawned and thoughts turned to organising the funeral.

And so it was, on a fine day in early February 1901 that Victoria, in her coffin, having been brought back from the Isle of Wight the day before, was drawn through London on a gun carriage. Thousands had turned out and apparently, at one stage something spooked the horses that pulled the gun carriage, causing it to become uncoupled. In the end it had to be manhandled by sailors all the way to St. George's Chapel, Windsor, for the service.

After the funeral Victoria lay in state in the Albert Memorial Chapel for a further two days before being taken to Frogmore Mausoleum to be finally laid to rest beside her beloved Prince Albert. The Mausoleum, of course, having been commissioned by Victoria for this very purpose shortly after Albert's death.

Grieving is a term generally ascribed to the experience resulting from the loss of a loved one, but it can apply equally, as in the cases of both Queen Victoria and Princess Diana, to the loss of a much-treasured public figure. Indeed, Prince Charles himself questioned what love was and, whereas we fully understand what we mean by love within a relationship or the family, we are probably not quite so clear about the concept when it relates to those in the public eye. Although this type of love clearly exists (a great proportion of the tears shed by ordinary people at Diana's funeral were genuine, I have no doubt about that), many are nervous of this type of love, thinking it 'cranky' – a sign of mass hysteria, perhaps. Consequently, whenever such an emotion is experienced under such circumstances, it may be suppressed, but the point is, it is still felt. There seems to be a consensus that grieving in all its forms follows several, well-defined stages. Interpretations vary, but essentially we are looking at:

1. Shock and denial

2. Pain (& guilt?)

3. Anger (& bargaining)

4. Sadness (& depression)

5. Acceptance and reconstruction

(Usually in something like that order.)

The initial shock and disbelief requires no explanation. 'I was only speaking to him the other day, I can't believe it!'. Then the pain, 'the world will never be the same without him!'. And, of course, it won't.

The guilt bit depends very much on the circumstances. 'I should have done this'. 'I shouldn't have done that'. 'If only…' etc., etc. In Victoria's case there was not a great deal anybody could have done. She was 'getting on a bit', particularly for the time and that was really all there was to it. Diana, on the other hand, was still relatively young and there was a palpable crisis of conscience in her case. A feeling that she had not been properly protected and, especially amongst her many admirers, not fully appreciated.

The next bit, anger, is the most dangerous. Anger is an almost inevitable consequence of pain and guilt in most people. The deeper the pain and the longer it goes on the more unbearable it becomes. The guilt begins to drive a hunt for scapegoats; 'I should have' becomes 'they should have' and before you know it the conspiracy theories: Where was the security? He was drunk! A foreign plot!

The sadness and depression stage Victoria knew only too well as, following the death of her beloved Prince Albert, she continued to wear black for the remaining almost forty years of her life. There was perhaps slight evidence of acceptance, though, and there may even have been something of an attempt at a reconstruction in the form of her subsequent relationship with her servant, John Brown. But could Victoria have ever been considered to have embraced this final stage of grief? I think not.

Naturally analyses vary and we are told that a stage or two may sometimes be missed out, some stage or stages may last longer (sometimes a lot, lot longer) than others and different people may experience more of one aspect (or aspects) than others. Where one could have a nervous breakdown and thus be locked in stages one and two, another may ferment grudges and be locked in stage three, whilst yet another, who could have reduced emotions etc. may jump straight to stage five. One example of where the 'anger' bit won out, though, must surely have been Austria's reaction to the death of the Archduke Franz Ferdinand in 1914.

Essentially everybody reacts slightly differently given the same set of circumstances, and only the overall mood can be described when it comes to the loss of a public figure. But, with time, some sort of stability eventually resumes, as it did following Victoria's death, and it would not be until two reigns later, that those grieving family members turned from comforting each other to being 'at each other's throats'! That is not necessarily to say that Queen Victoria's death, in itself, led either directly or indirectly, to conflict. I am merely exploring the consequences of bereavement and heaven knows, there were plenty of them still to come.

As the grieving process was progressing, then, thoughts turned towards the implications. The matter of the succession, the political future, both at home and throughout the Empire – while the Second Boer War was still raging in South Africa, across the Channel, the Kaiser's Germany was becoming increasingly bellicose. There was certainly no shortage of grist to feed the mill of the 'anger' (and 'bargaining') stage!

*

The Boer Wars were costly conflicts, in terms of both money and lives, and born out of pure colonialism. Britain first acquired influence in South Africa during the Napoleonic Wars, when it took over the Dutch province of Cape Colony, ostensibly in order to protect its trade routes with India. In truth, however, the takeover was probably as much to do with extending British influence in Africa as part of the vying between several European powers to secure influence there. At first there was not a great deal that the Boers (the descendants of the original Dutch settlers) could do about it, but with the adoption of English as the official language in 1822, and then the abolition of slavery by 1834 (the Boer farmers relying heavily upon slave labour), although, generally retaining the best, easy to farm, land, they started to become increasingly incensed. As a concession in the early 1850s the British recognised the Republic of Transvaal and the Orange Free State as independent Boer states but then, in the late 1860s, diamonds were discovered at Kimberley – virtually where Cape Colony, the Transvaal and the Orange Free State meet. Britain immediately annexed the Transvaal (the weaker of the two Boer states) and, by so doing, started the First Boer War.

Far from being the walkover that the British had predicted, this underestimation, combined with poor leadership, soon led to disproportionate British losses culminating in the disastrous Battle of Majuba Hill in February 1881. In all it only took just over three months before a negotiated settlement saw the Transvaal ceded back to the Boers as 'suzerainty'. (A state of affairs that left Britain with only a limited level of control). But the '*Uitlander* [essentially 'foreigner' or 'stranger'] Question' over the still-persistent influx of more and more British colonials into the Transvaal throughout the 1880s (particularly after the discovery of gold near Johannesburg in 1886) would continue to ratchet up tensions towards levels approaching those in Sarajevo in 1914. And, although less widely noted than the assassination of the Archduke, it was another violent death that would be 'the straw that broke the camel's back'.

Tom Edgar, a British *uitlander* living in Johannesburg, was shot dead one evening in December 1898, by a Transvaal police officer, who (the *uitlanders* felt) literally got away with murder. But the truth is never quite that simple, is it? Apparently, Edgar, on returning home drunk, is said to have overheard a neighbour shout "*Voetsak*!" This is an Afrikaans word for something along the lines of 'f*** off' or 'p*** off' and thinking that it was aimed at him, the incensed Edgar reacted by punching his neighbour to the ground. There had been a witness, but he thought that Edgar had killed the man and immediately went for the police. When the police arrived, they found Edgar at his home, and when they went in to arrest him a scuffle broke out during which Edgar was shot dead.

It turned out later that, no doubt because of the dark and the fact that he was drunk, Edgar had not realised that the neighbour was actually addressing his own dog when he shouted the word. Apparently, he was relieving himself and the dog had got in the way.

On the face of it then, it looked as though an unarmed Briton had been shot dead at point blank range in his own home by the Transvaal Police for what was merely a drunken brawl with his neighbour. However, shortly after holding the policeman for murder, the charge against him was dropped to manslaughter and he was bailed. As word got around it enraged the British *uitlanders*, and protestors in Johannesburg raised a petition to Queen Victoria for a fair trial. This was granted but the trial was held before a young and inexperienced Boer judge. However, it turned out that Edgar was built like the proverbial 'brick outhouse' and the police gave evidence that, when they had tried to arrest him, he had attacked them with an iron bar. An iron bar was indeed found at the site and, as a result, under the direction of the judge, the policeman who had shot Edgar was acquitted.

Despite political posturings the disquiet rumbled on, and another petition, now with over 20,000 signatures, was raised, asking for British intervention. This time British troops were sent and began to mass along the borders of the Transvaal and the Orange Free State. While the British Government was planning its next move the Boers played right into their hands when, on 9 October 1899 President Paul Kruger issued his ultimatum that if British troops were not pulled back within twenty-four hours there would be war.

Behind the scenes the British were thrilled by this move because they did not believe that the Boers had 'a cat's chance in hell' of prevailing and furthermore, it would now be the Boers, not the British, who had started it.

For the first couple of months the Boers, who knew the lie of the land, managed very effectively to continually defeat and besiege the British. The strategic garrisons at Mafeking, Kimberley and Ladysmith, place names etched indelibly into the annals of British history, were all besieged within three weeks or so of the outbreak of war. Mafeking, involving Lord Baden Powell, at 217 days, was to last the longest, but Kimberley, involving Cecil Rhodes, and Ladysmith, involving Churchill, both went on for well over one hundred days.

In early 1900, however, heavy British reinforcements under Roberts and Kitchener were able to relieve the sieges and the tide of the war began to change. By the autumn, control had been wrested over all the major towns including Johannesburg, Pretoria and Bloemfontein, but, although things were beginning to look up for the British, the war was far from over, as the Boers changed tactics and took to the hills.

The Afrikaans word *boer* comes from the Dutch meaning 'farmer' as many of the *Afrikaners* of the time were. Indeed, they were often farmers descended from the original Dutch settlers or *Voortrekkers* (pioneers) of the early nineteenth century. Brought up on newly settled land along the lines of the Wild West, they were well used to killing 'for the pot' in order to avoid starvation. In so doing, therefore, they were accustomed to the land, tended to be good shots, and were well practised in camouflage; the very stuff, you might say, of successful partisans.

Guerrilla warfare is generally a 'hit and run' affair, often with small groups attacking and ambushing as and where they can. Mostly these attacks are planned to take place in remote places while the enemy may be distracted or relocating (and, therefore, encumbered) and so depend on good intelligence. The lack of numbers is counterbalanced by the element of surprise and the object is to do as much damage as possible before the enemy realises what's going on. Of course, as soon as they do, it is equally important to skedaddle before they can respond. This is where familiarity with the terrain comes to the fore and, as adumbrated, nobody knew the *veldt* like the Boers, the escape of the Boer General De Wet from Kitchener's clutches after Ladysmith being a case in point. When British soldiers were sent to recapture him, they were led a 'merry dance'. After two bamboozling months scouring the land, the hapless pursuers were forced to give up. And, as if to add insult to injury, while all this was going on, De Wet had been able to draw some significant additional Boer strength from the Orange Free State. But not everything went his way as, ironically, De Wet's own brother was to turn against him by leading a group of Boers who, towards the end of the war, would change sides and fight alongside the British.

Despite all the bravado this guerrilla phase of the war proved more of a frustration to both sides than a meaningful counteroffensive by the Boers and it is fair to say that the tactic was pretty ineffective, overall. It did, however, succeed in leaving the British continually trying to work out where the next skirmish would crop up.

In an attempt to break the stalemate, Kitchener ratcheted up one of the most controversial aspects of the war: the so-called 'scorched earth policy' where homesteads, sources of food and even whole settlements were totally destroyed by fire in order to starve and deprive the Boers into surrender. This inevitably led to thousands of homeless (mainly) women and children who were then herded into what were initially referred to as 'refugee camps' but later labelled the 'Boer War concentration camps'. Presumably originally used to denote that the incumbents were 'concentrated' into the camps, later this term was to become very controversial, of course, and it would not help that many of the black African people interned were held (it was said) with the intention of using them later as forced labour in the gold mines.

Although there is no evidence of mass murder, as in the case of the Nazi concentration camps, there is no doubt that neglect was so rife and conditions were so bad that, by the end of the war, sadly something like 30,000 (some believe as many as 50,000) had perished

– again mostly women and children – as a direct result of being held in this way. Understandably, when things came out, it left Britain facing considerable opprobrium from around the globe, not least from the rest of Europe.

In the light of events, then, it is perhaps unsurprising that in Parliament a minority but nevertheless a significant proportion of Liberal opposition MPs, including Lloyd George, were beginning to struggle a bit with their 'loyalty to the government in times of war' maxim and so sent the radical campaigner Emily Hobhouse to South Africa to inspect the camps. Her report made for some grim reading, with opponents labelling her 'hysterical' and Kitchener calling her 'That Bloody Woman'! Essentially it painted a picture of abject neglect. Huddled in tents stiflingly hot by day and freezing cold by night, lack of hygiene, poor food (and/or lack of it), disease and the inevitable deaths were simply being ignored. In effect, the drama surrounding the death of little Richard Warren, some fifteen years before was being replayed over and over again. Even worse was that whilst Richard's death was virtually unavoidable, those in the camps were not. It is a sad reflection on human nature that the brain can come to accept the unacceptable the more familiar it becomes. Strangely Hobhouse noted that some incumbents were surprisingly uncomplaining of their situation. I am no psychologist but maybe it is rooted in a sort of deeply buried survival instinct related, say, to 'Stockholm Syndrome', where captives start to socialise to some degree with their captors, possibly in an attempt to introduce some level of normality into an obviously abnormal situation. Even today the foreboding nature of those camps, especially when viewed through the lens of the full horror of the Nazi Holocaust and its abhorrent racial connotations that was to take place some half a century later, is deplorable, and should be enough to send a shiver down the spine of many a right-minded Brit.

Clearly something had to be done about it and the British Government set up a committee of inquiry led by Millicent Fawcett, a women's rights campaigner, whose findings only served to confirm the whole sad and sorry affair.

As the war dragged on, more and more British and Empire troops were funnelled in, until eventually, at the end of May 1902, the Boers were finally defeated, but it had taken close on half a million troops to do it. The full human and financial cost of the war, not to mention the crisis of conscience about the methods used, though, had made the victory somewhat Pyrrhic. As a result, the peace terms offered by the British were fairly considerate and included an agreement to pay war reparations.

Subsequent analyses began to draw into question the doctrine of imperialism as a legitimate basis for war and just how compatible it was with modern politics. Indeed, was the British Empire even as strong as it was thought to be? After all, the sheer struggle, that the war in South Africa had been, had surprised many. In a nutshell, it was a bad day for jingoism, and it began to dawn that the dogma of 'Splendid Isolation', which held that British foreign policy be decided without any regard to foreign interests might, in reality, now be obsolete arrogance. A new frame of thinking was needed, a more co-operative one, based on alliances, and it would be the alliances that would decide how Europe would polarise when push came to shove during the summer of 1914.

All this said, the British did not have a monopoly on exploitation, far from it. During the 1880s Germany had succeeded in colonising the area in Africa now known as Namibia (then called *Deutsche-Südwestafrika* or German South-West Africa). Looking back at what happened there in the early 1900s, one could perhaps be forgiven for thinking it more typical of the Nazi era than that of Imperial Germany but then, instead of the Jews, it was the native Herero and Nama people who were on the receiving end.

This vast expanse of land was seen as fertile ground on which the German people could grow in numbers in line with the philosophy of '*Lebensraum*'. Literally meaning 'habitat' or 'room to live', *Lebensraum* was the political philosophy of German expansionism being expounded at around this time by Friedrich Ratzel. The only problem seemingly being the existing inhabitants, whom incidentally the Germans regarded as 'racially inferior'. When, after twenty or so years of being exploited and robbed of their land and possessions, the indigenous inhabitants could stand it no longer, the Herero people rose up against their German oppressors. In response the German government sent 14,000 troops under General von Trotha, not only to quell the rebellion but probably with a view to exterminating the entire indigenous population! After pushing them into the desert, Trotha had the drinking holes poisoned and the Herero had no alternative but to surrender. Both the Herero and Nama people who had survived were then shamelessly abused and enslaved in concentration camps. The Germans would remain determined to finish them off, but only after wringing out of them what was left of their free labour, on the construction of a new railway system.

One of the worst of these camps was on Shark Island. Not an island as such, but a short peninsula jutting northwards into the sea near to the town of Lüderitz. Also known as the 'Death Camp', it certainly lived up to its name in that there is evidence that awful experiments took place there, very similar, in fact, to those that would later be carried out by the Nazis during World War II. Here, instead of Joseph Mengele, it was Dr. Hugo Bofinger who headed these earlier sadistic and futile attempts to test various misguided theories including whether abilities were somehow decided by bodily characteristics and the like.

In so doing, thousands were murdered, and it is said that body parts, after the Herero women had been forced to prepare them, were sent back to Germany for so-called 'research'. When word of what was going on began to spread, though, the Kaiser was pressed (probably reluctantly) to put an end to it. And not before time either, since, by then, it was estimated that the Germans had annihilated some 80% of the 100,000 plus native population.

Mercifully, relatively early on in the First World War, German South-West Africa was successfully invaded and taken over by South African troops.

*

At around the same time as the Second Boer War broke out another problem arose, half a world away, in which Germany and Great Britain were allied. I mention it because it is the origin of the soubriquet by which the Germans later became known; a term that sums up the perception of the malevolent, violent mob that many would come to perceive the Germans as, in just four letters. No, not that one, something else when, hackles raised, Kaiser Wilhelm II, typically unable to suppress his irascible nature, blurted out a bellicose diatribe and in so doing managed to make a bit of a fool of both himself and German people in general into the bargain.

A group of young hot-headed peasants in China known as the 'Society of Righteous and Harmonious Fists' emerged, mainly as a result of the growing resentment at the rapidly increasing foreign (mainly European Christian) influences there. Because of reference to 'fists' and the pugilistic nature of many of the society's members, this group became popularly known as the 'Boxers' who had apparently convinced themselves that they were immune to bullets.

For some reason the European Christian missionaries were exempted from certain Chinese laws and, in frustration at the unfairness of this, alongside the appearance of a newspaper article about a proposal to destroy the Great Wall, which later turned out to be a complete hoax, the Boxers retaliated by attacking the Christians and their churches. During 1900 the situation worsened when the numbers of Christians killed and churches burned increased until eventually, when a railway line was attacked, the Germans captured a Boxer and, I am not quite sure why, killed him. The dead Boxer was described as a 'boy' but to what extent he was still just a boy is not clear. The term 'dead boy' always stirs up more emotion than 'dead man', though, and its use here certainly swelled the ranks of the outraged. The incensed Boxers stormed into Peking (Beijing), dealing summarily with anyone of European appearance as they went. Most of the European delegations were situated in one particular quarter of the city and although the resident US Marine Corps put up a valiant defence, the Boxers were eventually able to surround and besiege this area. For almost two months the embassies' staffs, as well as all the other Europeans who had sought shelter there during the attack, were pinned in and harassed.

The deadlock was eventually addressed when the countries whose citizens were most affected, namely UK, France, Germany, Russia, Japan, US, Austria-Hungary and Italy, formed an alliance, each supplying varying numbers of troops and equipment. In spite of having whipped the situation up in the first place, the Germans sent a relatively light force, but the faux pas came when, in his farewell speech to his contingent shortly before they set sail from the port of Bremerhaven, the Kaiser railed:

> *"No quarter to be given, no prisoners to be taken… Just as a thousand years ago the Huns under their King Attila went down in history, so may the name of Germany in China, such that no Chinese will ever again dare so much as to glare at a German."*

(Or words to that effect; the point being that the word 'Huns' was unequivocal.)

Even at the time this caused embarrassment and the above section was omitted from the official published version of the speech, but the word 'Hun', with its barbarian savage imagery, stuck and came in very handy later for propaganda purposes. From adding colour to such reportage under the banner 'The Rape of Belgium', where babies were said to have been bayoneted, to the outspoken former maverick Labour MP, Horatio Bottomley's delightful labelling of the Germans as 'Germhuns' (get it?) in his satirical magazine *John Bull*. Nor did it help that many German helmets and belt buckles were inscribed with '*Gott mit uns*'. Literally meaning 'God [is] with us' but the '*uns*' bit, being so close to 'Huns', only served to underscore the epithet.

*

September 1901 saw the quelling of the Boxers' Rebellion but the second Boer War was to drag on almost until the summer of 1902. Meanwhile Victoria's death meant that her eldest son, Bertie (Albert Edward), inherited the throne as Edward VII but, due to a period of illness, he was not crowned until August 1902. By this time, he was almost sixty-one years old, and the parallel here with the present Prince of Wales would be difficult to miss. As I write, Prince Charles is already in his seventies and, since the Queen seems to continue to enjoy good heath, it may well be a while yet before he succeeds her. Having said this, being in your seventies now is not quite the same as being in your seventies one hundred plus years ago, and the present Prince of Wales is obviously fitter than Edward was at the same age. However, there remains the 'Camilla Factor' to take into account. Harking back to the Edward VIII and Mrs. Simpson affair, I think that the jury may well still be out as to whether or not Camilla would make a queen 'acceptable to the British system' and, were the Queen to live to over a hundred, as did her mother, making Prince Charles getting on for eighty, putting this to the test may be considered pointless. That is, of course, assuming that neither Charles nor Camilla predeceases the Queen. Whatever, if Prince Charles does survive the Queen, the possibility that he may abdicate in favour of William seems, to me at least, an increasingly likely probability with the passage of time. But then again, I was wrong once before...

*

By the time that baby Leonard was born, in April 1902, the family had moved across the road into No.53 Tewkesbury Street. The complement was now eleven, four of which were still at school: Fred, at just turned thirteen, no doubt in his last year; Frank, just turned ten; Albert, aged seven and Syd, at only five, would have just started. Whilst I know that Fred attended Deacon Street School, Frank attended Mantle Road School and Syd went to (the then new) Narborough Road School, I have been unable to trace where my grandfather (Albert) went but, under the circumstances, Deacon Street or Mantle Road must be the most likely contenders.

Although both the Narborough Road and Mantle Street buildings still exist, I am not really sure where the school on Deacon Street stood. This is perhaps not surprising, as the area was significantly redeveloped during the late twentieth century in order to accommodate the new De Montfort University buildings.

For school, as for work, the 'tin can' alarm continued to sound its daily reveilles. Often its strident ring would be somehow anticipated in the dream, a train ride perhaps, a steady build of speed, then a jolt – points? In reality, no doubt the paroxysm of another incumbent of the bed. A case falls from the luggage rack, the train swerves, the dreamer now frozen with fear and 'trinnnggg' – the train crashes! Relief, it hasn't, it's quiet, pitch-black, it's cold, it's morning again; another Monday morning. As usual Jack is up first and, lighting the oil lamp, the shadows dance across the room as it splutters into life. At first no words, just grunts, faces and eyes rubbed, sighs, yawns and then the first conversation. Usually a brief exchange – one boy has irritated another in some way – an arm trapped, a foot knocked, possibly deliberate, something condign for some half-remembered recent injustice perhaps or, just as likely, an accident. A clearly directed rebuke with a profanity or two for good measure would usually follow. Whether things went any further largely depended on mood, but more often than not, that would be the end of the matter.

The routine had evolved into something like this: with Richard washed and sitting in front of the fire, cup of tea in hand, Flo would appear, then Jack and Arch, followed by Fred. The younger boys, being still at school, did not have to get there until nine o'clock and so were allowed an extra half an hour in bed, an aspect that certainly eased the bottleneck at the sink. In return, it fell to them to tidy up the bedroom and get rid of the contents of the *guzunder*. With such a number in a small house, routines like this were an absolute necessity if confrontations like that described above were to be minimised.

Yet, on occasion, things would go wrong. Like the time that both Richard's and the boys' alarms failed to go off. There were plenty of 'knocker-uppers' but Richard had refused to pay for this service or allow anybody else in the family to do so even though, with four workers in the household, they could well have afforded it. Sometimes you could hear next door's window being knocked but not on this occasion. Richard, generally a fairly light sleeper, was the first to hear the factory hooters go off. With only half an hour to spare, swearing under his breath, he shot out of bed and was dressed, shaved and out of the house with a lump of bread in his mouth for breakfast and, in so doing, had skilfully managed to avoid the hell that was to break loose shortly afterwards. The accelerated upheaval of getting up caused mayhem. Jack was shouting at Flo to 'hurry up or else', Arch and Frank were engaged in a full-blown fight, while Louisa, in tears, attempted to rectify the situation. In the end everybody got off half-dressed, half-washed and half-fed. All who had jobs were late for work and lost half an hour's pay and those at school only just arrived in time, which was as well because the punishment for being late was a summary swift crack across the behind with the cane. That day Richard invested in a new alarm clock and Jack decided to invest sixpence a week in a knocker-upper despite what his father had decreed. His eighteen years and growing confidence saw to it that Richard did not challenge his decision.

Before the Victorian era, Britain's status as the greatest power in the world was considered so assured that there seemed little need to change the ad hoc education system that had developed where, essentially, only the rich elite were schooled beyond elementary level. Although the state began to realise the need to reform the system as long ago as the 1830s, particularly regarding better provision for teacher training, before Foster's Education Act of 1870 there was no specific requirement at all for children to attend school. When it dawned, however, that foreign manufacture was beginning to compete directly with domestic production and that Britain needed a better equipped work force if it was to deal effectively with this challenge, it became clear that there was a requirement to look again at education. By 1880 it was made compulsory for all children between five and ten to attend school, and committees known as School Boards were set up to see that they did. Where there were insufficient schools, the Board had the power to provide them or where the schools were inadequate the Board had the power to take them over. At first the results were a bit hit and miss but improved after 1891 when school fees were abolished. Additionally, the school leaving age was raised, initially to eleven but, by 1899, to twelve years old. The Boards in England were replaced by the Local Education Authorities that we know today under the Balfour Education Act of 1902. This Act also paved the way for what was to become a natural progression to secondary education.

The walk to school in winter was often a pretty grim affair; in the half-light, along the streets lined with grimy buildings. But absolutely no concessions were ever made for bad weather. Neither rain, fog (often as smog) nor even snow made any difference. Obviously severe snowfalls could and did affect school attendance in the countryside but, unlike nowadays, there would have had to have been a catastrophe along biblical lines for a town or city school to close as a result of the weather.

In the playground, huddling, waiting to go in, hands drawn into sleeves, ears burning with cold. Then inside – a cold, poorly insulated, high-ceilinged Victorian building. Rising damp and often a leaky roof imparted a musty smell which slowly mixed with the sulphurous, dusty odour from the coke stove as the fire built. The third element was the smell of the children themselves. Through no fault of their own some children were cleaner than others. Then, as now, some people's idea of hygiene was different to others' and often they struggled to pay for washing powder, soap, hot water or even to find the time to wash either themselves or their children effectively. Most did their best, but the worst cases of neglect became undeniable when damp clothes were hung to dry on the guard around the stove.

Fred, Frank, Albert and Syd sat in a sort of 'sit-up-and-beg' double desk of which the seat was an integral part. In some cases, there was a backrest, in other cases not. If they slouched the teacher would require them, in no uncertain terms, to, "Sit up straight!" Anything other than immediate compliance with such a command might be taken as disobedience and could well land the offender with a summary whack. And woe betide anybody who literally blotted their copybook!

With up to fifty or so pupils, class sizes were generally much larger than those of today, but the teacher would have had a monitor or two to assist them. These were selected trusted pupils, sort of teaching assistants if you will, who would act, now and again, as an intermediary between teacher and the class by giving out books or topping up ink wells, etc. Teaching methods were robust and no nonsense; 'the three Rs' being delivered through 'talk and chalk'. Chalk was used by the pupils too because, as well as the teacher's blackboard, pupils also used it to write onto their small slates. In cases where tasks were set and then examined by the teacher shortly afterwards, this saved on costly paper, pens and ink – sums or practising handwriting, for example (the latter now very much a thing of the past I fear). To write on a small slate with a thick piece of chalk is not easy though, especially for a small hand, but long before the consequences of failure had healed, poor performance could simply be wiped away, leaving a 'clean slate' on which to try again.

'Writing' was in fact the second of the Rs, 'reading' being the first and, of course, the only one actually beginning with 'R'. Reading was taught with the aid of a fairly limited selection of approved books or poetry or from newspaper articles, etc. and the third 'R' – 'arithmetic' was a matter of addition, subtraction, multiplication and division. Thinking about it, these functions can be as simple or as difficult as you want them to be. Starting with, say 2+2=4, through pounds, shillings and pence (£sd) and stones, pounds and ounces (st, lb(s) and oz) eventually to the dreaded long division. In essence the stuff of the elementary school was everyday commerce. It did not run to concepts such as quadratic equations or calculus, but what was learned was learned well. Drummed in by rote, as they say, to the extent that the tools necessary to conduct everyday business became almost instinctual: how to weigh or measure out an order, the ability to understand how much to charge and how much change to give and how to record such. No doubt considered unrounded and basic by today's standards, it was an education of its time and no matter how better educated in comparison we consider ourselves today, I wonder what proportion of those having received a more recent education can swear, hand on heart, that they can do long division. (Without a calculator, that is.)

School meals would not be introduced for several more years and in the middle of the day the children would eat whatever they had taken with them. A sandwich or two, perhaps, or bread and dripping ('bread and dip') or bread and honey or a Tickler's jam sandwich; the bread, more often than not stale, though. Or even a cold potato – anything to be used up. Some may have had a piece of fruit from time to time, often apples from their own trees if the parents owned or had access to a tree. Remnants of these fruits would rarely find their way into the dustbin, though, because well before the best bits were eaten, the owner would be pressed: "Can I 'ave the core?" A pre-sucked, coarse apple core may not be to everybody's taste but, for the lucky recipient (or highest bidder), it may well have been one of the rare occasions that he or she would enjoy any fresh fruit and enrich their diet with the vitamins and minerals, considered these days to be essential for good health and development, into the bargain.

Around the turn of the twentieth century, life expectancy for a male was around forty-five. Not that you could always expect to live that long, it being a statistic, of course. It's just an average; just a simple addition and division. In fact, closer analysis reveals that most people died at an age other than forty-five. Although many would have died within a relatively narrow grouping of ages either side of that figure, some people, as now, still made it to ninety and beyond. The factor bringing the average down was the unacceptably large number who would not make it beyond their first year. Although vaccinations for smallpox, typhoid and cholera were available, there were only limited treatments for a large number of other serious childhood illnesses, including tuberculosis, measles, mumps, diphtheria, scarlet fever, rubella and so on. Not to mention the host of other conditions that sprang from deprivation such as infantile diarrhoea, influenza and rickets etc. If you could survive these in infancy and childhood, and the effects of household arsenic in, say, the wallpaper, didn't get you and you didn't get drawn into bloody warfare, then you might just be okay.

School in the afternoon meant more of the same and, as the day dragged on, any child perceived by the teacher as lacking in concentration or caught talking in class would also put themselves at risk of physical chastisement. The total silence of the class was essential following such a punishment because it reassured the teacher that discipline had been restored. He or she (more often he in those days) might gaze slowly around the room, from one lowered head to the next, as if searching for the slightest reaction that would have otherwise gone unnoticed, anyone evidenced as anything other than totally deferential and reverent risking a similar fate. (With interest if the indiscretion were in any way considered tantamount to insolence!)

Eventually the school Monday came to a close, as do all Mondays sooner or later. It was time for the walk home. Louisa had told them 'not to dawdle' on this journey as she knew full well that, with no particular arrival time to respect, they could easily be delayed by any of the numerous distractions likely to confront a child on foot. If the clothes had been wet in the morning the boiler should have seen to it that they would be dry on the way home. Unless, that is, yours had fallen off the guard (or, indeed, had been pushed off as part of some vendetta that had arisen through a playground conflict or the like). Occasionally distractions along the way would protract these journeys but sooner or later it would be home again around the fire, toasting forks at the ready.

Apart from hymns every morning at school, it was the Sunday School movement that generally provided for spiritual education. Each Sunday, best clothes would be donned, and the children would gather for their weekly enlightenment. Church vestries, nonconformist halls and other makeshift buildings would be made available across the land to those dedicated groups who gave cheerfully (in the main) of their time in order to deprive the Devil of as many souls as possible. Hymns – Easter carols at Easter, harvest songs at the Harvest Festival and Christmas carols at Christmas. Then a story from the Bible; often aimed at the vicissitudes of youth – Moses found among the reeds by the Pharaoh's daughter, Joseph and his coat of many colours, the return of the Prodigal Son, David and Goliath, the Tower of Babel... and who would not have known Psalm 23 verbatim. These stories were often from the Old Testament but naturally the story of Jesus Christ himself would have been the most important of all: '...before the cock crow, thou shalt deny me thrice.' Then a picture to colour – after the story of Abraham and Isaac, for example, where God requires that Abraham sacrifice his loving son Isaac in order to test his faith: just as Abraham is about to kill his son God realises that he means business and steps in. The drawings that followed would not rival Caravaggio's 'The Sacrifice of Isaac', I grant you, but they would capture the moment all the same: Abraham, dagger raised above his son, who is recumbent on an altar, the angel in the sky, word bubble under mouth with the word 'STOP!' written in it in thick crayon.

Occasionally the darker side of religion may be alluded to: 'the wages of sin', etc. No doubt seen as a guiding mechanism, or the prospect of hell if you 'fell short' in some way, but this sort of thing could well also play on a young mind, particularly if you were to wake up in the early hours.

Then another hymn or two and home.

I am not really sure to what extent Sunday School still lives on, but I fear that it is not the institution that it was. No doubt some would regard it as indoctrination, and others as irrelevant, but it did espouse values and stimulate thought, even if only the criticism of Christianity rather than its aggrandisement. I suppose other (more important?) pursuits, such as computer games, Sunday television or football may well have taken over today and the concept of Sunday School may now be considered somewhat passé. If so, I have to confess (no pun intended) that, although I am no religious zealot by any manner or means, I do find that a bit sad, particularly where there may be little, if any, such guidance at home.

Everyday home life, at that age, was also much simpler than it is today; with no television, radio or the dreaded computers, entertainment was limited, to say the least. Naturally there were jobs to be done; room tidying, cleaning – especially boots and shoes; with ten or so pairs walking in and out of the house daily it would soon be a mess if the soles were not regularly cleaned – and there was always an errand or two to run. With the essentials out the way, though, there would have been some time to relax. Simple games such as 'hunt the thimble' (fairly self-explanatory) or 'funnel ball' helped pass the time. With the latter you take a sheet of newspaper (the smaller the sheet the harder the game) and, holding one corner between the index finger and thumb, fold it around your arm to make a cone shape. The end held by the finger and thumb is twisted together to make the closed end of the funnel. Next make several paper balls by screwing up other sheets of newspaper. The funnel can either be supported on a table or on the floor in order to make a paper basket, or it can simply be held in a player's hand. In the first case the object would be to take turns in throwing the paper balls into the funnel from a distance. The winner would be the one who got the most balls onto the funnel or the one who caught the most balls in their funnel, depending on which way you had decided to play the game.

Consequences was another amusing pastime, no doubt originating amongst the parlour games of old. In its essential form much more popular with girls than boys, no doubt, because it can turn out a bit soppy. However, older girls would inevitably have played it with their younger brothers and younger boys may well have played it between themselves. But, come to think of it, given imagination it is a game that, by extending the possibilities and adding a bit of 'double entendre' and 'spice', could well be extended to the desires of older boys, if you follow. I'll show you what I mean.

The game is a complementary rather than competitive one and can be played by between two and twelve people: the greater the number of participants the better. You take a sheet of writing paper and fold it about ten or twelve times from top to bottom in a pleated or concertina fashion. The first player writes secretly on the strip above the first fold and then folds the strip back so as both to hide what is written on it and reveal the second blank strip. The next player then writes secretly on this second strip, folds it over to reveal the third and so on. It is important that no player knows what another has written as it would spoil the fun. The nature of what was written varied but essentially, it may well have gone something like this:

> The first player is asked to write:
> 'The...' followed by an adjective (or adjectives) to describe a man, e.g. 'The scruffy, bald...'
>
> The second player is asked to write:
> A man's name, e.g. 'Richard Warren'. Sometimes the more personal, the more fun.
>
> The third player is asked to write:
> Who they met (with as full a description as possible) followed by an adjective (or adjectives) to describe the person, e.g. 'Met the fat, old...'
>
> Next player:
> A woman's name, e.g. 'Mrs. Blucas'.
>
> Next player:
> Where: 'In...', 'On...', 'At...' etc. followed by where they met, e.g. 'Down the pub'.
>
> Next player:
> 'They... [what they did].'
> (See what I mean about the wider possibilities.)
>
> Next player:

'She said...'

Next player:
'He said...'

Then, often after the addition of several more details, the last player is asked to write what the consequence was:
'And the consequence was...'

The game could be extended with a wide range of eventualities such as 'What various other people said'; 'What the world said about it', 'What happened next'; there were no hard and fast rules. The point was that, with nobody knowing any more about the story than the line or lines that they themselves had written, the results could sometimes be amusing when, at the end of the game, the paper was unfolded to reveal the scandalous libel in its entirety. Nobody, either known or unknown to the writer, famous or infamous, was immune to inclusion. I understand that the Prime Minister (while drunk) once met up with a prudish vicar's wife in Monte Carlo where they drank beer and sang Christmas carols together. When she asked him for a stick of rock, he said he'd got to feed his cat and the consequence was that they both ended up in Wales. How those long winter's nights must have flown!

Of the other games played in the Warren house, draughts was probably the favourite, played by every member from time to time but especially enjoyed by the boys. Richard liked the game too and prided himself on being the best player. He liked to win and to be fair, in the main, he did. When he didn't, though, he was inclined to question the validity of the outcome, an attitude inclined to rub off on the boys. As a result, there evolved a sort of league table and because the result of each game could change a player's status in the table, they were played with the utmost concentration. Charges of cheating or not playing by the rules were common and sulks about what happened and why sometimes went on for days.

In the winter, outdoor activities were generally confined to Saturdays, when hoops could be propelled along with sticks, tops were kept spinning with whips and football could be played in the street. In summer it was a different matter, though. In such a crowded house, making the most of the freedom that the great outdoors brought was essential and, especially in the summer holidays, the boys would go for long walks.

Situated to the north-west of Leicester, Tewkesbury Street was then only a fifteen or twenty minute walk (half a mile or so) from fields and the open countryside that lay beyond. Glenfield, Anstey and Kirby Muxloe, which are now all but subsumed into the urban sprawl, were then still quite distinct, separate villages. A little further afield was Groby, with its pool, and nearby Newtown Linford with its entrance to Bradgate Park.

*

Bradgate Park is a large deer park with woodlands, in the middle of which sits the ruins of Bradgate House – a once-great Tudor mansion that was the ancient seat of the well-connected Grey family (Henry Grey, 1st Duke of Suffolk and Lady Frances Grey, who was one of Henry VIII's nieces). Their young daughter was Lady Jane Grey, who was destined to become, ostensibly, queen regnant of England, albeit for only nine days. A record for a British monarch but perhaps surprisingly, not for all monarchs. Apparently two of them only lasted twenty minutes! Both Louis XIX of France, who abdicated after twenty minutes' reign and Luis Filipe of Portugal, who was heir to the throne but was fatally wounded by assassins along with his father, the king, but survived for twenty minutes longer than he did, lay claim equally to this title.

Although now just roofless, red-bricked ruins, there is evidence that grand stone buildings may also have formed part of this great home. Even walking amongst what remains today one can still get a sense of the opulence in which the Greys must have lived. Vast halls, servants' quarters, of which there must have been many, grand kitchens and fantastic views over the park. Life must have been privileged indeed for the young Jane growing up in such a style, and if ever such ruins were haunted, these must surely be. In the chill of a quiet autumn's afternoon, perhaps the sounds of a child are heard... is it a young girl running from room to room? Is there someone there, or is it just the wind jostling the leaves?

When Henry VIII died in 1547, his only son, Edward, his sole male heir – through Jane Seymour, the only one of his six wives to produce the son and heir that Henry had so desperately longed for – and who was not yet ten years old, succeeded him as Edward VI. Because of his tender years a Regency Council was set up to advise the new King, led by his uncle and close friend of his father, Edward Seymour, 1st Earl of Hertford (Jane Seymour's brother). He was to be known as Edward's 'Protector'.

The prime purpose of a regency is to assist a reigning monarch who, for one reason or another, may need help in conducting day-to-day matters of state, etc. and, therefore, invests its members (particularly the 'Protector' himself), albeit vicariously, with a great deal of political power. A handy commodity when things are going well, but when they are not the resultant criticism from opponents could often prove fatal. And in Seymour's case things certainly did go wrong! He managed to upset so many influential people that he lost his job as Protector and, in 1552, ended up being beheaded. John Dudley, Earl of Warwick (later Duke of Northumberland), would take over as Regent, and although he adopted a much more laissez-faire approach, was also power-hungry. Later, he too would end up with his head on the block.

Whether it was anything to do with his mother, Jane Seymour, having died within a few days of his birth, is not clear but Edward had always been a sickly child. So when he started to cough up blood, it was clear to all that his health had taken a serious turn for the worse and sadly, in 1553, after only just over six years on the throne, Edward died of tuberculosis. Meanwhile Dudley had managed to marry off his son, Lord Guilford Dudley, to Lady Jane Grey only a few weeks before Edward's death. What's more, there was a 'Device for the Succession to the Crown' in Edward's will which named Lady Jane Grey as his heir. But few failed to grasp that this was a thinly veiled attempt by Dudley to usurp power for himself, and that the legal heir to the throne was, in reality, Mary, Henry VIII's elder daughter. The only caveat being that she was the daughter of Catherine of Aragon, his marriage to whom Henry had denounced as invalid, ostensibly on account of her previous marriage to his brother, Arthur. In reality, though, he had really wanted to marry Anne Boleyn and the whole affair became known as 'The King's Great Matter' which, of course, led to Henry's rift with Rome and the Reformation. Through all this Mary had remained a staunch Catholic, however, and there were fears that she might well reverse the Reformation and reintroduce Catholicism to England. Nonetheless, Mary had managed to gather much more support than Dudley anticipated, even to the extent that some of those who had been sent to arrest her, changed their allegiance. As a result, Jane's supporters were forced to back down, despite her having been proclaimed Queen on 10 July 1553. With her arrest and imprisonment on the following 19th, though, her reign would last a total of just nine days.

Dudley, Jane and Guilford were all tried and found guilty of treason and Dudley duly executed but, through fear of stirring things further, Mary was reluctant to execute Jane or Guilford. Unfortunately, though, she had little alternative when further mootings of rebellion arose. First Guilford and then Jane – this young girl, still in her teens, who never really wanted to be queen anyway and who had been cynically manipulated and exploited for political gain – were eventually beheaded in the grounds of the Tower of London on 12 February 1554.

Chapter 6

The Uncle of Europe

> 'I never can or shall look at him without a shudder...'
>
> **Queen Victoria**
> (About her son, Bertie,
> the future King Edward VII.)

Because of everything else that was going on at the start of the twentieth century, preparations for Edward's coronation took longer than normal, being eventually set for late June 1902. It then had to be postponed further because he was taken ill with appendicitis, but after surgery (somewhat pioneering for its day), the Coronation was able to go ahead at Westminster Abbey on 9 August 1902. His full name was, in fact, Albert Edward Wettin of Saxe-Coburg-Gotha, I think the 'Wettin' bit coming from his father's (Price Albert's) original family surname. Although the modern Royal Family name of Windsor is said ostensibly to be derived from Windsor Castle, it may well have been that the similar word 'Wettin' lent a greater degree of congruity when Edward's son, George V, brought about the change in 1917. This name change, of course, became necessary in order to distance the British monarchy from their German origins, especially since Britain was now being bombed from the air by Gotha bombers! And other things would change for the same reason. For example, the sea to the east of Britain that had long been known as the German Ocean on account of its focus on trade within the historic bloc of northern Germanic states known as the Hanseatic League, began to be called the North Sea. Likewise, German biscuits became 'Empire biscuits' and the Battenberg family – closely connected to the British royal family – would anglicise their name to Mountbatten.

On ascending the throne Bertie had decided to reign as simply 'Edward' rather than 'Albert' or 'Albert Edward', possibly in order to emerge as 'his own man' from the long shadow of his parentage. Whatever, I rather suspect that he did not choose the name in order to bask in the reflected glory of some preceding monarchs who went by the same regnal name. Although Edward VI's reign lasted less than six years, Edward V's comes in fourth shortest, after that of Lady Jane Grey, at around just eleven weeks, on account of his uncle Richard, Duke of Gloucester, who was supposed to be looking after him but usurped the throne instead, as Richard III. Richard is believed to have been behind the murder of Edward V and his brother, Richard of Shrewsbury, Duke of York (the so-called 'Princes in the Tower'). Although Edward IV's reign was interrupted, Edwards I, II and III each had fair cracks of the whip, but they all courted controversy in their times, Edward I especially, through his harassment north of the border, which earned him the soubriquet, 'Hammer of the Scots' – an association not entirely lost when criticism of this twentieth-century Edward emanated from that quarter.

Because Edward was related in one way or another to practically all the other royal families of Europe (notably fairly closely to some) the great gathering of these 'crowned heads' for the Coronation served to relieve political differences somewhat and lifted the mantle of grief that had prevailed since Victoria's death. After some sixty years of wealth and privilege (without real responsibility) mixed initially with the catalyst of youth, it is perhaps not surprising that, long before his accession, Edward or 'Bertie' as he was originally known, had developed something of a 'reputation'. Being the eldest son of Queen Victoria and Prince Albert and therefore heir apparent, in order to shield the boy from any undesirable outside influences, his early years were confined to intense and continuous study. And, whilst his older sister, Vicky; the Princess Royal, was considered bright, Bertie was regarded as rather lazy and clumsy and it was said that his mother, often comparing him unfavourably to his father, had made Bertie feel as though he had been a disappointment to her. Inevitably this led to frustration and anger and the boy became more and more petulant until eventually the strictures that had been imposed upon him, rather than being the making of him, contrived to turn him into rather a difficult and obstreperous young man. Understandably this did little to improve his relationship with his mother, instead providing her with even more reasons to dislike him.

Bertie was born at Buckingham Palace on the morning of 9 November 1841; by no means a small baby, his birth had been something of an unforgettable experience for the petite Victoria. I do not know exactly how much he weighed but, in a letter to her Uncle Leopold (King of the Belgians) a few weeks later, she wrote, 'Our boy is a wonderfully strong and large child, with very large dark blue eyes, a finely formed but somewhat large nose and pretty little mouth'. (Whether the mouth was 'little and pretty' or just 'pretty little' i.e. not much of it, was not qualified.) She is also said to have written that he was born after 'very severe suffering'.

Later, as a young boy, Bertie is said to have angered and upset his parents when he fell and badly lacerated his face while climbing on an iron gate. But probably his most inflammatory act was his dalliance with Nellie Clifden in the summer of 1861 when, as a young man of nineteen, he was sent to experience army life in Ireland. Nellie Clifden was described as an 'actress' and apart from that, there is not a great deal else known about her. Whether she was an actress in the theatrical sense of the word or in the 'as the actress said to the bishop' sense must remain conjecture but whatever, Bertie and she would share what was probably the prince's first sexual experience. However, that would not be all there was to it as, to the absolute disgust of Victoria and Albert, Clifden's attitude following the liaison was hardly 'the sole of discretion' and word soon got around.

Later that year, when Bertie had returned to Cambridge, Albert, despite complaining of feeling ill, felt the need to visit him for a 'fatherly chat' about the affair. He badly wanted to make his son fully appreciate all the distress that his actions had caused, how these matters were unbecoming of the heir to the throne and all the rest of it. However, the bad weather during the visit had made Albert feel much worse and, after developing a fever, on 14 December 1861 (just a year or so after Richard Walter Warren Sr. had been born) he died, ostensibly of typhoid fever; a disease often caused by drinking infected water. And, with sanitation then not as it is now, there was plenty of contaminated water to be had, especially when travelling. No doubt with a depressed immune system then, as a result of the stress and cold that he experienced during the journey, and well before the advent of antibiotics, what happened is perhaps not so surprising.

Bertie himself would go down with typhoid some ten years later but, of course, he survived it.

The devastation that visited Victoria following the death of her beloved Albert is legendary: the natural consequence of losing the one great love of her life. Then, when she subsequently wrote about Bertie to her eldest daughter, Vicky, saying that, 'I never can or shall look at him without a shudder...', it was quite clear that she deeply begrudged the stress and embarrassment that his behaviour had caused and the extra burden on Albert's health that had clearly resulted from his need to visit. I do not think that it is going too far to suggest that she blamed Albert's untimely death (he was only forty-two) entirely on Bertie's stupidity.

Just over a year later, Bertie married the Danish Princess Alexandra but, much to Victoria's dismay, this did not stop his philandering. Far from it – his name would go on to be linked to those of many other women, including the famous actresses Lillie Langtry and Sarah Bernhardt, and aristocrats such as Lady Frances Brooke, Lady

Randolph Churchill (Winston Churchill's mother) and Alice Keppel (Camilla, Duchess of Cornwall's great-grandmother and interestingly, also a distant relative (by marriage I think) of the first UK *Who Wants to be a Millionaire* winner, Judith Keppel). How Victoria must have despaired then when, on top of all this, her son, Bertie, the Prince of Wales no less, appeared in open court on a couple of occasions as a direct result of his indiscretions. Firstly in 1870, when he gave evidence voluntarily in an action for divorce brought by Sir Charles Mordaunt against his sex-mad (literally) wife, Lady Harriet Mordaunt. Although not cited as a co-respondent it was well known that he had visited her on many occasions and so felt it necessary to declare that there had never been any impropriety... As a result, whilst some felt that his treatment in court was deliberately over-moderated, he did spend an uncomfortable few minutes in the witness box, and the subsequent newspaper coverage of the matter would draw his suitability as a future king into question.

The second occasion was somewhat later, in 1891, when, at fifty-odd, the prince could hardly claim the callowness of youth as an excuse. This time he was compelled to attend court as the result of a writ for slander issued by Sir William Gordon-Cumming, a lieutenant-colonel in the Army, over the suggestion that Sir William had cheated at baccarat, a card game which at the time was, in fact, along with various other gambling games, illegal. It became known as the 'Tranby Croft Affair' on account of the Yorkshire mansion where the card game in question had taken place. In the end Gordon-Cumming lost the action, was kicked out of the Army and vilified by his circle. The public, however, were not so sure and retained a certain sympathy for Sir William which certainly did nothing to improve the prince's image.

The German Kaiser Wilhelm II, on the other hand, was said to have been Victoria's favourite grandson, so could it have been that some degree of animosity may have developed between Edward VII and his nephew, the Kaiser, and if so, by extension, between Britain and Germany as early as this?

Not that Edward's popularity was improving within the rest of

Europe at this time, either. Just prior to his ascending the throne, the 'Fashoda Affair' had brought Britain and France to the brink of war.

In 1898, at the same time as the British were fighting the Mahdist revolutionaries in Sudan, the French were seeking to secure a continuous route west to east across Africa, stretching from what is now Mali (but then under French colonial rule) on the Atlantic Ocean, all the way to the Red Sea. The only thing in the way was the troubled Sudan which, coincidentally, served Britain in a similar way, north-south, and without passage through it there could never be a continuous route from South Africa to Egypt and the Mediterranean. To cap it all, Britain had by now become particularly sensitive about anything to do with Sudan, what with the killing and decapitation of General Gordon at Khartoum and the continued unrest there. So, when a small contingent of French troops turned up on the Nile at Fashoda (now Kodok), Kitchener's Army, fresh from its victory at Omdurman, was sent upriver to 'sort things out'. When both sides met up, however, neither could see any advantage in direct confrontation and the resulting stand-off lasted for several weeks. Eventually the French, promised additional land elsewhere if they agreed, made an embarrassing withdrawal. Although what happened at Fashoda did nothing to endear France and Britain to each other, it did show that, where mutual interests were at stake, they could at least, co-operate.

Neither were things too great between Britain and Belgium. En route to Denmark and accompanied by Alexandra in April 1900, Edward (then still Prince of Wales) was the subject of an assassination attempt when a young anarchist by the name of Jean-Baptiste Sipido shot at him through a train window. Young indeed; Sipido was only fifteen years old at the time, but clearly old enough to have been indoctrinated. Luckily nobody was hurt in the drama and Sipido was quickly disarmed and detained. Under interrogation he fully admitted that he intended to kill the prince in order to avenge the British atrocities in the South African War. However, it was not the assassination attempt in itself that caused the unease, but what happened afterwards.

When the matter came to court, as would Princip be in 1914, Sipido was mitigated by his youth and the defence successfully argued that, at such a tender age, he could not be expected to understand fully the difference between right and wrong. Initially this seemed fair enough, as at least he would be detained. However, the detention was appealed and with the various other legal arguments that ensued, the case got rather bogged down. Such was the muddle, that in the end Sipido was released, whereupon he immediately fled to France.

Although the Prince of Wales had asked that Sipido be treated reasonably, his release came as a complete shock to all and the British Government complained bitterly, calling it a miscarriage of justice. Then, despite Belgium having requested Sipido's extradition, the process again seemed to drag on unnecessarily, King Leopold II even at one stage personally pressing the French President, Loubet, on the issue. In the end, Sipido was sent back to Belgium but it was through deportation rather than extradition and so he retained his freedom. In fact, he survived into his seventies and was said even to have returned to live in France in later life.

Leopold II was a second cousin to Edward VII, Leopold's father (Leopold I) being Queen Victoria's maternal uncle. What's more, he was said to have been her favourite uncle so if Edward had begun to become a bit paranoid by this time it really would not have been too surprising!

So, in spite of Britain's close royal familial connections to the other crowned heads of Europe, her political tangency with the Continent at the time of Edward's coronation remained tenuous. And if anything, she was probably still tied closer to Germany than the ancient enemy, France. It would be the twists and turns of events, during the course of Edward's subsequent reign and beyond, however, that were to alter attitudes irretrievably and bring about a series of polarisations that would decide the final outcome.

*

The turn of the twentieth century, as with all turns of centuries, precipitated reflection but perhaps markedly more so than normal, in view of the great strides made during the Victorian era. Britain had come a long way from the abject poverty and cruelty depicted by Dickens through the developing technology of the Industrial Revolution and the educational and social reforms that grew out of its increasing wealth. The Britain of the twenty-five-year-old Richard Walter Warren in 1885 would have been virtually unrecognisable to that of the similarly aged Richard Ward Warren (his grandfather) in 1824, when slavery, for example, although in the process of being abolished throughout the British Empire, was still being widely exploited in other parts of the world. If I am to retain the reader it would be impossible to allude to all the achievements of these times, but I feel that to mention a few of the most important pivots goes some way to illustrating the metamorphosis that Victoria's reign saw.

To start with, the introduction of the Penny Post during the 1840s, which, for the first time gave all and sundry the ability to communicate over long distances, while the simultaneous development of the railways significantly reduced delivery times and revolutionised personal travel. As an example, the young Richard Ward Warren, wanting to make the one hundred-plus mile journey from Leicester to London by stagecoach, would have had to allow something like a whole day for the journey; often longer if undertaken during the winter months. Granted, the main highways, at least, were generally reasonably surfaced by this time and the coaches fairly well-sprung, but you could get very cold, especially if you did not have an interior seat. The poor coach lights, sometimes just candle lamps or powered by oil, greatly increased the risks that accompanied night-time travel and meant that to travel any distance, overnight stays in coaching inns along the way were often necessary. (With additional stays perhaps, where progress was hampered by the myriad other unforeseen delays that might arise.) Some of these inns would have been good but others, no doubt, not so and certain 'arrangements' between coach drivers or operators and inn landlords along the way meant that you didn't always get the best value for money.

Although confined to the more affluent, coach travel at this time was still a risky business. Not only might you catch a chill or worse, but brakes sometimes failed, horses bolted, wheels could fall off and even open fights could break out as the tedium and confines of the journey began to tell. Not to mention being relieved of your possessions by a highwayman. Not too surprising then that timetables and announcements regarding itineraries were often appended with 'God willing' or something similar. Presumably, this was in order to remind the traveller of the level of risk involved and giving him or her a final opportunity to change their mind. Or, at least, to mitigate any resultant legal action by implying that, should the passenger ignore this 'final warning' and the worst happen, then it would be God, rather than the coach company, who was principally liable.

Not difficult to work out then, why a significant number of the coaching inns were named 'The Rest and be Thankful' or variations on that theme.

In contrast, the young Richard Walter Warren undertaking the same journey by rail, although crammed into a carriage with the masses, would have been much more likely to have arrived in one piece. Better still, rather than taking a whole long day, his journey would have probably lasted less than three hours. In fact, although it would have been a long day, he could well have expected to get to London, complete his business there and arrive back within the same day, all at a fraction of the cost that his grandfather would have paid.

In terms of world travel it was the construction of the Suez Canal that achieved for sea journeys something akin to what the railways had done for journeys over land. Opened in 1869, it connected the Mediterranean to the Red Sea and enabled large vessels to travel between Europe and the Far East without having to go all the way around Africa. In particular there was no longer a need to brave the frequent storms off the Cape of Good Hope, so that voyages became safer, quicker and cheaper. All of this would help Britain in particular, not only by improving access to its colonial interests in the Far East but also by improving access to its Empire as a whole.

In the air, although the Montgolfier brothers had pioneered balloon flight in the late eighteenth century, it was left to the American cycle manufacturers, the Wright brothers, to develop heavier-than-air flight during the very late Victorian era. They did not, however, succeed in flying a powered aeroplane until 1903 when, at Kitty Hawk, North Carolina, they managed to take off and fly 100 feet or so before safely landing the machine. Somewhat surprising then, that planes had developed to the degree that they had done by the time of the Great War; only just over ten years later. But, although Blériot had flown across the English Channel in 1909, it would not be until the war had ended that Alcock and Brown were able to make their historic first non-stop crossing of the Atlantic.

In medicine the concept of vaccination was developed into the highly effective preventative measure that we rely on today. Not only does it protect the inoculated but also those with whom they come into contact. Initially against smallpox, it would become the means by which the world would eventually rid itself of this deadly scourge. Although the virus still exists in secure research establishments, ostensibly in case any beneficial use is ever found for it, there have been no recorded outbreaks since the late 1970s and smallpox was declared eradicated by the World Health Organisation (WHO) in 1980.

Although a pre-Victorian, having died some fourteen years before Victoria came to the throne, it was Dr. Edward Jenner who paved the way for all this through his research into the association between smallpox and the similar disease, cowpox. He was born in the small town of Berkeley in Gloucestershire, midway between Gloucester and Bristol, in 1749, and went on to study at both St. Andrews and London. But it was to Berkeley that he would return to work as a country doctor. Many of his patients were farmers, who had noticed that milkmaids rarely, if ever, contracted smallpox. And it was this perception, along with the notion that small exposures to diseases, prior to infection by them, could reduce their severity, which led Jenner to ponder whether the milkmaids' apparent immunity to smallpox was acquired as a result of their having been in contact with cattle infected with cowpox. Although cowpox is principally a disease of cows, causing lesions to form on their udders similar in appearance to the lesions caused by smallpox on human skin, it can also be passed to humans. However, it is a much milder disease in humans than smallpox; the skin lesions tend to be more localised and less disfiguring, and sufferers are much more likely to survive.

Jenner demonstrated his theory when, in 1796, he introduced tissue from a cowpox-infected milkmaid – Sarah Nelmes – into James Phipps, the young son of a friend, who had had neither cowpox nor smallpox. Although rendered mildly ill by cowpox, thankfully the boy soon recovered. Imagine how anxious Jenner must have felt about this and then how relieved but, nevertheless, he then went on to deliberately infect the boy with smallpox! He must have been very sure of himself as, if the boy had died, he may well have been left facing a charge of murder! Fortunately, though, the boy did not succumb to the disease and Jenner had proved his point.

Basically, Jenner had harnessed the action of specific antibodies. These are produced in the bloodstream in response to foreign protein material, in order to attack and destroy invading pathogens. They are specific because they attack only a specific type of pathogen (or group of pathogens with similar characteristics). The problem is that, even in the otherwise healthy body, there may not be sufficient antibodies produced in time to deal effectively with the pathogen and, especially in Jenner's time, sufferers were more likely to be already compromised through poor nutrition and living conditions. Anyone lucky enough to survive a dose of smallpox was unlikely to contract it again but, by this time, the disease would have done its worst and most survivors could expect to have been left severely weakened and disfigured by it. So, with cowpox much less symptomatic in humans and not so disfiguring, infection with it seemed a small price to pay if it were to prevent the subsequent contraction of smallpox.

At the risk of getting out of my depth here, my understanding is that, put simply, antibodies are proteins produced by the body in response to its invasion by 'antigens' (foreign substances or pathogens). Being fairly specific to a particular type of antigen, having attached themselves to it, they can then destroy it. As the cowpox and smallpox viruses are so similar, generally somebody who has encountered cowpox will produce and retain enough antibodies also effective against smallpox and, therefore, impart immunity to that disease as well.

The word 'vaccine' and its derivatives, largely as a result of Jenner's work, derive from *vacca*, the Latin for 'cow', however, modern vaccines are by no means all derived from cows and are not always live. Even in Jenner's day the concept of vaccination was not an entirely new one and a form of it known as 'variolation' (after 'variola', the alternative name for the smallpox virus) had been practised down the ages. Variolation differs from vaccination, however, in that infected material is taken from a patient known to have smallpox but who is only displaying mild symptoms. This makes some sense, in that you would perhaps expect, along with a small amount of the pathogen, there to be a high count of antibodies in such material but it was, nevertheless, a very risky business and the recipient was still at risk of developing the full-blown disease and dying. In fact, Jenner himself was variolated as a child and became very ill as a result, an experience that, no doubt, spurred on his ambition to protect others from such suffering.

Rather paradoxically, Jenner's legacy, although great, has not always been applauded by all. In order to be effective, mass vaccination requires almost everybody to co-operate and the vast spectrum of views that exists within populations can militate against this, not to mention the 'fake news' that spreads so widely, so quickly these days. Although perhaps not universally unreasonable, since bad reactions and unforeseen side effects can and do arise and you can never win everybody over, unless some specific risk is identified (and they are rare), getting vaccinated would be, very much, my personal choice.

Another fatal disease that needed addressing was cholera. This time a bacterium, rather than a virus, which so dehydrates the body that it can totally destroy the metabolism. When it arose in Britain in the early nineteenth century, it was popularly thought by the so-called 'miasmatists' to come from 'miasmas'; the vapours exuding from rotting waste. But in fact, it had been brought in from recent large outbreaks on the Indian subcontinent.

When, in the 1850s, a serious epidemic broke out in London, the challenge this time fell to another gifted physician, a doctor to Queen Victoria: John Snow.

Snow believed that cholera was ingested rather than breathed in and when he noticed that the London outbreak was centred around one particular water pump, in Broad Street, Soho, he wondered whether contaminated water could be the cause. He was able to prove it, too, when he managed to establish that all those infected had drawn water from that particular well. Further confirmation came when the pump was disabled, and the disease began to decline.

Although cholera had been shown to be waterborne (as opposed to an airborne disease), the miasmatists were also proved right to a degree, in that it did indeed come from smelly waste, such as cesspits, etc. which, at the time, were often exposed and could easily contaminate sources of drinking water. It was clear that better waste management was needed if such diseases were to be controlled and, as a direct result, higher levels of sanitary inspection were introduced, and better sewage systems built.

Before the end of Victoria's reign, a vaccine against cholera would appear and, through similar methods, it would not be long before many other vaccines, against many other serious illnesses, would emerge.

Great strides were also made in surgical techniques; the use of chloroform as an anaesthetic, for example, acting both to reduce pain and alarm during operations and extending the time that could be spent on surgical techniques. It was also to prove a great aid during childbirth – Queen Victoria herself was said to have been given chloroform (by Dr. Snow, mentioned above in relation to cholera) during the births of her last two children: Leopold and Beatrice. Likewise, the wider understanding of germs, the need for hygiene and the development of antiseptics by Lister reduced incidences of post-operative infections, which often posed a much greater threat than the invasive procedures themselves.

As well as great strides in disease prevention and cure, the medical profession became more organised, with the introduction of formally recognised medical qualifications and formal training for nurses. Although many attempts had already been made to differentiate between qualified, learned professionals and the various quacks, impostors and charlatans who claimed to cure every known disorder with little more than coloured water, it was the 1858 Medical Act and the establishment of the General Medical Council that proved most successful, the original purpose of this organisation being essentially to keep a register of qualified medical practitioners. What's more, the Medical Register was to be a public document, and so anyone unsure could consult it at any time. Eventually, however, its role would be extended to exercise more control and supervision over the profession, enabling it to investigate and weed out the incompetent and unqualified.

*

There was yet another disease that was to make its presence felt during early Victorian times; although a disease neither of humans nor animals, it was estimated to have caused the deaths of up to a million people during the 1840s and 50s. That disease was, of course, potato blight, and it struck in Ireland worst of all. The result: famine – a disorder no medical advances can prevent. Although the lessons learned through this devastating catastrophe were to improve the understanding of crop diseases, they came at a very high human cost indeed.

The potato is a new world plant and exactly how it was first introduced into Britain is a little unclear. Although some credit is given to Sir Thomas Harriot (or Herriot?), a close associate of Sir Walter Raleigh, it is commonly held that it was brought back by Raleigh himself during his early voyages to the Americas (along with tobacco, a closely related plant) in order to impress Queen Elizabeth I. And he is said to have been the first to cultivate it, on his estate in Ireland. In the event the potato turned out to be easily cultivated in Northern Europe and its tubers proved to be an extremely rich source of nutrition. It is said that a diet of potatoes and milk alone fulfils all the essential dietary needs, and over the years the Irish became more and more dependent on this combination, to the exclusion of pretty well everything else. Unfortunately, almost all the crops were of one variety – 'the Lumper', which had proved particularly suited to Irish conditions. Initially, since potatoes had been taken out of their indigenous environment, there were very few, if any, natural pests or diseases to affect them in Europe. That is until somebody decided to import a fertiliser derived from the bird and bat droppings that collect by the ton on certain coastlines and coastal islands of South America. Called 'guano', it did turn out to be a very effective potato fertiliser, but it is generally held that it brought with it the spores of the fungus *Phytophthora infestans* which is the causal agent of potato blight. Eventually the disease was to spread throughout Europe but the reason that Ireland was so badly affected was that their almost exclusive variety, the Lumper, proved to be particularly susceptible to this disease.

Unlike crops which multiply through true seeds and have some degree of genetic diversity, all the plants within a single variety potato crop, since they can reproduce asexually through the tubers that they produce (biologically modified stems), barring mutations and rogue plants, are genetically identical. So, whereas within a genetically variable crop, some plants are likely to be more resistant to a disease than others, within any single variety potato crop, each plant is equally susceptible. In other words, if one plant succumbs, all are likely to.

The result throughout Ireland was catastrophic, and the slow and often inappropriate reactions to the crisis by the British Government certainly did nothing to improve its already tarnished image there. Indeed, the consequence would only serve to reinforce that long-held vision of the British in Ireland as an occupying dictatorial, colonial power. The stories of how poorly the victims of the famine were treated are manifold. Tenants unable to pay their rent were often simply turfed out, sometimes with the roofs of their former dwellings being removed in order to make their return pointless. The only shelter, in many cases, was the hedge. Emergency relief, when it came, was in the main too little, too late, of poor quality and often of an unfamiliar or inadequate type. There was also a lack of information as to how to prepare and consume these alternative foodstuffs, especially with regard to maize, imported from America, which needs to be well chewed and, as a result, proved difficult for the Irish stomach to digest. And woe betide anybody caught stealing food, as they would soon enough find themselves like Michael in the song 'The Fields of Athenry' – on a prison ship bound for Botany Bay!

As a result, many became so desperate that they decided to emigrate and, although estimates vary, what records do exist suggest that something like two million of the surviving population of seven plus million may have moved overseas as a direct result of the famine. What became known as the 'Irish Diaspora' would scatter the Irish, not only to England and the United States, but far and wide across the entire world.

Unlike with human or animal diseases, there are no 'magic bullets' when it comes to plant diseases and the emphasis is very much on avoidance, rather than cure. Once a disease establishes itself in a crop there is very little, if anything, that can be done. Prevention, therefore, is very much a part of good crop husbandry and ranges from the regular application of insecticides and fungicides (not always popular with the public, it has to be said) through plant breeding to total soil sterilisation, where nothing else will do. As for blight itself, despite modern potato varieties being selected for resistance, it is still very much with us today and relies on the application of chemical treatments for its continued control. Thankfully, though, modern methods mean that it is nothing like the problem it was back in nineteenth-century Ireland.

*

Problems, however catastrophic, nonetheless always present opportunities for improvement and, to the inventive Victorians, the devastating occurrences with which they were presented carried with them lessons to be learned. The dogged investigations into the reasons for the disasters such as those described enabled them to be more fully understood and not only produced new cures and treatments but also precipitated the improved practices and procedures of modern times intended to reduce inherent risk, that we often take for granted today.

Technology was also coming on in leaps and bounds; witness, for example, the construction of the London Underground. At first only a fraction of the system that exists today but, nevertheless, the start of something that would significantly ease getting about the capital by relieving the intense pressure on London's crowded streets. Similarly, the likes of Brunel, Telford and Stephenson, with their great works of engineering, would improve travel elsewhere and electricity, the telephone system, radio and films, etc. would all enter the public domain. Then, as always, though, something would happen from time to time to remind man about his limitations when it came to taking on nature, one event in particular being the Tay Bridge Disaster.

Anybody crossing the present Tay Rail Bridge may well notice some stumps sticking out of the water alongside it. These were part of the original bridge that suddenly collapsed while a train was crossing on the evening of Sunday 28 December 1879. Spanning the Firth of Tay just south of Dundee, the bridge, at almost exactly two miles long, was the longest in the world at the time. Designed by Thomas Bouch, it had only been opened the year before. Just after 7pm the train from Edinburgh, carrying six carriages, began crossing northwards into Dundee in the middle of a wild storm. Unfortunately, when the train was part-way across, the bridge simply gave way, and the engine and carriages were plunged into the water. Everybody on board (some seventy-five souls) was lost. At the time the cause was put down to the poor structural integrity of the cast-iron supports leading to inadequate loading against the severe weather. As a result Bouch, who had been knighted by Queen Victoria for his work on the Tay Bridge, was so affected by the disaster that he would be dead within the year, after having completely abandoned his design for a bridge across the Firth of Forth even though much higher loadings were said to have been factored into that project. The Forth Bridge was still built, of course, but the structure we see today is down to a design by Sir John Fowler and Sir Benjamin Baker instead. Many felt, however, that Bouch's design was unfairly criticised, and that poor construction methods, resulting in weakened riveted joints, together with poor subsequent maintenance, were the more probable causes.

*

On a lighter note, nothing lifted the Victorian spirit like a grand event, and the Great Exhibition which took place during the summer of 1851 certainly was a grand event. The inspiration for it was said to have arisen out of the French capability to arrange such spectacles, and in particular the magnificent Paris Exposition of 1844, which had turned heads and invited imitation all over Europe. The organisers of the Great Exhibition included no less than Prince Albert, the Prince Consort, and the innovator Henry Cole. Designs were invited for a suitable building to house the event and, of the many forwarded, it was one for a gigantic greenhouse sent in by Joseph Paxton that seemed to fit the bill. As well as being impressive in itself, it could be built in time and within budget, but probably above all, nothing else like it existed. The huge greenhouse being the 'Crystal Palace', of course, or the 'Great Shalimar' as it was also known – presumably alluding to the term often used in conjunction with gardens in India. It was to be erected in Hyde Park and, although boasting a truly international flavour, the exhibition was essentially to promote British and British Empire achievements, developments and knowhow.

Over the course of the summer, the 100,000 or so individual exhibits attracted over six million visitors. From jewellery and textiles through innovative printing presses, photography, firearms, transport and agricultural machinery to steam engines and machines and devices of all types. Queen Victoria summed it up when she wrote in her journal of there being 'every conceivable invention.' I can think of the two that probably commanded the most attention, though. The first must surely have been the magnificent Kohinoor (also spelt Koh-i-Noor) or 'Mountain of Light' diamond, then only recently taken from India and presented to Queen Victoria. Originally thought to be the largest diamond in the world, it was still an impressive 186 carats; about 37 grams or 1.3 oz. when cut. People expecting it to throw the light in a spectacular way were said to have been left disappointed, however, and possibly as a result of this, the gem was later recut and now forms part of the Queen Mother's Crown, kept with the Crown Jewels in the Tower of London.

Another 'big pull' must surely have been the new public toilets. They were designed by George Jennings and are said to have been the first ever 'public' toilets. Also called 'Monkey Closets' (not sure whether or not Thomas Huxley 'went' – read on) they cost a penny a time to use and thus would establish the going rate for such an experience for some years to come.

Following the Exhibition, the Crystal Palace was dismantled and re-erected a few miles south of the river at Sydenham Hill near Croydon, just a couple of miles north of Selhurst Park, where Crystal Palace FC play today. Sadly, though, late in 1936 the whole edifice was razed to the ground by fire, after which it was considered too costly to rebuild. Winston Churchill, on witnessing the conflagration first-hand is said to have declared, "This is the end of an age!"

*

As well as the great strides made in education already alluded to, the actions of trade unions were to improve the working conditions of many and, for women and girls, the idea of female suffrage began to gather momentum. There had been calls for changes as early as Victoria's ascent to the throne but the Suffragette Movement had still not fully established itself by the time of her death, and the paucity of power extended to females and their practically non-existent levels of influence persisted into the nineteenth century. However, this inadequate state of affairs had begun to meet with increased resistance, the growing discontent over how little say women had when it came to divorce being a prime example. As a result, divorces were rare before the Matrimonial Causes Act of 1857 and almost always depended on an Act of Parliament having to be passed! Naturally this made them completely out of reach of ordinary folk and left the wives of violent, drunken wasters locked into their relationships, come what may. Furthermore, there seemed to be little or any real consequence if a husband did attack his wife, even on a regular basis. Often quoted tongue in cheek, the phrase, 'no thicker than the width of his thumb', attributed to Judge Francis Buller when hearing a case during the 1780s, is said to have been an attempt to define the legal limit to which a man could chastise his wife while remaining 'reasonable'. In other words, he appeared to be saying that it was all right to use a stick on your wife provided it was under a certain thickness. Although sometimes quoted as an actual historic legal statute, in reality it never was, but if it was said, and I believe that something along these lines was said, then it gives us something of an insight into the received views that many men would have held towards women at the time.

Even if they could obtain a separation or divorce, it was only just prior to Victoria's accession that women were attributed rights over any children that may have resulted from the marriage. When writer and campaigner Caroline Norton left her violent husband George (then an MP), however, she was successfully able to petition Parliament for access to her children and paved the way for the 1839 Custody of Infants Act. This, in turn, would lead to the Matrimonial

Causes Act mentioned above and then the Married Women's Property Act of 1870 which, for the first time, gave wives at least some measure of ownership.

In addition, William Foster's Education Act of 1870 addressed inequalities in education too, by incorporating girls, who had hitherto been excluded from elementary education, into the system.

Interestingly George Norton went on to sue the then Prime Minister, Lord Melbourne (unsuccessfully as it turned out), for 'criminal conversation' with his wife, Caroline – after she had left him. Essentially this meant adultery but is there not also hidden in the phrase the idea that the co-respondent had violated the husband's property – his wife's body?

In all, conditions for women had continued to improve throughout the final years of Victoria's reign, with the amendments to the Married Women's Property Act of the 1880s finally enabling wives to own property in their own right. Slowly but surely such measures would begin to destroy the long-held concept that a wife was a chattel, i.e., owned by her husband. The rights of mothers over their children were further strengthened and women would soon be given some tiny degree of political franchise. However, it would not be until 1918 that women would become eligible to become MPs and be able to vote in national elections. Even then they had to be over thirty, and fulfil certain other property criteria. Indeed, it would not be until 1928 that a woman would be treated in exactly the same way as a man when it came to the ballot box.

As well as the changes towards how women were regarded in society, with better education, communication and literacy came wider views regarding other aspects of life. Several researchers were coming to conclusions of one sort or another that life on earth had developed over a very long period of time, rather than being suddenly created only a few thousand years before. The most memorable being Charles Darwin, of course, the son of a well-to-do physician. His most famous work, his treatise entitled *On the Origin of Species by means of Natural Selection* first appeared in 1859, its tenet, that plants and animals had 'evolved' over many millions of years, putting him in direct conflict with the widely held belief of the time that they had all been created in their present form by God in just six days. If the full implications of this were not at first appreciated, they soon would be when, within the next few years, Darwin's subsequent publication came out: *The Descent of Man and its Selection in Relation to Sex*. Controversy simply was not a strong enough word for it! Instinctively, what we truly believe to be the case always gets in the way of fresh thinking, irrespective of whether our beliefs are sound or not. So, although we may struggle to appreciate today why the idea of evolution was so contentious back then, it has to be understood that it was a time when the workings of God, Heaven and Hell were held as unquestionable truths throughout the Christian world. To suggest otherwise struck at the very fabric of society, not only for fear of one's own eternal damnation but also politically; this level of fear probably being about as powerful a political tool as you can get. That is, of course, only if everybody believes it, because when they no longer do, it very quickly becomes a pretty useless one.

One of the most fanatical supporters of Darwin's theories was the scientist Thomas Henry Huxley and one of the most vociferous opponents was Bishop Samuel Wilberforce (son of the slavery abolitionist William Wilberforce). Their risible verbal exchange on the subject at Oxford in 1860 went something like this:

> Wilberforce: "*Was it through your grandfather's or your grandmother's side that you claim to be descended from a monkey?*"
> Huxley: "*I am not ashamed to be descended from a monkey but would be ashamed to be associated with a man who used his great gifts to obscure the truth.*"

Though still denounced to this day by a few, evolution has now become an accepted biological theory that, with the redefining of certain biblical terms and timescales, etc., can even manage to coexist alongside traditional religious beliefs. And, evidenced as it is, through the emergence of the so-called 'super rats' – rats that have developed resistance to the traditional rat poison warfarin or the peppered moth which, in order to blend in, turned a darker colour during the Industrial Revolution, and the various pathogenic bacteria that have developed resistance to antibiotics, there can be little doubt that selection based on tolerance to adversity does take place. God moves in mysterious ways, you might say.

*

The very end of the nineteenth century saw a new railway station open in Leicester; the Central Station, off Great Central Street, serving the Great Central Mainline Railway as it passed through the town. It was born out of the vision of the politician and rail entrepreneur Sir Edward Watkin. His idea was to link the industrial north of England with London and eventually the whole of Europe via a tunnel under the English Channel. There had been talk of such a tunnel since Napoleonic times, and with the advent of the railways, the extent of the commercial benefit that the creation of such a structure would bring to both Britain and France, was now greatly increased. After agreeing the development, the British began tunnelling from Dover and the French from Calais during the early 1880s. And there is little doubt that, given the technology of the day, if the work had been allowed to carry on unhindered, there would have been a Channel Tunnel in place some hundred years sooner. The sad fact was, however, that despite political cooperation on ad hoc projects such as this, France remained 'The Old Enemy'. After all, the Napoleonic Wars, where Britain feared invasion almost to the point of paranoia, were still in living memory and it did not take much for something to flare up. (The Fashoda Affair referred to earlier in this chapter, for example.) Although nothing really did occur or, at least nothing that really threatened British sovereignty, many a mickle makes a muckle, as the Scots say. So when the inevitable day-to-day differences, which under normal circumstances would simply have been regarded as minor political irritations, were mixed with anxieties about the increased threat from France that the tunnel might pose, the British Government began to have serious doubts about the wisdom of such a project. For one thing, political stability in France was still somewhat shaky after her defeat at the hands of Prussia in 1871. For another, in Africa, Britain and France were still vying for control over the Suez Canal, while the pinch point that had developed between French Equatorial Africa to the west and the British-influenced Sudan to the east was still somewhat sore. With time, all these matters and others, set as they were against the backcloth of the risk-averse policy of so-called 'Splendid Isolation', began to conjure up scenarios of mass invasions through the tunnel, say during the night or at other unsuspected times. The sensationalist aspect of the prospect of such perturbations were not lost on the popular press either and in the end, despite assurances that we could blow the whole thing up at very short notice in the event of any such invasion, the government, with only about a mile of tunnel dug, shelved the project.

Looking through the crystal-clear optical instrument that hindsight is, though, a completed Channel Tunnel would have undoubtedly proved an invaluable asset when it came to deploying troops to Northern France at the outbreak of the First World War and it is difficult to imagine that its existence then would not have significantly altered the thinking behind the opening gambits of both sides. It may have even altered events to the extent that the combination of alliances that precipitated the war may have been different. Who can say? If things had gone along similar lines though, even with the tunnel in place, what about the Second World War, where France was simply overrun? If ever there had been 'a best time' to blow it up, it would certainly have been then. In any event, with everything that was to overtake Europe and indeed the world, during the first half of the twentieth century, if a Channel Tunnel had been finished at its turn, I have my sincere doubts as to whether that same tunnel would have survived until the present day.

Notwithstanding, in the early 1890s work began to extend the

Manchester Sheffield and Lincoln Railway (MS&LR) line that ran from Manchester to Annesley (about ten miles north of Nottingham) on to London. This 'London Extension', as it was known, later to be named the Great Central Railway, would pass through Nottingham, Loughborough, Leicester, Rugby, Woodford Halse (near Daventry), Brackley (near Banbury), Grendon Underwood (near Bicester) and then on to Marylebone Station in London. The last stretch was owned jointly by both the Great Central and Great Western Railways, and you could go alternatively via either Princes Risborough and Wycombe or Aylesbury and Amersham. The new line was opened for the first time to the public in 1899. In line with all intentions, it was built to European loading gauge standard and was so straight and level as to be admirably capable of handling both Continental and domestic high-speed traffic. As well as laying the track, building all the necessary bridges, tunnels and infrastructure, etc. all the stations along the way from Nottingham (although this station also served the Great Northern Line) to Brackley were newly constructed ones. Naturally it was costly and, as so often with such projects, came in many times over budget. Against an initial estimate of just over £3m, the final cost was around £11½m – no doubt equivalent to billions today. Initial returns were not very encouraging, either, as the new line was in direct competition with the Midland Railway to the east that ran into St. Pancras. The subsequent introduction of faster trains, with more comfortable carriages, however, improved the Great Central's popularity, particularly amongst business travellers, whilst its freight services became more competitive too. Sadly, though, Watkin was to die at the ripe old age of eighty-one, only two years after the line had become fully operational. Although his creation did indeed provide the fast route into London from the north that he had envisaged, the Master Cutler service from Sheffield being a prime example, his dream of trains travelling along it bound for and coming from the Continent was, sadly, never to be fulfilled. Neither was the period that the service ran for to be a long one. Perhaps inevitably, the Beeching Report of the 1960s, aimed at reshaping the railways in the light of rapidly increasing road transportation, flagged up the duplication of purpose that the coexistence of the Midland Railway and the Great Central Mainline caused and so concluded that one of these two lines had to go. It was the Great Central that lost out, and by 1970, after less than eighty years in service, the whole stretch had been closed.

But it would be an ill wind indeed that blew no good at all and the silver lining was that the closure restored some badly needed open space to Leicester. Instead of the trains thundering past and the shunting yards, gazing over the garden walls of the many homes that once backed onto the old Great Central Line, the observer's eyes now meet with a green expanse through which a leisurely footpath and cycle path run. Elsewhere, notably along the Birstall to Loughborough stretch which, as I write, I understand is planned to be extended further, the line has been restored by enthusiasts, enabling one, if one so wishes, to relive live those halcyon days of steam transport.

*

In addition to the new developments that took place to the north-west of Leicester at the end of the nineteenth and beginning of the twentieth centuries, St. Mary's Parish to the south-west was also further developed. An additional 2,000 or so domestic dwellings and other buildings were erected alongside the construction of the Great Central Railway running south out of Leicester. And it was to one of these houses that Richard Warren moved his now completed family around 1907, specifically to No.192, Western Road, an address I remember well from childhood as it was where the youngest of his family, Doris (my Aunt Doll), continued to live for most of her life.

192, Western Road was one of those properties that backed onto the old Great Central line. Behind it ran the shunting lines and engine sheds that I remember gazing over the wall at as a kid, watching in fascination as the steam engines shunted up and down. Sometimes the trains were a bit too close for comfort, my dad often regaling us with the story about how his Uncle Jack's dog was once tragically killed there, under one of those trains!

As well as the house move, the family was changing in other ways, too. Firstly Richard, not so young as he used to be, began to settle down a bit. He no longer stayed out half the night and, after coming home from work each day, seemed quite happy with a cup of tea in his armchair reading his newspaper in front of the fire. Jack, nor anybody else for that matter, never really did get to the bottom of the riddle that the 'Mrs. Blucas Affair' was. But certainly nothing at all that he had heard relating to it afterwards had gone any way towards allaying his suspicions. The other thing was, and I have no way of knowing whether it was anything to do with living next to the train track, my grandfather (Albert) was to renew the family's connection with the railways that had been broken almost fifty years before by the death of his own grandfather, John.

By the summer of 1907 Richard would have been forty-six, Louisa forty-seven, Flo twenty-four, John (Jack) twenty-three, Arch about to turn twenty, Fred eighteen, Frank fifteen, Albert just turned thirteen, Syd about to turn eleven, Ernie eight, Leonard (Little Joe) five and Doris (Doll) just three years old. And it was at around this same time that Flo married Sam Kirk, whom she had met at work. They set up home together in Spalding Street, a short terrace in the North Evington district of Leicester and, in those days, at the very easterly extremity of the town – the last terrace before nothing but allotment gardens and open countryside. I say 'town', rather than 'city' as, although Leicester's status was that of a city in Roman times (known then as *Ratae* or variants of) it somehow lost the status in the Middle Ages, only to regain it in 1919 – enabling the celebrated football club, 'Leicester Fosse', from then on to be legitimately renamed 'Leicester City'.

One of Leicester's many boot and shoe factories stood to one end of Spalding Street, so if Sam and Flo had worked there, they would certainly not have had far to travel each day. By all accounts, the course of their marriage did not always run smoothly, however. Apparently, Flo was known as 'The Vixen' as a young woman; allegedly she would hit Sam over the head with a frying pan when he came home drunk and, from what I can gather, this was quite often. According to family legend, Sam would later spend some time in Wakefield Prison. Not after rounding on Flo, I hasten to add, but after going awol while she was pregnant during the First World War. While in jail he contract pneumonia and, afterwards,was sent back to the front, only to be gassed. Although he did survive for some years after the war, sadly he would never fully recover.

Also, at around this time, Jack married Lydia (I think Jones) and went to live back in Mill Lane, just down from where the family had been back in the early 1880s. Arch (Richard Archibald) must have left to join the regular forces – the Royal Marines, I believe – and, although by 1911 Fred had also left, I have not been able to establish to what or to where he went. Through contacting their descendants through genealogy websites and from family anecdotes, I also know that, although Arch was wounded during the Great War, both Arch and Fred survived well beyond 1918, indeed Arch into the 1960s. Beyond this I have not been able to find out a great deal more about them. Possibly, like my grandfather's, most of their service records may not have survived – destroyed in the Blitz in 1940 perhaps?

When Frank left school around 1905, he followed his father into the hosiery industry, whilst my grandfather, Albert, who must have left school around 1907, initially went into the butchery trade. It could have been down to the family's new location, as I have suggested, or that butchery did not suit him or for some entirely different reason, but sometime between 1911 and the outbreak of war in August 1914, he gave up butchery and took a job on the railways, starting as a lowly carriage cleaner. But whatever it was that caused this reconnection of the family to the railways, it was to last a lifetime, and I still have to this day his National Union of Railwaymen fob that used to hang from his pocket-watch chain.

By 1911 Syd had left school and was working as an errand boy, I think for a carrier's office, whilst Ernie, Joe (Leonard) and Dolly had all started school.

Possibly as a result of the ever-increasing prospect of a European war, or maybe just as an escape from the daily grind, Frank, now the eldest of the younger generation in the household, had joined the TF (the Territorial Force or 'Terriers' as they were known; the forerunner of the modern Territorial Army or TA). He had presented himself on Monday 14 November 1910 and was admitted into the 1/4th Battalion of the Leicestershire Regiment, part of the North Midland Division. His Enlistment Form E. 501 confirms that he took the oath to be:

> *'faithful and bear true Allegiance to His Majesty King Edward the Seventh, His Heirs and Successors... as in duty bound, honestly and faithfully defend His Majesty... [etc.]... in Person, Crown and Dignity against all enemies, according to the conditions of [his] service'.*

The rest of the form is fairly perfunctory and merely confirms his name, place of birth, age, occupation, employer and various clarifications about work and status, etc. along with what was generally expected of him.

If Richard and Louisa were at all concerned by their son's actions, they did not show it, and both were proud of him. His period of service was to last four years but, as we now know, the subsequent unravelling of events was to change all that.

Chapter 7

Taking Sides

> 'Sooner or later... one has to take sides,
> if one is to remain human.'
> ***The Quiet American* – Graham Greene**

In order to begin to understand the reasoning behind why Britain went to war with Germany in 1914, it is necessary to take a look at the history of Belgium and the area in and around it, traditionally known as Flanders. I am not suggesting for one minute that if Belgium, as an independent state, had never existed then Britain would never have gone to war. Far from it, it was becoming increasingly obvious sometime before the outbreak of war that, given the growing belligerence of Germany at the turn of the twentieth century, Britain would eventually have found it impossible to ignore either the subjugation or the threat to her global authority. Nevertheless, at least one of the reasons for Britain's entry would have been undeniably different.

The name 'Belgium' is derived from the 'Belgae' which were the tribes occupying North-Eastern Gaul during Roman times. However, ever since the French and German powers to either side of it began to emerge, the relatively small and disjointed region that now contains the modern state of Belgium has served as a geographical and political barrier between them. All three regions were somewhat artificially held together within the Carolingian Empire under Charlemagne, the so-called 'Father of Europe', and his successors towards the end of the first millennium. When Pope Leo III formed an alliance with Charlemagne in 800 and crowned him Emperor, it reignited that powerful political concept of Roman Imperialism with Charlemagne effectively the first 'Holy Roman Emperor', although the term had yet to be coined. After his death, however, conflict again arose as both west and east strove to dominate. Things came to a head when Charlemagne's son and heir, Louis the Pious, died in 840, and his three sons, Lothair, Louis and Charles, fell out over their legacies. As eldest son, Lothair had naturally assumed that he would inherit the lot, but his two brothers had other ideas and civil war broke out. Lothair's side did not prevail and the war ended in 843 with the signing of the Treaty of Verdun. This saw the old Empire divided into three: the West Frankish Kingdom (essentially the French) under Charles (*le Chauve* – the Baldy) being confined to the west of the River Scheldt (in the north), the East Frankish Kingdom (essentially the Germans) went to Louis, leaving Lothair with the bit in the middle known as the Kingdom of Lothair. This middle bit, incidentally, was not just confined to the north but spread all the way down, to what is now, Northern Italy.

To the French mind at least, central to the Treaty of Verdun was that this small city, in view of its geographical position, was France's 'gateway' and needed to be defended at all costs. At the outbreak of the First World War (with Alsace-Lorraine then part of Germany) Verdun was the first city encountered when entering France from Germany on the road to Paris. In view of this, it is perhaps not too difficult to appreciate why Verdun was so rigorously defended and the Battle of Verdun turned out to be the longest battle of the war.

Although a kingdom in its own right, Luther's 'bit in the middle' remained disjointed, in that it was derived from the amalgamation of several (often very) different former realms and peoples and it is partly as a result of this ad hoc arrangement, together with subsequent reorganisations, that Belgium still remains to this day regarded by many as a contrived and artificial nation. By partitioning the two competing eastern and western powers through the cooperation of the 'triumvirate', however, it did provide for some degree of stability and cohesion which facilitated trade and would enable the development of the fine cloth industry for which Flanders subsequently became renowned.

Despite the title 'Roman Emperor' being handed down to Charlemagne's successors, in reality its meaning and purpose began to loosen somewhat with time, and it was only when Otto I (Otto the Great) came on the scene in the tenth century that the term 'Holy Roman Emperor' began to be used, and some degree of order was restored. He was a fierce but clever leader and enthusiastically accepted the title after successfully defending Christianity against the Magyar invasion from the east. Following his coronation, he took the opportunity to try to establish the role a bit more through his *Diploma Ottonianum* – his treaty with the pope. Although this extended the pope's influence (theoretically at least), it also consolidated Otto's powers as Emperor in that, while confining the right to elect a pope to the people of Rome, it also gave Otto a considerable hand in deciding the issue too! Then, when Otto went on to conquer and control large areas of Italy, the pope became so concerned about his rising influence that he turned against him. When Otto got wind of all this, he marched on Rome, causing the pope to flee. Now free to exercise his new powers, a delighted Otto sacked John XII as pope and installed the more compliant Leo VIII to replace him as 'antipope'. What followed turned into a bit of a fiasco, however, as the Roman people promptly kicked the inexperienced Leo out and reinstalled John. John then died, the cause of which is not clear but, by all accounts, he was not the most 'well behaved' of popes, which could well have had something to do with it. Anyway, John was replaced by Benedict V but when Otto eventually realised what had gone on, he sent Benedict packing too and reinstalled Leo VIII, this time as pope. At the time the people of Rome can't have known whether they were coming or going when it came to popes!

Over the following several hundred years the title of Holy Roman Emperor was passed down via heredity through a series of mid-European kings, eventually ending up, in the fifteenth century, with the first Habsburg King, Frederick III. Then, as described in Chapter 3, Frederick's son, Maximilian, and then Maximilian's grandson, Charles V (Charles I of Spain), were subsequently chosen. When, eventually, the Habsburg dynasty was divided up between the Spanish (senior) branch and Austrian (junior) branch in the sixteenth century, Spain ended up with the provinces in and around Belgium which became known as the Spanish Netherlands.

Struggling with the effects of the English Reformation, and in ill health, in 1556 Charles decided to abdicate. Although a complicated, drawn-out affair, it left Spain with his son, Philip II (the one who married Mary I in the hope of reintroducing Catholicism to England). If Charles had been unpopular in his colony in the Low Countries, then Philip was even more so, what with his little or no knowledge of Flemish, little if any connection with the area and the dividing issue of Catholicism. Despite the Netherlands' very strategic positioning in Europe (the entry and distribution of gold and silver from Spain's colonies in South America being greatly facilitated by its importation through Antwerp), Philip continued taxing the people to the hilt while neglecting them to the point of abandonment. Just as with the American colonists a couple of centuries later, this 'no taxation without representation' policy very soon led to war. Religion also fuelled the fire, particularly in the north, where Calvinist Protestantism had become particularly deep-seated and where hostility towards Philip and Catholic Spain was particularly strong. Then, when the Dutch demanded independence from Spain in 1568, it led to 'The Eighty Years War' (like the Hundred Years War before it – no need to tell your grandchildren about it; they'd be in it!). The effect of all this was to deprive Spain of the northern part of its Low Countries colony leaving the (debatably) even more heterogeneous region that was to become modern-day Belgium, and Luxembourg, with its majority of protestant Flemish speakers in the east and its majority of catholic French speakers in the west.

Things would come to a head again in 1700 when Charles II (the last Habsburg king of Spain) died. His early demise had been widely predicted, almost certainly without an heir in view of his compromised physical and mental health; no doubt the result of many generations of inbreeding. Thus, speculation as to what would happen when this event arose was rife. Despite his handicaps Charles almost made it to his thirty-ninth birthday and, at over thirty-five years, his reign had been a relatively long one. The resultant power vacuum created by his death, therefore, was enough for Louis XIV to send his troops north-eastward in a bid to take the Southern Netherlands for France. To make matters worse, on his deathbed, Charles is said to have chosen his distant relative, Philip, Duke of Anjou, to succeed him, who was incidentally also Louis XIV's grandson. This set both Dutch and English alarm bells ringing, as fears grew over the emergence of a combined Spanish-French superpower, and in the following year 'The War of the Spanish Succession' broke out. In Vienna, the then head of the Austrian side of the Habsburg dynasty, Leopold I, was understandably a bit brassed off by it all since, with some justification, it has to be said, he believed that he was the rightful heir to the province. As a result, the 'Grand Alliance' of European countries, which had been used before against Louis XIV's expansionist aspirations, was revived. In addition to Austria, it included England, the Scots and the Dutch.

By 1708 the Spanish Netherlands had been wrested from France, but Spain and France remained undefeated and so political pressure mounted to end the war. The subsequent talks resulted in the Treaties of Utrecht and Baden which recognised Philip (or Philippe) d'Anjou's sovereignty of Spain (as Philip V) but stipulated that the Spanish Netherlands be ceded to Austria, and so in 1714 under the Treaty of Rastatt, what was left of the 'Spanish Netherlands' became the 'Austrian Netherlands'.

By this time both Leopold and his eldest son, Joseph, had died, leaving Austria to Leopold's other son, Charles VI. This Charles, however, also had difficulty in the heir-producing department and, with thoughts of what had happened before, tried to make amends by decreeing the right of female descendants to inherit. Then, when in 1740 Charles himself died after naming his daughter, Maria Theresa, as heir, it sparked 'The War of the Austrian Succession'. Honestly, you wait years for a war of succession then two come along in short order!

The war ended in 1748 with the 'Treaty of Aix-la-Chapelle' confirming Maria Theresa's right to the throne of Austria and thus the Austrian Netherlands but, as time wore on, the Austrian hegemony started to grate with the Belgians. Insurrections and unrest followed, to the extent that when Napoleon's forces entered in 1792, they were hailed as liberators and, although the Austrians managed to kick the French out again shortly afterwards, the French retook the territory in 1794, swallowing it up as part of their then, ever-expanding Empire. When Napoleon was defeated at Waterloo, some twenty years later, however, Belgium and Luxembourg were reunited with the Dutch to form the United Kingdom of the Netherlands under William I. Nevertheless, the old problems just would not go away and once more, divisions led to trouble, this time in the form of the Brussels uprising of 1830.

To those who continued to seek political stability, it was beginning to become increasingly clear that there could only be hope of such, within the pinch point that Belgium was, if the Belgians were simply left to sort things out for themselves. It is somewhat ironic, therefore, that what happened next would, over eighty years later, have the exact opposite effect. It was the British-initiated London Conference, a few months after the uprising, that effectively laid the foundations of the new independent nation of Belgium, even to the extent of inviting Leopold Saxe-Coburg-Gotha (Queen Victoria's uncle), who had only just declined the throne of the newly independent Greece, to become its first king. Naturally the Netherlands had a bit of difficulty with this and tried to retake Belgium by various means over the following few years. But under mounting international pressure, she too was eventually persuaded and, in the end, agreed to respect the sovereignty of Belgium.

Now, the document signed in London on 19 April 1839; the so-called 'Treaty of London', is the critical element in all this as it guaranteed the neutrality of Belgium by both Britain and Germany (through the Prussian signatory). Specifically, Article 7 states:

> *'Belgium, within the limits specified in Articles I, II and IV,'* [the Articles that defined the territorial boundaries of the Belgian state] *'shall form an independent and perpetually neutral State. It shall be bound to observe such Neutrality towards all other States'.*

Further treaties in 1870 were to reaffirm this resolve. So, since Germany's first attack on France via Belgium on 4 August 1914 violated Belgium's neutrality under the terms of the treaties, Germany had not only broken its promises but also international law (such as it then was).

When the issue was raised with the German Chancellor, von Bethmann-Hollweg, in an attempt to downplay the severity and consequences of such an act, he dismissed the treaty as just a 'scrap of paper':

> *"Just for a word 'Neutrality', a word which in wartime has so often been disregarded. Just for a scrap of paper Great Britain is going to make war on a kindred nation who desired nothing better than to make friends with her."*

True enough, but no matter how many wrongs are added together they never amount to a right. If a nation signs a treaty, then ignores it, what is the point of treaties? Surely 'civilisation' as such depended on people honouring agreements and the law. Lloyd George would sum it up eloquently when he ridiculed von Bethmann's comment in his speech at the Queen's Hall, London, on 9 September 1914 by asking the audience:

> *"Have you any £5 notes about you, or any of those neat little Treasury £1 notes?"*

He continued:

> *"If you have, burn them, they are only scraps of paper!"*

Later picture postcards would be printed with an image of the Treaty of London on the front, above which was written, THE 'SCRAP OF PAPER', designed both to publicise the issue and to belittle the remark even further.

The subsequent invasion by Germany, very soon labelled 'The Rape of Belgium' by the popular press, only served to confirm the uncivilised way in which she was behaving. There is little doubt that their policy of 'do it to them before they do it to you' saw many innocent Belgians imprisoned, tortured, raped and murdered. But once the propaganda machine got to work, the Germans were apparently 'eating babies' too!

If Britain was going to go to war, it had to be for a very good reason, especially if it was to be against a 'kindred people' with whom she had never really had any conflicts before, especially in alliance with 'the old enemy', France! What better reason could there have been, therefore, than to confront this 'denial of civilisation'?! Even the dubious justification of its invasion of Serbia by Austria-Hungary in far-off Southern Europe paled against the 'rape' of one of Britain's nearest neighbours. The sceptics, however, and there were quite a few of them, argued that Germany had declared war on France, not Belgium, and the real purpose of Britain entering the war was the defence of its own sovereignty. But, by now, war had become inevitable, precisely because the existence of the Treaty of London meant that Britain had to require Germany to withdraw from Belgium while knowing full well that she would refuse. So, at 11pm British time on 4 August 1914, when Germany had failed to respond to Britain's ultimatum, the conflict that would become known as the Great War, the war to end wars, began.

So why, as signatories to the treaties supporting Belgian neutrality, did Germany attack France through Belgium? After all, it had over 200 miles of direct border with France. The simple answer is that it suited her better strategically. The flat terrain of the Low Countries was a much simpler route than the mountainous, afforested Franco-German border, which had also been heavily fortified following the invasion of 1870 – when the Germans had taken this route and managed to besiege Paris within a couple of months – these fortifications being heaviest where it was easier to cross. In other words, if it was going to be done then it would best be done as quickly and as easily as possible.

Unlike Britain in its 'splendid isolation', Germany under the Kaiser was eager to exploit rising European tensions for its future political advantage and, for some while, had been considering, as and when the time arose, how it might best attack France. It was also obvious to Germany, even at the turn of the century, that she would almost certainly have Russia to contend with to the east at the same time. Germany's plan assumed, however, that the lumbering beast that was Russia would take a considerable amount of time to mobilise. Hence France should be swiftly overwhelmed first and then Russia dealt with as soon as possible afterwards. Over-simplistic? It would certainly prove so.

Contrived by General Alfred von Schlieffen, the so-called 'Schlieffen Plan' was for the Germans to sweep into Northern France through Belgium and Luxembourg, surround Paris and take it from the north and west. Once Paris was safely in German hands, troops could then be sent swiftly east to face Russia via the elaborate rail networks of France, Belgium, and Germany. As for the Treaty of London, Germany either didn't give a damn or hoped that it would not seem important enough to Britain for her to go to war over – in reality probably a bit of both. But, in spite of the writing being on the wall as far back as the turn of the twentieth century and the threat of war heightening significantly through the summer of 1914, it was undoubtedly only when Britain stood resolute against Germany's complete disregard for the treaties she had signed, that the full, frightening potential consequences of everything that had gone before dawned, not least in Germany and Britain, but also throughout the world.

*

"Things *ain't* lookin' good on the Continent *y'* know," said Richard, looking up from his newspaper one Saturday afternoon. "Them Germans won't listen to anybody and them *un* the French 'ave *allus bin* at one another's throats. And what with us allyin' wi' France *unall*, we'll get pulled in too. Why else would the Germans be building all them new battleships and the Kaiser spoutin' off *un* that? *Y'* know what they say when they've 'ad a few, don't *y'*? They 'old up them great big beer mugs, click their 'eels and shout '*Der Tag*'! It means 'the day' *y'* know; the day they're *gooin' tek* over the world."

Louisa, having overheard, turned away from the cooking towards him. "Oh, don't say that, duck. With Frank just joined the Terriers *un* that." Her face looked pale and worried because, although she was well aware of all the rumours, until now, out of deep concern for the boys, she had continued to hope desperately that that's all they were – just rumours – and that nothing would ever come of them.

"Things 'ave changed on the Continent," she continued. "They're not so much at each other's throats these days, the Kaiser's just hot air. In any case what's it to do with us if they want to cut each other to pieces. Let 'em. Why should it affect us?"

"It *ud* affect us because we're too near 'em," Richard replied. "They can be over 'ere in hours nowadays. Thank God they never dug that tunnel under the sea! That's all I can say."

Oh why can't everybody just get on with each other? thought Louisa. *It's all so depressing.*

Just then Frank walked in, making Louisa turn quickly back to the simmering pans, and Richard shake the paper back towards his face and carry on reading.

"Have you read the bit on German domination of Europe, Dad?" Frank asked. "And 'ow we'd stand by France if they were attacked?"

Louisa (before Richard could reply): "It's not going to 'appen, Frank, so why bother with it?"

"Oh I think it will, Mam. But you'll be safe enough if it does because if the Germans get anywhere near *y'* we'll see 'em off! Anyway, if Germany did start anything it wouldn't last long. As well as us and the French they'd 'ave Russia to contend with and the whole o' the Empire too. And then what about America? The Kaiser 'ould 'ave to be really stupid to take 'em all on."

"Germany's got their friends too *y'* know," said Richard. "Italy, Austria, the Turks..."

"Austria and Turkey are falling apart, Dad, and I doubt Italy would make much of a difference."

"Exactly," replied Richard, "exactly, they're all unstable – anything could 'appen."

"Well," replied Frank, "as I said, I don't reckon it'd last long if it did start and so, the more people there are like me, the better. That's my view, for what it's worth... oh and by the way, Syd says he's going to join the TF too."

"What?" cried Louisa, trying not to sound too alarmed at the revelation. "He's only fourteen!"

Sensing his mother's rising concern at what he had just said, Frank tried to tone things down a bit by adding, "Not now, of course. I mean he wants to when he's older... perhaps..."

The thing was, that Frank and Syd had always been the closest among the brothers. In fact, it was fair to say that Syd idolised Frank. It was Frank who had first started to call him Syd; Syd rather than Walter and, because he was always talking to him or about him, the name had stuck. Even family and friends were apt to forget from time to time that he was really Walter and that Sydney was his middle name.

Understandably this was not too difficult for Richard or Louisa, after all the pain and suffering when poor little baby Richard Walter lost his struggle for life.

Louisa did not only have Frank and Syd to worry about, though. She had another six boys, including Arch, who was already in the regular armed forces. If the balloon did go up would they all get drawn into it? *Oh God, it's too horrid to contemplate*, she thought. *I just hope to God that it won't happen.*

When Syd came home later that afternoon, he found his dad alone, sitting in front of the fire and beginning to doze off. When he realised Syd's presence, however, Richard, having pulled himself round, asked, "So *y' gooin' te* join the Terriers *unall* then?"

"Hope so, Dad," replied Syd, matter-of-factly.

When Richard asked him why, though, Syd's mood seemed to change and, as if he had not bargained on going any further with the subject, his head fell and he gazed silently down at the floor for a few seconds. After a while he began to explain that, although it was not all about Frank, he had made his mind up when Frank had told him all about the comradeship and fun to be had at the weekends and during the annual camps. Afterwards, and perhaps more tellingly, though, Syd continued that he had suggested to Frank that they would be better off and safer together, especially if the worse came to the worst.

"Are you doing all this because you feel that you can protect Frank in some way, then?" asked Richard.

"No, not really, Frank can look after himself well enough. I know that," replied Syd. "It's just that we're better watching out for each other – *y'* know."

Syd was by no means always as open about things as this and he made Richard promise not to say anything about the last bit and, if he was asked, to say that he simply wanted to join the Terriers for the life.

"Of course I won't say anything, *milad*," Richard assured him. But, at the same time, a pang similar to that Louisa had felt earlier ran through his body and he too hoped that there would be no war. Surely there was still plenty of time to defuse mounting tensions, hopefully at least long enough to keep his sons out of it.

Throughout the first decade of the twentieth century, despite a great deal of speculation about the prospect of war in newspaper articles and through discussions, etc., it actually seemed so outrageous as not to merit serious consideration. Even with Germany's sabre-rattling regularly making the column inches, very few, if any, could truly have foreseen how events would conspire so catastrophically. Around 1910, however, the general mood turned a little more cynical and, although still regarded by most people as improbable, the prospect that war could well break out started to loom. The general air was something like: 'sooner or later something will certainly kick off but thankfully, not for a bit yet'. The result of all this optimistic procrastination meant that, when war finally did arrive, Britain was sorely underprepared. Although she still had the biggest navy in the world, Germany's had been greatly strengthened and, since there were no land borders to defend, the British Army was very small in comparison to those on the Continent. Indeed, the Kaiser was said to have referred to the British Expeditionary Force in 1914 as that 'contemptible little army' – an epithet that 'The Old Contemptibles' would embrace and become proud of, despite the original derogatory intention.

Also, as far as weaponry was concerned, there was nothing like enough, and although rapid increases in production, together with the floods of volunteers that came forward, soon made for remarkable progress, the limited supply of all resources was to remain an issue for some time to come.

After the Archduke had been assassinated during the summer of 1914, despite the incident being worrying, its full consequence was still to dawn on many, and even when war was actually declared, in view of the carnival-like atmosphere that arose, who could have appreciated the full extent into which this devastating worldwide conflict would develop. 'Our boys 'll show 'em what for and then they'll all be back home for Christmas' (to spout off about all their great adventures, no doubt)! If only.

*

After their constant squabbling down the ages, the one thing that was never going to happen was that Germany and France would 'leave it at that'. As things stood at the middle of the nineteenth century, they were always going to be on opposing sides, whatever. The bitter taste of Napoleon Bonaparte's humiliation of the Prussians was still in living memory and enough to make the very idea of any co-operation with France tantamount to treason. Even Napoleon's sound defeat at Waterloo in 1815 had failed to pacify the Germans. The Prussians in particular simply could not get the humiliation of their proud armies, at the hands of Napoleon, out of their minds. On the other hand, France's Second Empire (as it was then), being under Emperor Napoleon III, who was Bonaparte's nephew and carried the same name, cannot have helped either. Furthermore France, already dogged by internal political problems, was now looking at the prospect of Bismarck's brainchild: a united Germany under the umbrella of Prussia with the unified southern states on her border.

It had almost been the last straw when, after the Spanish Revolution of 1868, the Prussian Prince Leopold was offered the Spanish crown. Had it happened it would have left France surrounded but, to what must have been a collective French sigh of relief, the offer was declined.

Nevertheless Franco-German relations had reached breaking point, and when the French Ambassador met the Prussian King, William I, apparently by chance while out strolling one day, he was said to have asked the King to confirm informally that Prussian aspirations towards the Spanish throne were finally at an end. Instead of receiving any such clarification, however, the matter was deliberately blown out of all proportion, with Prussia implying that the Ambassador had made a nuisance of himself and had threatened the King with war. By the time the newspapers got hold of the story the meeting had been nothing but insult and counter-insult. The French were outraged, and frenzied demonstrations in Paris led to mobilisation and eventually Napoleon III, convinced that he could prevail, declared war. Prussia's subsequent invasion of France in July 1870 and the resultant Franco-Prussian War would this time leave the French humiliated, and serve only to increase the level of belligerence between the two old enemies, which was, of course, exactly what Bismarck had intended. It was he who had 'sexed up' the incident between King William and the French Ambassador in his famous 'Ems Dispatch'; his report on which the press reports were based. Not only had he achieved the long-awaited war with France but he had successfully induced the French into declaring it and, in so doing, had also managed to assuage any misgivings that the Southern German states may have harboured about reunification – all at the same time!

As far as Britain was concerned, though, this was just France and Germany slogging it out again so why should it be any of her business? The frightening speed at which France had been overpowered was, nevertheless, still a bit worrying. Yet was it not France, our old enemy, and Germany, our 'cousin'? After all, France had started it. Cousins can fall out though, so when it came to the Germans being just 'next door', in Northern France, might that be a bit too close for comfort? The books and articles that began to appear after the invasion did nothing to allay these anxieties either, particularly through their graphic scenarios. A good example is *The Battle of Dorking* by George Chesney, which sees Britain invaded by a European power; although not directly identified as such, clearly meant to be Germany.

The German sweep into France had been so fast that Paris was besieged within weeks and, after three months under bombardment, without fresh food supplies, the French forces were eventually starved into capitulation in January 1871. And as if to add insult to injury, the Prussian King, William I, had seized the opportunity to be crowned German Emperor or Kaiser of the newly united Germany in the Hall of Mirrors at Versailles.

This time round France's nose really had been rubbed in it. Napoleon III, who had found it difficult enough to aspire to Emperor in the first place, was captured by the Prussians at Sedan. Although released after the war, he was no longer accepted in France and was forced into exile in Britain. It was to be the end of the Second Empire and Napoleon III would never again return to France, dying in London in 1873. France was made to pay war reparations, relinquish territories in Alsace and Lorraine and totally reorganise itself. Germany had made it crystal clear to all concerned that this newly united nation intended to hold sway over Europe.

By now, alongside a united Germany, stood the various Italian states which had also recently been unified, making Europe start to look something more like it does today. With time and effort France eventually managed to settle into its Third Republic (as it was known) and Britain's ever-optimistic attitude returned, with the matter soon being regarded as 'over and done with'. After all, there was the British Empire to think about, with troubles in Egypt and South Africa, not to mention Ireland, and the ever-increasing internal industrial disputes. However, on the death of William I in 1888, the subsequent, brief reign of his eldest son Friedrich (which lasted only a few months on account of his illness) and the accession of Kaiser Wilhelm (or William) II, France particularly, but also Britain, would continue to be faced with Germany's bellicose view of where she felt she stood in the new order of things.

*

By early 1914 the Warren family had been living on Western Road for five or six years. Richard, now in his fifties and very much regarded as an 'old hand' in the hosiery industry, continued to enjoy steady employment. Louisa, also in her fifties, was fit and well. Of the boys, Frank, Albert (Bert), Syd, Ernie and Len (Joe) all still lived with their parents, as did the younger daughter (and youngest of the family), Dolly. Both Frank and Syd now worked in the hosiery industry too,

Albert on the railway, and Ernie, after leaving school, had followed his older brother, Arch, into the grocery trade. Len, at eleven, and Dolly, still only nine, had not yet left school.

Frank's twenty-second birthday had fallen on Thursday 19 February and, although a basic one and within her means, Louisa had prepared a birthday tea that evening. It consisted of tinned soup for starters – Maconochie's, ironically a brand that would soon become famous (or infamous) for its 'subsistence stew' so widely consumed in the trenches, ham sandwiches, the meat of which had been cut from a bone which Ernie had brought back from work and, for sweeteners, a tray of cakes; Frank now considering himself a bit too old for a birthday cake. Louisa had also bought some Lipton's tea, a luxury indeed, in comparison to the normal cuppa that Richard called the 'sweepings up'. Richard sat with his plate on the side of his chair beside the fire whilst Louisa sat at the extended table with her sons and daughter. The table hummed with conversation, sometimes getting so loud that Louisa had to shush them. As the evening passed the older boys began to try and outdo each other with increasingly outrageous stories, throwing in the occasional innuendo or veiled sexual reference just to see how far they could get away with it in front of their parents. Although Richard and Louisa were fully aware of all the connotations (most of the time anyway), on this occasion they did not object. It was, after all, a celebration; a happy occasion, and what might lie ahead was as far from anybody's thoughts as it could have been.

After tea Richard gave Ernie half a crown to fetch some bottles of beer from the off-licence and when Little Joe and Dolly had been sent to bed the rest of the family settled down around the fire.

Frank and Syd sat together as usual and, while the general attention was elsewhere, Frank turned and asked in a low voice, "Have you said anything yet?"

"Well, sort of," Syd replied. "I've mentioned it to Dad. But..."

No doubt because the beer was now flowing a bit, before Frank could stop himself, he blurted out, "Syd's got *summat* to say!"

Immediately all the other conversations stopped abruptly and all eyes fell on him. During the silence that followed, Syd's mind seemed to swim with everything that he was about to say and do. After a brief pause, he began: "You know that I've always wanted to join the Terriers like Frank. Well… now I'm just about to." The smile fell from Louisa's face as if she had been struck dead. She had been expecting this day for some time but had lived in the hope of never seeing it. Richard's expression was one of acquiescence: he had long since come to terms with the inevitability of this moment.

Louisa, in the vain hope that Syd's enrolment was still some time off, spoke in a voice meant to sound optimistic but which was betrayed by her expression. "When do you join up then?" she asked.

"Tomorrow, it's tomorrow, Mum."

"Tomorrow?" replied Louisa. "Why… why so soon, and why didn't you say before?"

"I did, Mum, you know I did. It's something I've always wanted to do."

"Well yes, I know, but why didn't you give us a bit more warning?"

"Sorry, Mum, it's just that I've been putting off telling you, I suppose because I know how you feel about it and all that but… but Frank's another year older now and I'm old enough… so, well… that's it really."

Louisa, not in the least amused by it all, "Oh, I see. That's it, is it?" and, sniffling away a tear, added, "Not much more to be said then," with which she swept off out of the room and up the stairs.

"Well, I think that went down rather well," said Frank.

"*Shurrup*!" snapped Syd. "I was going *te* tell 'er in *me* own way. If you *anna* shouted out—"

"Big day then tomorrow," said Bert, trying to rescue something from the situation. In the event it didn't, and, after another period of silence, he added, "Well, better be off up too, early start tomorrow," and with that, he too went to bed.

A minute or two later Frank got up and put his hand on Syd's shoulder. "Sorry mate," he said. "Me *un me* mouth, eh?"

"It's okay, mate," came the predictable reply – Syd, of course, would forgive Frank anything without so much as a thought (and vice versa).

When Frank went to bed, Richard realised that Ernie was still up, sitting in the corner, evidently spinning a top on the floor with his fingers, but in reality, having listened to and taken in every word. Although his concept of military service was fanciful, gained through the media of books, comics and what his friends had told him, Ernie was now old enough to understand something of the concept of war and was proud of his brothers' military aspirations. But his mother's reaction had frightened him a bit and made him think. Certainly, galloping across a field at the enemy with sabres drawn was an exciting prospect but what about being on the receiving end? The comics only depicted victory and the death of the enemy. Rarely, if ever, did they describe defeat or the true human cost. But Britain always won anyway, didn't she, so why should they?

"*Oy*! Off to bed you or you'll not be up for work in the morning," Richard shouted. Ernie, quickly brought back to reality, got up and, stuffing the spinning top in his pocket, followed the others to bed. "Night Dad, night Syd," he said and with that Syd was again left alone with his father.

After a bit Richard began again, "So that's it then. You're determined to go through with it, are you?"

"Yes, Dad, I said so, didn't I?"

"Right enough, you did son, but all the same, I knew it'd affect your mum."

More silence as Syd and his father stared at the fire, Syd's hands together over his chin with the point of his index finger pushing up his top lip. "The fact is, Dad, it's not really out of duty. Frank's tales of the weekends sound really good. I want to train and get fit like him and, if war does come, well… we'll all be needed anyway."

"It's your life, son, you must do what you think best. At seventeen *y'* can't stay tied to *y'* mum's apron strings!"

In reality, however, Syd had not been quite so sanguine as he would have had everybody believe. For the last year or so he had become increasingly anxious about his military aspirations, in the light of all the rumours about the possibility of war. As long ago as the previous September, when he had turned seventeen, Syd had been eligible to join the TF as he had said he so dearly wanted to do. But now, some five months later, he was still only just about to. The same things kept whirling around in his mind. As and when the time came, would he be up to it? At the first sign of danger would he run away? His idol Frank had always seemed so calm about it and loved the Terriers. He lived for his one or two evenings a week and those practice weekends away but despite them being 'David and Jonathan', they were as chalk and cheese in many ways. Frank was outgoing and gregarious, whereas Syd was quiet and introspective, and when you are fourteen and your brother is eighteen, it is only natural to look up to them and think, *I want to be like him!* When it actually came down to it, though, Syd's nature took over, so much so that he began to doubt himself and lay awake some nights, all the various scenarios running through his head and how he would cope with them. As things went on he became yet more obsessive until one Sunday morning, after a particularly restless night, he felt so desperate that he asked to have a word with the vicar after church. When the service was over, Syd approached the vicar as he stood by the church door bidding each of his flock farewell. "Good day… oh good day, Mrs. Johnson. I do hope Mr. Johnson is better next week. Good day… good day." (A parishioner whispers in the vicar's ear.) "Oh yes, yes I haven't forgotten… on Tuesday, yes…" As all this went on Syd increasingly began to consider calling the whole miserable thing off, telling the vicar that everything was okay now and that he had just been a little unsure of himself, that was all.

After what seemed like an age, when everybody had gone, the vicar signalled to Syd to follow him and by the time they were at the vestry door Syd was no longer able to prevent all his anxieties and pent-up emotions spilling over. As if listening to somebody else's cathartic outburst he heard himself blurt it all out.

"Oh God… Father, I can't… I don't think I can… I'm really muddled up!"

Naturally concerned by the manner of Syd's outburst, "Come now my son, come on in and sit down," the vicar replied, quickly opening the vestry door and pointing to a chair in front of his desk. "Now then, sit there and tell me exactly what's troubling you."

Syd stumbled in. When he was seated he began to squeeze his cap between his hands as though hoping to ring out his anxiety from it. "It's just that... it's just that I'm not sure that I can live up to the reputation I've so stupidly made for myself, Father."

"How so?" replied the vicar, "and slowly now. This evening's service isn't until seven and I am all prepared, so just take your time."

"Oh Father, I don't know where to start. I'm just deluding myself. I wanted to be like my brother, be him, but I'm not sure I can anymore. I thought the Terriers were all fun but now there's talk of real war..."

"You're Dick Warren's son, aren't you?" Syd nodded. "I don't often see him nowadays. More likely down the pub, I expect."

The aside made Syd forget himself momentarily and, shifting his head on one side with a faint smile, "Oh, he's not that bad these days, you know, Father, his age has slowed him down a bit, *y'* know."

"Yes, I suppose so," said the vicar. "Now do go on, what's this all about?"

"Well, you know my brother Frank..."

"I'll say," said the vicar, "a very popular lad, and a fine, handsome young fellow too!"

Although Syd was well aware that his brother was indeed these things, the vicar's words still came as something of a shock to him when he wondered how he was thought of in comparison.

"Well, I suppose that's really it, Vicar. I've been so stupid. I've compared myself to him and said I'll do everything he's done and I'm not so sure that I can. I know that if the worse came to the worst and either of us had to face death he would take it like a man, but I might not. I can't be sure that I can live up to who I've made myself out to be!"

"Now look," replied the vicar, "exactly what is it that you are afraid of my son? Is it really about not being able to be just like your brother or is it really the fear of death itself?"

"Oh, I don't know, both I suppose," and then, as if just realising the irony in the vicar's questions, reeling back in his chair, Syd repeated half under his breath, "Just death, just death I suppose," and then he sighed, his eyes began to mist over and it became obvious to both that Syd was totally emotionally drained.

The vicar silently and carefully considered his reply. "Well, for a start, son, you aren't Frank, and never will be. That's not to say you're not every bit as good as him, or any man for that matter. We're all different, you see. Some things that Frank can do you can't and yes, I daresay that some things you can do, he can't."

Syd thought for a bit and then, "Yes, it's about courage, I know. Frank's stronger and braver than I am, that's all there is to it, Father."

"No, it's not," replied the vicar. "That's not all there is to it. It's about fear. If anybody tries to tell you that they're afraid of nothing they're either a liar or a fool! Yes, even Frank. God made us to have fear; why, do I not say all the time that I am a God-fearing man? It's about your fear, and since God gave you that fear he can also make it go away."

"Can he?" asked Syd. "And what about war itself and being badly injured and everything that goes with that, too?"

"Ah, those are different matters," replied the vicar.

"And I think I know what you are about to say about death but I'm not so sure that your vision of death is the same as mine," added Syd.

"How do you know what my vision of death is?" the vicar retorted.

"Fair enough," Syd conceded. "I just assumed that it was the conventional Christian one, I suppose."

"Well, yes… it's like this, you see. Whilst I know that I will see my Lord when I die, I also know that He can save me or you or anybody from death. It's nothing new, don't take my word for it, you can find out for yourself."

Syd's tone sounding somewhat weary, "I know all that, Father. He died to save us and as a result, we will live for ever."

"That much is very true my son, and never forget it, but no, I didn't quite mean it like that. He can really save you from death in *this* world. It's *all* there in the Bible, all you need to know is where to look. Mathew 7:7 – seek and ye shall find!" With that he stood and with a single wave from the back of his hand, "And now be gone, my son! And do try to cheer up a bit. I'll see you next week with some further guidance. In the meantime, don't be so hard on yourself. There really is no need, you know."

"Yes Father, I'll try," said Syd as he got up to leave. "See you next Sunday, then," added the vicar.

"Oh yes, Father, of course, and thank you, see you then."

As Syd closed the vestry door behind him, he could just make out the vicar's parting words; sincerely spoken but nevertheless said half under his breath, "And the Lord be with you, my son."

Since the vicar had been so convinced that the answer to everything lay in the Bible, by the time he had got home, Syd had determined that he would start to read it from cover to cover. Sure, he had learned parts of the Bible in Sunday School but had never read it in any great depth. Maybe that was the problem. Hadn't the vicar said seek and you shall find and that all the reassurance needed lay within its pages?

As he took the family Bible down from the bookshelf in the parlour, he heard his father come in. Whilst the Bible was always on the bookshelf, it was hardly ever (if ever) taken down and read, and Syd knew that if his father saw him clutching it he would want to know why, so he stuffed the book under his jumper, shot upstairs to the empty bedroom and, lying on his bed, opened the cover. Although Syd's intention had been to read the entire book from start to finish, so as to be sure to find all the relevant bits, by about halfway through Genesis he began to waver and, more out of boredom than anything, started just flicking through the pages from one part to another. It then occurred to him that if, instead of reading whole chapters, he held the book in such a way as to allow pages to fall open at random, it would be God who decided the parts he should read. But, despite his greatest efforts in considering all manner of hidden or esoteric meanings in the many texts he managed to get through in this way, by the time it was Joe's bedtime, Syd was forced to concede that, although he had sought, he had certainly not found. *What am I supposed to be looking for anyway?* he thought. *What did the Reverend Buxton really mean?*

The following Sunday was Advent, and Syd made a point of attending the special service that day as he had promised, not least in order to quiz the vicar as to exactly how he could find the solace he sought. At the end of the service he again stood near to the vicar as the congregation left, this time having to dodge the remarks of a couple of his friends: "You 'elpin' the vicar again, Syd?" "You the new vicar or something?" When the church had emptied, just as Syd was about to talk to him, the vicar swept over to the bookshelf and took a small book from it, which he pressed into Syd's hand.

"Keep this, it's for you, read what it says and keep it safe. And may God be with you."

"And with you, Father," replied Syd, instinctively. "Oh, and thank you very much for this, yes, I certainly will read it… and keep it safe."

On the way back, Syd opened the small volume and flicked through the pages. Being a black book with a gold cross on the front cover, at first he'd thought that it was a miniature Bible, but inside was written: 'The Book of Common Prayer' opposite a print by the Victorian artist, Emma Irlam Briggs, entitled 'In the Workshop at Nazareth' depicting the young Jesus with his father Joseph. At first Syd still didn't quite understand, though he knew that this book must be relevant otherwise he would not have been given it. Then he noticed the brief handwritten inscription on the flyleaf:

Sydney W. Warren

Advent 1913

Psalm 116

So, Psalm 116 must be where the answer lies, he thought. After flicking through the pages, he found it and began to read it:

Day 24
Morning Prayer

PSALM 116
Dilexi, quoniam.

> I AM well pleased: that the Lord hath heard the voice of my prayer
> 2 That he hath…

By the time he got home Syd had read the psalm several times over but was still not quite sure what it meant. Then he read it again and this time, the significance of verse eight began to dawn on him:

> 8 Thou hast delivered my soul from death: mine eyes from tears, and my feet from falling.

Is this what the vicar meant? he thought. *If I keep this passage in mind and keep this book safe, will I overcome my doubts and fears?* One thing he did know was that he needed to decide once and for all about joining the TF alongside his brother. But when the day before Frank's birthday arrived, he still had not, and when the subject came up as the two of them were chatting, Syd had realised that it was now or never. So it was then, that on Friday 20 February 1914, the day after Frank's twenty-second birthday, that Syd turned up at the Drill Hall and signed up to four years' service. His Medical Inspection Report has him as 5ft. 5in., all but the same height as Frank was when he had joined, but his chest size and expansion measurements were slightly lower, and his physical development was only described as 'normal' whereas that of Frank's was described as 'good'. In fairness though, at only seventeen and a half, Syd was a year or so younger than Frank had been when he had joined. For some reason or other, neither's weight was recorded. Nevertheless, Syd was proud that he had finally gone through with it and been accepted. Despite his reservations, as he had hoped, he began to enjoy the TF every bit as much as his brother and the more he experienced, the more his confidence grew. If war did come, he knew that the training would serve him well and above all, he would be shoulder to shoulder with Frank.

*

Looking back today, we may well ask why the Great War came as such a surprise to the British public. After all, Germany under Kaiser Wilhelm II had become increasingly bellicose, the rumours of war were rife and German militarisation clearly posed a real threat. Surely the expansion of the German Navy alone to a level rivalling that of Britain's cannot have escaped even the most blinkered eye. But on the other hand, the Kaiser was directly related to the British Royal Family; being the King's cousin, making Germany, in effect, England's cousin. Tribally too: Anglo-Saxons were descended from Saxons and their languages had developed from the same stem. The alliance with France must have seemed a bit strange as well. After all, didn't it take a Prussian-British alliance to defeat the nuisance that Napoleon had become? What possible circumstance could prevail, therefore, for Britain to end up at war with Germany and worse; in alliance with France! Essentially it may have seemed better for all concerned to remain in 'splendid isolation' and continue to leave Continental business to the Continentals.

However, as international tensions mount, the reasoning behind extant treaties and agreements can quickly blur and drag those dreaded 'unintended consequences' to the surface, so there were still many other factors on which Britain's involvement in the Great War depended, including the threat that German expansionism posed, her continued belligerence towards France and the stability of Europe as a whole, to name but a few. Yet, it would remain the undeniable, callous and forthright way in which Belgian sovereignty had been violated that proved elemental in deciding the issue, simply because it was the most emotive aspect. But, had the Schlieffen Plan not been enacted, in that Germany had invaded France without crossing another country, I have little doubt that one or more of those 'other factors' would, in themselves, have brought about the same end. The fact remained, though, that Germany had invaded via Belgium and her decision to do so would prove very difficult indeed to defend, not least because Germany was a big country whereas Belgium was only a fraction of her size, therefore, Germany was an outright bully, Germany had agreed to guarantee Belgium's neutrality but had invaded it, therefore, Germany was also a liar and Germany's abuse and atrocities towards the Belgians were widely and quickly reported, therefore, Germany had to be stopped! And the sooner, the better.

If the Kaiser had full control of events in the period leading up to that fateful evening of 4 August 1914, then the Schlieffen Plan certainly robbed him of it shortly afterwards.

When Germany first declared war on France, because of the implications of sending troops into Belgium, she had, in fact, asked the Belgian king, Albert, for permission to 'cross through'. After all, he and the Kaiser were related and what's an invasion or two when it comes to familial cooperation? But, although I say Germany 'asked' Belgium, in reality the request was clearly a veiled ultimatum. It started by implying that Germany feared attack from France via Belgium (a bit cynical in view of the fact that the Schlieffen Plan was, by then, some nine years old) and therefore, that it was vital for Germany to enter Belgium in order to prevent the attack. It then warns Belgium about the consequences of refusing and goes on to say that any obstruction would be regarded as an act of war.

The Belgians were left devastated by it all and refused the request point blank, citing its direct confliction with the assurances that she had already received from France on the issue and reminding Germany of her obligations under the 1839 and 1870 treaties. It left no doubt that any invasion would be vigorously resisted. Despite all this though, German troops simply marched into Belgium anyway.

Belgium's reaction had shocked Germany so much that the Kaiser began to panic. He called in the Chief of General Staff, Helmuth von Moltke, suggesting he abandon the Schlieffen Plan. But, by now, the gauntlet had been thrown down. It would have been like running away from a duel. Her pride would lie in tatters and Germany would be finished!

So, despite all the rhetoric, posturing and warmongering, had the Kaiser really weighed up the odds of all-out war properly? Because, having clearly wanted to build on Germany's successful recent past, it was all now looking more like a gambling stake – a very big stake, in a very big game! And furthermore, was he really up to it and did he fully appreciate what was going on? Often labelled as 'mad', his decisions were now starting to become increasingly rash. He was not in the best of heath physically either, not least because of his withered arm which, although he always tried to conceal it, clearly frustrated him by the effect it had on his stance. Possibly as a direct result of this, the Kaiser's relationship with his mother, Vicky, had also been a bit shaky which, if you believe all that Freud wrote on the subject, can really screw you up! She is said to have blamed herself for his deformity and had gone out of her way to do anything (that she felt) necessary to 'make it better'. Unfortunately, however, whatever she did never seemed to work and, if anything, only made matters worse. By the time of her death in 1901, her relationship with the Kaiser would be described as 'distant'.

Then, as now, culturally Germany is often taken as a geometrically militaristic and controlling state, and in pictures the Kaiser often appeared 'formal' and over-serious, dressed in overly ornate military garb with a turned-up moustache; the sort of combination the British find risible. The French and British societies to the west must have seemed liberal in comparison, but Russia to the east, possibly not so much so. However, the main concern must surely have been that important political decisions were increasingly being made by the Kaiser and his generals rather than by a democratically elected German government and that their belligerent bias was beginning to have all too strong an effect on things.

By five o'clock in the afternoon on Saturday 1 August 1914 all the frantic exchanges between Germany and Russia over the situation in the Balkans had finally failed and the Kaiser, surrounded by glaring generals, intent on enacting the Schlieffen Plan, had no alternative but to declare war. After signing the Mobilisation Order he was now clearly torn on the whole issue and is reputed to have thrown the pen down and growled, "*Meine Herren, ich glaube Sie werden diesen Entschluß nochmal bereuen!*" – "Gentlemen, I think that you will live to regret this decision!"

Cynically, of course, it is also possible that the Kaiser fully appreciated all that was going on and regarded war with Britain as inevitable: his protest, perhaps, merely to 'cover himself'. Whatever, he must have dearly hoped that, with all that was at stake, Britain would, in the end, see fit not to intervene and so the way things did turn out must have come as a considerable disappointment to him.

*

When Europe awoke on Sunday 2 August 1914, the domino effect of Germany's declaration of war on Russia was in full swing. Even though the Kaiser had advised against it, Austria had already invaded Serbia, in spite of the fact that Serbia had agreed to virtually all of Austria's absurd demands. But since Germany had agreed to support Austria whatever, the Kaiser was now party to all this as well. Predictably this slight on their Slavic cousins riled the Russians and, although domestic revolution was to take them out of the equation before the end of the war, they mobilised, ostensibly against Austria but of course, this meant against Germany, too. By the Monday Germany had declared war on France, claiming that she had bombed Nuremberg from the air and German troops had entered Belgium en route for France. On Tuesday 4 August France reciprocated and declared war on Germany and, as the British ultimatum requiring Germany to vacate Belgium expired at 11pm that same day, Britain would also be at war with Germany.

Thus, the scene was set but, ironically, the initial public response in Britain was more one of elation rather than sadness. Could it have been a sort of relief that the question of European stability was now to be settled once and for all and that the British would be among those who were going to settle it? After all this was to be 'the war to end all wars'.

Whatever, as there was nothing in history with which to compare the situation, the reality that all were standing on the precipice of that monumental catastrophe that would spread to many other parts of the world, could never have been fully appreciated so early on.

Chapter 8

A Call to Arms

'The call is not alone to guns,
This is not but a battle test;
The world has summoned free men's sons
In every field to do their best'.

Edgar A. Guest

Even as late as the period between the assassination of the Archduke Franz Ferdinand and the outbreak of war; essentially the month of July 1914, at home the prospect of war was still considered unlikely, let alone that Britain would be drawn in, as it was strongly felt that Russia and France could deal adequately with Germany and Austria-Hungary by themselves. In fact, even during this period, the Irish and Indian questions, the Suffragette Movement, industrial disputes and the increasing divisions being brought about by rises in fascism and socialism, etc. still loomed higher in many a British mind than the prospect of all-out war.

The weather was typically that of a 'British summertime': after a very warm but cloudy start to the month, the second week of that July was mainly dry, sunny and warm but by the end of the month it had cooled, the clouds had returned and conditions had become more changeable. Then, as July moved into August the weather in Britain, like her relationship with Germany, became cool and unsettled.

During the first weekend of August 1914 (the first and second of August), reports began to reach London that German troops had entered France via Luxembourg. So, by then, it should have been clear to everybody but the most imperceptive that all the political posturing and rhetoric expressed before had failed and that the tranquillity that Britain had enjoyed since the death of Queen Victoria might well now be coming to an abrupt end!

Even within political circles, however, there still seemed to be some degree of viridity, ironically the Foreign Secretary, Sir Edward Grey, was not a keen traveller, in fact his accompanying King George V on a state visit to France in April 1914 had been his first official visit abroad since taking office over eight years earlier! Also, when the then Chancellor, David Lloyd George, discussed the prevailing circumstances with other cabinet members, many remained opposed to the war, citing the fact that it was not Belgium that had been invaded (at that stage) as had been anticipated. There was the proviso though, that 'should it be…' and so on, but in reality of course, they would not have very long to wait. In any case, this response must have seemed a little disingenuous because, although the first foray was indeed through Luxembourg rather than Belgium, similar guarantees had been extended to Luxembourg's sovereignty under the same 1839 Treaty of London. But there was another difference too; the Germans had asked permission to enter Belgium (if you can put it like that) and after Belgium's summary refusal, for them then to ask Luxembourg, I suppose, may well have been pushing rhetoric a little too far. Germany, for her part, claimed that her actions were in response to the French having bombed Nuremburg from the air and that she, therefore, had a perfect right to defend herself. This 'right', though, surely could not have extended to the event purported to have occurred shortly after one arm of the German invasion force crossed the Moselle and was challenged by a solitary Luxembourg gendarme who informed them, in no uncertain terms, that they had 'strayed' onto Luxembourg territory. If the few who still believed that the 'request' to Belgium had been sincere they would have certainly been disappointed by the German summary riposte: 'Go away or you'll be arrested!'.

Even when the Grand Duchess Marie Adelaide of Luxembourg complained to the Kaiser, she was 'assured' that it was by no means an act of war against Luxembourg but self-defence in response to attacks by France, and that full compensation would be due for any damage caused. I'm sure that that would have put her mind at rest.

In the meantime, further south, the Germans had also crossed directly into France – just north of the Swiss border at a place called Joncherey, near Belfort, the capital of the small *Département* of *Territoire de Belfort*. Although well into France, even by the geography of the day, looking at the positioning of Joncherey on a modern map one may well be forgiven for asking how on earth the Germans had managed to get so far into France without being challenged sooner. There were two main reasons. Firstly, Joncherey was quite a bit nearer to the German border in 1914, on account of the fact that the present day *Département* of *Haut-Rhin* was then part of Germany, as a result of the Alsace-Lorraine lands retained by Germany following the Franco-Prussian War. Secondly, the French had decided to withdraw ten kilometres from their border with Germany in order to prevent any suggestion that, in the event of war, they could in any way be considered the aggressors.

As the Germans approached, Leutnant Albert Mayer opened fire and wounded a French corporal, Jules-André Peugeot. The French returned fire and Mayer was killed. Sadly, Peugeot had also been fatally wounded and he too died shortly afterwards. So, although this happened just before war had been officially declared between the two countries, Mayer became the first German to be killed and Peugeot the first Frenchman of the so many military and civilian fatalities that that awful conflict would bring about.

On the first weekday after these events, 3 August, the Bank Holiday Monday, the *Leicester Daily Mercury* repeated *The Times* lead about the Government's latest response:

> *'After the example of what Germany has done in Luxembourg and on the French border we can no longer rely on the presence of her Ambassador as a security against some sudden surprise'.*

This was the day that the Germans formerly declared war on France and, as had been feared, began their march though Belgium. So, despite all that had been said and done Britain was left with absolutely no alternative but to issue Germany with an ultimatum to withdraw from Belgium or else. Pandora's box had been opened and the only thing now left in it was *hope* which was rapidly turning to fear, as the famous quote by Foreign Secretary, Edward Grey, to the journalist John Spender, clearly illustrates:

> *"The lamps are going out all over Europe; we shall not see them lit again in our lifetime."*

As we know, the deadline passed at precisely 11pm on Tuesday 4 August 1914, but the Germans, having flatly refused to withdraw from Belgium earlier, had already made war between Britain and Germany an inevitability well before Big Ben struck the hour.

Germany had already declared war on Russia, and since Austria-Hungary had declared war on Serbia with the full backing of Germany, Britain and Russia were, by virtue, also at war with Austria-Hungary. Accordingly, on Thursday 6 August, Austria-Hungary formally declared war on Russia. A week later Japan would declare war on Germany and so it had all begun.

Britain's declaration not only involved our 'Sceptred Isle' but also the overseas dominions, including Australia, Canada, India, Ireland, New Zealand and those on the Continent of Africa. And, when considered, the so-called 'British Empire' of the time made a formidable enemy. Naturally estimates vary, but essentially the Empire extended to something like 11½ billion square miles – in excess of 20% of the world's land mass, contained something like 430 million people – getting on for a quarter of the world's population of the day, and probably controlled something approaching half the world's total wealth! No wonder then that the Kaiser got the wind up when he began to realise exactly what he was up against.

There was something of a 'crisis of conscience' within the British Parliament too: could anything more have been done to prevent war? What effect had the Agadir Affair, where Germany had tried to muscle in on French interests in North Africa, had on the situation and could more have been said and done at this earlier stage? Similarly, despite things being directly drawn to a head by the dispute between Austria and Serbia, could more have been done to diffuse this tension as well? Had the threat to France been given enough thought? After all, the conflict between Austria and Serbia had absolutely nothing to do with France initially, her hand having only been forced through her alliance with Russia, when Russia had come to the aid of her so-called 'Slavic cousins'. And so on.

Britain had not been part of this alliance, however, and there had been some serious doubt, even up to the summer of 1914, as to whether Britain would automatically go to the aid of France in the event of all-out war. However, France was certainly not seen as the aggressor here and, although their shadows had often surfaced since, the Napoleonic Wars were long over. Now France had become our friend and, of course, our nearest neighbour. If she were attacked and we stood idly by, the consequences could be dire! As a result, Foreign Secretary Grey had already given assurances that, subject to the approval of Parliament, should the German fleet attack the north coast of France, the British fleet would give 'all the protection in its power'.

When all had been said and done, however, the invasion of Belgium was and would remain the essential pivot around which the

British decision to go to war swung. Put simply, after agreeing along with Britain, France, and others to preserve the neutrality of Belgium, Germany had gone back on her word, and this was 'uncivilised'. And, if she were to ignore it, Britain too, would be 'uncivilised'! So, as well as being 'the war to end wars', this was to be 'The Great War for Civilisation'.

*

As expected, on Wednesday 5 August 1914 the papers were full of it with the British Ambassador to Berlin, Sir William Edward Goschen, reported as having 'received his passport'. Essentially a euphemism for the expulsion of a foreign diplomat, presumably the implication being that the passport is 'kept safe' and only used when necessary.

As things stood Britain, France, Russia, Belgium and Serbia (the Allies) were ranged against Germany and Austria-Hungary (the Central Powers) and it was soon clear that other states too would inevitably be drawn in: Ottoman Turkey, although not officially until October, and Bulgaria, although not until the autumn of the following year, both threw in their hands with the Central Powers. The third arm of the Triple Alliance with Austria and Germany; Italy, had, at the last minute, declared herself neutral, but there remained fears that she might well come in alongside the Central Powers at some time in the future. In the event she was to declare war on Austria-Hungary and join in alongside the Allies during May 1915.

King George V thanked the Dominions for their loyalty and expressed his 'confident belief that, in this time of trial, my Empire will stand united, calm, resolute [and] trusting in God'. For their part the Colonies sent messages of support with Australia committing an initial expeditionary force of 20,000 men and placing the Australian Navy at the disposal of the Admiralty as and when required, and Canada pledging to raise a force of 10,000. There was also speculation as to how the United States, in the west, and Japan, in the east, would react. Japan, at least, had indicated her willingness to assist the Allies should the war spread to the Far East and, indeed, declared war on Germany soon after its outbreak in Europe.

At home the War Office requested that all regular reservists report to their stations immediately and there were assurances that, despite the circumstances, food supplies would be maintained and that there could be no justification for increasing prices. Nevertheless, and no doubt predictably, wholesale food prices did begin to rise almost immediately.

It was announced that Field Marshal Sir John French was to lead the British Expeditionary Force with Corps Commanders whose names would become as inexorably linked as that of French himself to subsequent accounts of the war, including Lt. Gen. Sir Douglas Haig, Maj. Gen. William Pulteney, Maj. Gen. William Allenby and Lt. Gen. Sir James Grierson. In the event, however, Grierson was to die from a cardiac aneurism within only a few days of arriving in France and was replaced by Gen. Horace Smith-Dorrien.

Reports were also being received of initial engagements in Belgium and the Netherlands. Naturally, in line with the mood at the time, they were very sanguine and spoke of the Germans being driven back. But, as they say, the first casualty of war is always the truth and, with time, many of these reports would prove apocryphal, not least as a result of the sketchy detail often associated with rapidly changing events.

In tones reminiscent of the former 'glories of war' the column inches spoke of advancing Uhlans and Lancers, references to engagements between German and Belgian cavalry, clearly reflecting the traditional view still then held about the way in which the war would progress. But perhaps the most worrying aspect was the portrayal of the German offensive as 'brutal'. Obviously, war, by its very nature, is brutal but there is a clear difference between its reasonable prosecution and what we today call 'war crimes' or 'atrocities'. Nowadays it is simply impossible to differentiate between what was fact, what was hyperbole and what was deliberate propaganda. There were reports of rape and pillaging and even babies being bayoneted. In one account, the town of Vise and the nearby village of Argenteau (just inside the Belgian border) were reported as having been set alight by the Germans, yet a captured German officer is said to have expressed surprise at the level of Belgian resistance after apparently being assured that he would be able to pass unopposed through the country.

In the Navy, Admiral Lord Jellicoe was appointed Head of the Fleet and there were already jingoistic rumours of victory at sea in that two German battleships had already been sunk and another captured. Although the report counselled caution, in reality at least one, the minelayer *Königin Luise*, had indeed been destroyed. The 'glory' turned out to be somewhat pyrrhic, though, in that the *Amphion*, the British cruiser that had sunk the *Königin Luise*, was herself destroyed by a mine laid by the very same ship the day before. Sadly, all on board were lost.

Although still in its infancy, this was to be the first of many wars where aviation would play a major role and there were also rumours that Austrian troops had downed a Russian plane and that a German plane had been brought down over Belgium.

*

In Leicester the start of August was traditionally the industrial holiday period and in 1914 3 August was the Summer Bank Holiday Monday. As a result, the streets were fuller than they normally would have been. As in other towns, crowds gathered around civic buildings in order to study the King's Proclamation, motorists displayed their patriotism by decking their cars with British and French flags and one became increasingly aware of the appearance of greater numbers of soldiers. The requisitioning of horses had begun and, although the authorities had the right to remove animals compulsorily if needs be, one report stated that no problems had, as yet, been encountered to which was appended 'and none were anticipated'.

The *Leicester Daily Mercury* of 5 August 1914 ran as follows:

'WORLD CONFLICT
GREAT BRITAIN DECLARES WAR'

[Interestingly the article below this headline includes as follows:]

'Seven nations are already involved in the titanic struggle, vis:

Great Britain,	**Germany,**
France,	**Austria,**
Russia,	**Servia,** [Serbia]
Belgium'.	

And that was exactly as it was written. Maybe I'm missing something here, but I cannot see any sort of order to this list – either chronological, alphabetical or anything else. So, as it stands, it would seem to suggest that Serbia (Servia, as it was then known) was allied with the Central Powers. Could this have been just poor typography or a fundamental misunderstanding of the role of the Balkans in all this?

Whatever, as well as the other inevitable column inches detailing the outbreak, its consequences and all the latest, page three carried the following large advert:

'YOUR KING AND COUNTRY NEED YOU

Will you answer your Country's Call? Each day is fraught with the gravest possibilities, and at this very moment the Empire is on the brink of the greatest war in the history of the world.

In this crisis your Country calls on all her young unmarried men to rally round the Flag and enlist in the ranks of the Army. If every patriotic young man answers her call, England and her Empire will emerge stronger and more united than ever.

If you are unmarried and between 18 and 30 years old will you answer your Country's Call? and go to the nearest Recruiter – whose address you can get at any Post Office, and

Join the Army To-day!'

Also, there was a letter to the editor, relating a message that he had received from the Chief Scout, Baden Powell, headed:

'WANTED, 1,000 BOY SCOUTS'

The correspondent urged Scout Masters to 'mobilise' 1,000 boy scouts from Leicester and its surrounding districts in order to assist with the distribution of information and poor relief, 'guarding culverts' and assisting the Post Office and emergency services, etc. He emphasised, however, that the Scout Movement was a non-military organisation, assured that all their duties would be non-combatant in nature, and that account would be taken of individual age, strength and capabilities in deciding specific tasks.

But alongside the ebullience there were also groups, not least the Christian Pacifists, who felt deep disappointment at the way things had turned out. At a meeting held in Leicester Market Place on the morning of the Sunday before war was declared, Alderman George Banton (who would serve as Labour MP for Leicester East shortly after WWI) declared that the assassination of the Archduke was no good reason to waste lives and denounced Russia's motives as oppressive, undemocratic and expansionist. He called for a meeting of the Town Council in order to petition the Government for neutrality, as did the local Free Churches, but, since war had already been declared, it was all now a bit too late. Nevertheless, confrontations between opposing groups on the matter were increasingly to result in public disorder.

The traditionally Liberal electorate of Leicester had only relatively recently turned towards the Labour Party as a way in which the lot of the common man could be improved, no doubt as a result of the perceived break in political inertia that the emergence of this new party might herald. And in 1906, the Independent Labour candidate, Ramsay MacDonald (who, after WWI, would of course become the first Labour Prime Minister) had been returned as one of its MPs. He was staunchly anti-war and had no qualms at all about telling anyone willing to listen. His stand was one of a 'negotiated peace' and, whatever your own personal standpoint is, it has to be said that, had this approach been at all possible, there may have been at least a chance that the monumental catastrophe that followed, which few, if any, had anticipated, could have been avoided.

These local dignitaries may well have had the feeling that they were getting their message across too, because, in the early stages of the war at least, compared with other nearby towns and cities of a similar size, in Leicester the proportion of the population volunteering for service was pretty low. Whilst the initial figure stood at fewer than 3% locally, Derby fielded in excess of 5% and in Nottingham the figure was over 18%. On the face of it the extent of these differences appear shameful and, indeed, Leicester was to carry the burden of this 'disgrace' for some time. I say 'on the face of it' as it may be fairer to add that Britain's chances of success also depended heavily on industrial output, not least on clothing, footwear, and engineering, the three staples of Leicester, and without manpower these industries could not run, let alone increase production. Additionally, perhaps, as levels of employment in the town were relatively high, and with rank and file military service having traditionally been regarded by many young men as 'an occupation of last resort', the proportion of able-bodied youth immediately available to serve would have been further reduced. Also, although the town had 'had its moments' when it came to the industrial disputes of the early nineteen-teens, relations between the workforce and management were probably, in general, better than average. As the war progressed, though, the balance was redressed and by the end some 50,000 men from Leicester and Leicestershire had served.

The most vehement group opposed to fighting, of course, were those who declared themselves conscientious objectors (COs). At first this did not cause any great concern as, unlike other countries, the intention in Britain was to supply troops on a voluntary basis alone. As time went on, however, and the full extent of the carnage became a reality, more and more troops were needed to replace those who had been lost. At recruiting rallies the pressure on young (apparently) fit young men to join up could be quite severe and it was not long before young ladies, with the best of intentions I'm sure, and eager to do their bit, began handing out white feathers to those who, for one reason or another had still not joined up. White feathers had been associated with cowardice for some time, but the P.G. Wodehouse book *The White Feather*, which had been published only a few years before the war, no doubt reinforced this image. Some of the young women concerned were quite intimidating too: perhaps gliding up with a smile in an amorous, provocative manner, as if meeting a close friend or lover, only to change into a scowling, insulting termagant in order to attract attention as she thrust a white feather into the face of her unfortunate victim. If it still did not make them join up, the shame and embarrassment that this could cause in many young men would, at least, have made them think about it which, after all, was part and parcel of the whole idea. I doubt that the committed CO, who had thought through and genuinely believed in the futility of war, would be similarly moved, however. In a way I suppose that in order to be a genuine CO you had to be a bit 'thick-skinned' as this sort of thing would surely have tended to 'weed out' those who merely called themselves COs in order to avoid service. And indeed, many were quite prepared to volunteer for non-combatant roles such as medical assistants or cooks, thus releasing others for active service.

When conscription began in 1916, all able-bodied unmarried men between the ages of eighteen and forty-one (with certain defined exceptions) were deemed to have enlisted and a system of tribunals was set up in order to decide whether or not those claiming exemption had genuine cases. Amongst the obvious reasons was essential employment, and factory owners often came in for personal criticism through testifying that the loss of a certain worker would seriously damage their business. Other reasons considered valid included serious financial consequences for dependants, poor health or infirmity and, largely due to the efforts of the No-Conscription Fellowship movement, 'on the ground of conscientious objection to the undertaking of combatant service'. If satisfied that an appellant fitted any of the requirements the tribunal would issue them with a certificate of exemption. Grants on the grounds of being a CO were rare, but some 16,000 did get issued during the course of the war.

So how would a supposed conscientious objector plead his case?

Definitions vary, but essentially a CO is one opposed to war for either religious, political, humanitarian or personal reasons. On the first count, if you could demonstrate that you were a practising Quaker, for example, or a Jehovah's Witness – religions with peace as one of their most basic and fundamental tenets – or could prove a history of devout Christianity, firmly holding to the Commandment 'Thou shalt not kill' (under any circumstances), then you were pretty well home and dry. In all fairness, however, only a very small proportion, even within these groups, refused to assist the war effort in any way at all.

Grounds on the basis of political beliefs, were perhaps a bit more difficult to demonstrate as a reason, for the ordinary man at least. Being an active politician, whose party had publicly and enduringly denounced war was one thing but somebody with a reputation as a militant trade unionist and/or out-and-out communist, who felt deeply that the war was merely the imperialist elite forcing the workers to 'do their dirty work for them', might have had a bit of a job on their hands. Similarly, one claiming to be a humanitarian, where killing is simply considered wrong but not necessarily for religious reasons, may also have struggled. And how on earth could anyone illustrate effectively the highly subjective concept of genuine neutrality – not having any standpoint whatsoever with regard to what was going on?!

The tribunals were local, and those sitting would inevitably have compared appellants to others who had either willingly volunteered or who had raised no objection to being conscripted, especially perhaps with regard to their own relatives, friends and neighbours etc. As a result of all this, the appellant would have been left with a very heavy burden of proof indeed and, predictably, the vast majority of pleas, brought on the grounds of conscientious objection were fairly summarily dismissed. Even where common sense prevailed and some sort of compromise was permitted, it did not always work. For example, a market gardener from Blaby was said to have ruled out serving as a medical orderly on the grounds that treating wounded soldiers would only prolong the fighting. Then, where a compromise could be reached, this 'singling out' could often exacerbate any subsequent bullying (perhaps especially from an over-enthusiastic NCO or the like). Those denied exemption but who still refused to serve were usually arrested and issued with fines before being handed over to the military but, if they persisted, risked being court-martialled and sent to prison.

Unfortunately, to give full voice to the experience of any individual Leicester CO is now difficult since, not only did they generally go unnamed in press reports, but the official records relating to them no longer exist as, for some reason, they were destroyed by the Ministry of Health in 1921. There were some whose particularly vociferous objections were widely publicised, however, such as Edith Ellis, a member of a local 'well-to-do' Quaker family and the daughter of a one-time Liberal MP for Rushcliffe (in South Notts.) and Undersecretary of State for India. After pushing things a little too far, she ended up in prison in 1918 for not having paid a fine imposed upon her for publishing a paper entitled 'A Challenge to Militarism' without first clearing it with the Official Censor, as required at the time under the Defence of the Realm Act (DORA).

Other Leicester Quakers were not quite so adamant, however, and helped form the 'Friends Ambulance Unit' which, as the war went on, continued to be very well supported by the town. And, in all fairness to Edith Ellis, she did turn her experiences to the benefit of others when, following the war, she began campaigning to improve prison conditions.

I suppose that what lies at the heart of conscientious objection is the dilemma that what is illegal in peacetime, i.e. killing, which at the time was punishable by death, is laudable in wartime. Many may well accept this paradox as a necessary evil in order to deal with oppression, but there are, and will always be, the highly principled (or dogmatic, however you see it) on one side or the other for whom there can be no compromise. Yet could it not be argued that, since such zealots tend to be few and far between, such single-minded COs could have been accepted for exemption without further challenge, thus avoiding all the rigmarole of tribunals and prosecutions, etc? Possibly, but in the end, when the levels of death and injury began to rise so dramatically, it is easy to see why the authorities became increasingly concerned that they might run out of 'cannon fodder'! Thus, along with the vilification of desertion, the determination to make an example of anybody who simply refused to join up inevitably hardened.

Arguably the most ironic CO was George Henry Powell, or George Asaf [*sic*], as he was known (presumably on account of the fact that he was born in St. Asaph, North Wales). He was the one who wrote the lyrics to 'Pack Up Your Troubles in Your Old Kit-Bag', his brother, Felix, who was not a CO and did fight, writing the tune. It was voted the best morale-building song of the war!

*

Another aspect of society then, the Suffragette Movement, with which the Government had had some considerable truck prior to the outbreak of war, and which could have continued to cause the diversion of attention, decided to call a truce for the duration of hostilities. Their motto was 'Deeds, Not Words' and although mayhem had been caused by activists demanding the vote, so far it had only met with intransigence from the Government. Even at the outbreak of war there was still a great divide over the matter, but the suffragettes were prepared to hold back on the strength of an indication by the Government to review the matter after the war was over. And it is hardly difficult to understand the reasoning behind this since, essentially, to disrupt the war effort would have been counterproductive to all concerned and would undoubtedly have turned public opinion against the cause. Moreover, many members would have had friends, husbands or other relations serving at the front and, due to the upper-class nature at the core of the Movement, many of these would have been officers whose respect they certainly did not want compromised. In short, it was a time to 'pull together' and, for the time being at least, put internal squabbles aside.

Portrayed near Leicester marketplace in statue form, Alice Hawkins was probably one of the most famous (if not *the* most famous) of Leicester's suffragettes. She was born Alice Riley in Stafford in 1863, the daughter of Henry Riley, a prison officer, and his wife, Ellen. Still living in Stafford, at around the age of thirteen Alice left school and started work as a trainee machinist in the boot and shoe industry there, as did her younger sister, Selina, some three years later.

I understand that Alice's mother, Ellen, died during the early 1880s and, possibly as a result, at around this time she moved to Leicester. It seems that Alfred Hawkins, who was to become her husband and who had also worked in the boot and shoe industry in Stafford (as a 'clicker'[**] [see footnote]), moved with her before their wedding, as the only record that I can find matching their marriage is one that took place in Barrow-upon-Soar (about eight or nine miles north of Leicester) in 1884. Presumably, therefore, they met in Stafford, as likely as not, either at work or through their politics, as both were activists. Probably it was the wide range of opportunities to be had in Leicester's then booming boot and shoe industry that drove them to relocate, and they obviously liked it because records show they

** 'Clicking' is a skilled occupation within the traditional boot and shoe industry. It is the process whereby parts of a shoe are cut out from a sheet or roll of leather. The name comes from the clicking sound made when the knife rebounds against the brass template around which it is cutting.

went on to live at various addresses in and around the place during the late nineteenth and early twentieth centuries: the time when the Suffragette Movement was in its ascendance.

Alice was from a staunch working-class background, considering herself 'confined to work as well as domestic duties', as the saying went and both she and her husband were passionate trade unionists. Many of the other prominent suffragettes, on the other hand, were fairly 'well-to-do', presumably for the very reason that they would have had that additional time on their hands to devote to the cause. As a young boy I'd often wondered why it was that my grandmother (on my mother's side – the only grandparent I ever knew) did not seem to relate to the Suffragette Movement as I would have expected. After all, it was at its zenith when she was a young woman and I understood, even as a very young boy, that denying women the vote was patently unfair. However, she too was brought up within a strong working-class family and, as a result, very much tied to her job and the day-to-day domestic grind. Because of this I can only assume that she may well have regarded the movement as a bit elitist or even, dare I say, a little patronising towards 'her kind'.

Shortly after Alice had moved to Leicester, a group of disillusioned boot and shoe workers formed a co-operative and began production from a small factory near to the Central Station. As production levels and their reputation grew, they were soon able to move into larger premises. This was the beginning of Equity Shoes where Alice worked and which, by 1895, had established itself in a large, newly built factory at 42, Western Road. This, incidentally, is the opposite end of Western Road to 192, where my great-grandparents (Richard and Louisa) lived – the other side of Upperton Road, which, following the removal of the Great Central Railway bridge, nowadays bisects Western Road so that you cannot travel its full length by motor vehicle. Sadly, although the buildings still stand, the recession of the late 'noughties' was enough to send Equity Shoes into liquidation and the company ceased trading in early 2009.

The rise in militancy within the Suffragette Movement at the turn of the twentieth century must have been sparked, in part at least, by the result of the 1906 General Election, which returned a landslide victory for Henry Campbell-Bannerman's Liberal Party following ten years of Tory rule. Could there have been a feeling that the Liberals would be more responsive to the cause or, given the higher-class nature of many prominent suffragettes, could the Liberals have feared for their seats, were women to be given the vote? Perhaps a bit of both, if the truth be known, but Emmeline Pankhurst certainly ratcheted things up when she organised a march on Parliament after the King made no mention of the cause in his speech of early 1907. And it could well have been this 'turning point' that drew Alice into the Movement, as she was very much part of that march, being arrested for disorderly behaviour and resisting the police when they intervened. In court she was found guilty and sentenced to two weeks in Holloway Prison – the first of five different prison terms that she would serve as a result of her protests. During her stay, the Leicester MP, Ramsay MacDonald, wrote to her, criticising the way she had behaved and warning her that she was harming her own cause by her actions. Alice replied with similar vigour that if the ILP (Independent Labour Party) were to turn against the cause she was 'afraid they will lose a great deal number of members' [*sic*].

Undaunted, on release she returned to Leicester where she set up a local branch of the Women's Social and Political Union (WSPU) and invited Sylvia Pankhurst along to speak. It is important here not to confuse the WSPU with the NUWSS (National Union of Women's Suffrage Societies) as they were two separate and distinct organisations. Whereas the NUWSS, under the leadership of Millicent Fawcett, had avowed to attain universal female suffrage through only legal and peaceful means, the WSPU held no such reservations.

Alice's next term of imprisonment came as a result of a visit by the then President of the Board of Trade and soon to be Home Secretary, Winston Churchill, when he spoke at the Palace Theatre in Leicester in 1909. On account of her reputation, Alice had been duly banned from the meeting. Her husband, Alfred, however, was admitted, but was thrown out after he started heckling. Then, when both he and Alice blocked the exit, they were arrested and subsequently fined. Alice, however, refused to pay her fine and so was sentenced to another two-week term – this time in Leicester Prison.

Still undeterred, she went on to break a window at the Home Office in 1911, for which she was again jailed, and in 1913 she served a further two terms – one for throwing ink into a post box and last but not least, for digging up a golf course!

1913 also marked what was possibly the most emotive protest by a suffragette when, on 4 June that year, the activist Emily Wilding Davison jumped out in front of the king's horse at the Epsom Derby. The field was in full gallop and she did not stand a chance. In a split second she was knocked to the ground, sustaining serious head injuries. She was to die in hospital four days later. The horse also fell as a result of the collision, throwing the jockey off but, despite sustaining minor injuries, both survived. Although martyring herself, Emily Davison's act met with a mixed response, with many, including Queen Mary, condemning her actions in no uncertain terms.

Another aspect of disruption in which the suffragettes did engage, but in which Alice Hawkins personally does not seem to have been involved, was arson. Without wishing to condone such acts in any way, there would appear to have been a clear intention throughout only to attack those objects least likely to endanger life. Pillar boxes proved popular targets as setting their contents alight caused inconvenience by disrupting the mail but confined the fire to within the box's strong metal structure. True, buildings were also set alight but, as far as I can tell, only those known to be vacant, such as the Red House in Burton Walks, Loughborough. (Probably something to do with the Corcoran sisters who actively 'fought for the cause' in that town. Today a commemorative green plaque hangs outside their former home there, in Castledine Street.) Then there was Stoughton Hall on the outskirts of Leicester. It was up for sale at the time but later demolished. (I am not sure what effect the arson attack had on this decision.) Also Nevill Holt Hall, near Market Bosworth – believed to date back to the seventeenth century and latterly the home of the Carphone Warehouse billionaire, David Ross. But when all these attempts literally fizzled out, none causing any serious damage, the Leicester suffragettes decided that more 'expertise' was needed in this department and for it, they turned to a renowned hothead (if you'll excuse the pun).

Katherina Maria Schafer was born in Germany and is said to have had a strict upbringing. As a teenager she moved to England, where she became an actress and was better known by her stage name, Kitty Marion. During the Suffragette Movement's escalations of the 1900s she had joined the WSPU in Brighton and, remaining convinced that the only way forward was through direct action, she was rarely out of trouble for her disruptive protests.

During the early hours of Sunday 12 July 1914, a fortnight to the day after the Archduke had been assassinated, Kitty, accompanied by two others, believed to have been Ellen Sheriff and Elizabeth Frisby, were trudging across fields towards the railway station at Blaby – no longer there today but back then a small main line halt, situated some five miles to the south of Leicester. Having availed themselves of all Kitty's experience, they were armed to the teeth with various flammable substances and an axe with which to break in. It must have been difficult in the dark, scrambling up the embankment to the line with all that kit, but they managed it and were soon able to make out the station a little further down the line by the glow of that night's three-quarter moon. After breaking in, they wasted no time in distributing the fire accelerants so as to cause maximum damage. Unlike the smoulderings that had gone before, when they put a match to the tinder there was an almighty *whoosh* and, as they stood back, the flames began to lick against the night sky. "Time to go, I think!" shouted Kitty and off they bolted – back along the line, sliding down the embankment and away over the dark fields. When they came to the road at the edge of the last field they must have stopped and, catching their breath, gazed back at the glowing results of their handiwork. Looking suspiciously dishevelled, the remainder of their journeys home must have been undertaken with some discretion, as none of the gang was ever prosecuted for this act. A bit of a 'turn-up' as it happened because, although I cannot find any reference to Ellen Sheriff ever having gone to prison, both Kitty Marion and Elizabeth Frisby had served time for similar offences in the past and so would presumably have been on the 'police radar'.

When day broke the station looked a right mess, with the cost of the damage done estimated at £500. Although modern comparisons vary, in terms of materials and labour, this may well have amounted to something like £50,000 or £60,000 in today's money.

Elizabeth Frisby, at least, was certainly one of the 'fairly well-to-do' suffragettes, the daughter of a footwear manufacturer and, to her subsequent credit, she undertook voluntary work during the 'war truce' for which she was awarded the MBE. Following the end of the war she became a JP and was elected to the council as a Conservative member during the late 1920s, eventually rising to become Lord Mayor of Leicester in the early 1940s. So it is perhaps unsurprising that she would never make any public mention of taking part in the Blaby Station incident.

Kitty Marion, during her several terms of imprisonment, like many other suffragette prisoners, had gone on hunger strike and had had to be force-fed. But, because force-feeding was dangerous and could seriously harm a prisoner, the response of Parliament was to draft the so-called 'Cat & Mouse Act'; officially the Prisoners (Temporary Discharge for Ill-health) Act, 1913. This allowed for the temporary release of those on hunger strike who, once free, would then start to eat again and regain their health, whereupon they would be swiftly rearrested – hence the nickname.

Whatever view you take of the Suffragette Movement, they clearly did have a point. But it has also to be borne in mind that this injustice was, by no means, confined to women alone, since a sizeable proportion of men did not have the right to vote either. Although rarely alluded to, many of the servicemen who fought in World War

I would have been ineligible to vote too! For one thing, male voters had to be over the age of twenty-one and many volunteers were not. Officially the minimum age for enlisting was eighteen but there are widely ranging accounts of much younger recruits, even some as young as fourteen, enlisting through lying about their age, a blind eye often being turned because the country was so desperate for recruits. Also, in order to vote, you had to be a landowner (of land valued at £10 or more) or a shopkeeper or a householder who paid more than £10 per annum in rent which, again, only a very few of the young men of the time would have been.

This 'elitism' became even more poignant when the choice as to whether to serve or not was removed by the introduction of conscription in 1916. But just why, in the first place, had the qualification to vote been so restrictive to men and women totally excluded? I suppose that one can only put it down to the established class system that existed, whereby 'some men' (the more wealthy) were 'more equal than others', the inference being that only the most influential need vote since the result of an election was seen to affect only influential men and was, therefore, their business and theirs alone. In contrast, the view of the role of women in society was seen as a 'stay at home' one, their concerns confined to cooking, cleaning, the bearing and raising of children and generally catering for the day-to-day requirements of house, husband and family.

Whatever, the Representation of the People Act passed in early 1918 would not only enfranchise women (well, some at least) but all men over twenty-one by dropping the property requirements for them. For women, however, the right to vote was still related to property and they had to be over thirty years of age. It would not be until 1928 and the Representation of the People (Equal Franchise) Act that women were given exactly the same voting rights as men. Somewhat ironically, however, the Parliament (Qualification of Women) Act, passed towards the end of 1918, which allowed women to stand for Parliament for the first time, placed no such restriction on age and applied to any woman over the age of twenty-one.

*

Another suffragette, another Alice as it happens, also described as a pacifist, an atheist and a staunch member of the Socialist Labour Party, was Alice Wheeldon.

Born Alice Marshall in Derby in 1866, after marrying William Wheeldon, she lived in Bootle, during which time she gave birth to four children: Nellie, Hettie, William and Winnie. Shortly after the turn of the twentieth century, though, Alice returned to live in Derby with her family.

She could in no way have been described as a 'shrinking violet' and the whole family had developed something of a reputation for (often profanely) 'telling it like it is' when something needed to be 'sorted out'. However, the outbreak of war in 1914 gave her a dilemma in that, although the suffragettes on the whole backed it, or at least women's participation in it, as a pacifist Alice did not, and resolved to support the cause of the conscientious objectors (COs). Things came to a head in early 1916 when conscription was introduced and men started to be sent to prison if they refused to fight. In response, Alice, who, like Edith Ellis, was a member of the No-Conscription Fellowship (NCF), along with friends and family, began to shelter deserters and those who had refused to serve on the grounds of pacifism. But it did not take long for the authorities to get wind of what was going on and in late December that year Alice answered a knock at her door to a man introducing himself as Alex Gordon and claiming to be in those very circumstances. However, he turned out to be nothing of the sort and was, in fact, a government agent.

Implicitly, Alice took him at his word and arranged to put him up at a friend's house. After a few days, though, Gordon returned to Alice's house with another man, Herbert Booth (said later to be Gordon's immediate boss), and this is where the plot thickens. Apparently, they told Alice, who was still unaware that both were government agents, that the camps holding COs were guarded by dogs. They then went on to suggest that the best way of dealing with this might be to poison the dogs so that the COs could escape. Alice is understood to have agreed to help but only if they, in turn, would help her son, William, son-in-law, Alfred, and another CO escape to the United States. William, or Willie, as he was known, had served a brief period in prison for obstructing the police and his application to be excused conscription on the grounds of being a CO had been denied.

Alice's daughter, Winnie, was married to a chemist, Alfred Mason, who agreed to supply her with the poison. Once this had been handed over to Gordon, however, both Alice and Alfred were arrested, along with Alice's daughter, Winnie and her other daughter, Hettie. They were then all charged with plotting to kill Prime Minister David Lloyd George and the then leader of the Labour Party, Arthur Henderson!

The case came to trial in March 1917 at the Old Bailey, and it soon became clear that, although most of the prosecution's evidence arose through the testament of Alex Gordon (the first government agent who had called on Alice), he would not be appearing in person and could not, therefore, be cross-examined. However, Herbert Booth did appear. As the trial got underway Alice's involvement in the Suffragette Movement was discussed and Booth claimed that Alice had admitted to him that she had taken part in various arson attacks, including the one that severely damaged the ancient All Saints' Church at Breadsall in 1914. He also claimed that Alice had made threats against several politicians including Lloyd George and Henderson for taking the country to war and had already devised a plan to poison Lloyd George. He also claimed that she had even tried to carry these threats out, only failing to do so when the Prime Minister was not present at his supposed location.

Sir Frederick Smith, prosecuting, presented evidence linking Alice to the poisons (strychnine and curare) supplied by her son-in-law, Mason. Both are alkaloids (organic compounds found in plants), and both have medicinal uses but, like many such substances, can also be deadly poisons. Even when administered in relatively small quantities they can kill, as they act on the nervous system and so seriously disrupt the body's vital functions.

Strychnine is derived from the strychnine tree, native to the Far East (*Strychnos nux-vomica*) and has been commercially extracted for some 200 years. It is often laced into bait food used to kill rats and other vermin. Curare originates from the forests of South America. It is derived from a number of different plants including pareira root (*Chondrodendron tomentosum*) and a form of monkey orange, another *Strychnos*; *Strychnos toxifera*. Both strychnine and curare had long been used by indigenous peoples as so-called 'arrow poisons', that is to say, arrows or darts are dipped in them before being shot at invaders or prey and it was suggested that Alice and her co-conspirators intended to use these substances in this way in order to kill their victims! The legendary Home Office pathologist, Dr. Bernard Spilsbury (later Sir Bernard Spilsbury) was called to give evidence on the effectiveness of such poisons but, when it came to curare, he could not recall any documented cases of it ever having been used to kill a human being.

Perhaps not too unusually, when it comes to being a secret agent, as the hearing progressed the background of Alex Gordon took an even more sinister turn when a Maj. Melville Lee (said to be Booth's boss and so presumably over Gordon too), gave evidence. Although he accepted that he had instructed Booth to look out for potential saboteurs, when asked about Gordon and specifically whether he had known that he had a criminal record, Melville Lee refused to answer, rather curiously adding that he didn't even know the man! As it later turned out, Alex Gordon was not Alex Gordon at all but William Rickard, a mentally deranged journalist who had been detained in Broadmoor and was a convicted blackmailer.

When it was Alice's turn to give evidence, she did not immediately endear herself to the jury when, being an atheist, she refused to swear on the Bible. She willingly admitted to obtaining the poisons, however, but insisted that they were only intended for use against the dogs that she understood were guarding the COs. She also admitted that she had told Gordon that she wished Lloyd George and Henderson dead but that this had nothing to do with her obtaining the poisons. Furthermore, her daughter, Hettie, testified that it was Gordon's and Booth's suggestion that they murder the Prime Minister and that she had suspected the two men were spies from the start, warning her mother to have nothing to do with them. She went on to say that she thought the idea of killing Lloyd George was obviously absurd anyway, if for no other reason than that if you were to kill one politician, they would be replaced and so you would have to keep on doing it, over and over again.

When it came to Alice's other daughter, Winnie, she agreed that she had helped in the supply but said that her husband had assured her that it was highly unlikely that either strychnine or curare could be effectively used to kill humans.

The suffragette leader, Emmeline Pankhurst, was also called and confirmed that the Prime Minister was certainly not in any way considered a target by her Movement.

As it was becoming more and more difficult to see how the jury could arrive at the correct verdict if Gordon did not give evidence, Alice's defence lawyer, Saiyid Haidan Riza, felt it necessary to insist that he appear. The reality was, however, that this was never going to happen, which seemed to convince the judge, at least, that the case was doomed to fail. These were strange times, though, and it took the jury less than half an hour to return verdicts of guilty to conspiracy to murder on Alice, Winnie and Alfred, whereas Hettie was found not guilty. Alice received ten years, Alfred, seven and Winnie, five and, looking at the difference between these sentences, together with the fact that Hettie was acquitted, it is pretty clear that the judge felt that Alice had been, by far, the overriding influence.

Nevertheless, public opinion remained somewhat divided, with some continuing to call for Gordon to give evidence. The Government was accused of a witch-hunt and the suggestions that the secret agents had encouraged and therefore, entrapped the defendants, would not go away.

From the other side of the debate there were calls to rearrest Hettie under the Defence of the Realm Act (DORA) but after some consideration the idea was dropped since it was felt that, after all that had gone before, a conviction appeared unlikely. She did lose her teaching job, though, and unfortunately what remained of her life was dogged with bad luck. Following her marriage in 1920 she gave birth to a daughter who sadly died shortly afterwards and, by the end of the year, Hettie too would be dead; as a result of complications after developing appendicitis.

At first Alice was sent to Aylesbury Prison along with her daughter, Winnie, where she remained as resolute as ever. Stirring things up and refusing to co-operate, she had to be force-fed after going on successive hunger strikes. (I don't envy whoever had the job of trying to force-feed her, though.) She was then moved to Holloway, where again she refused to eat, this time making herself very ill as a result. With the possibility that, after such a controversial trial, Alice might now die in prison, she was released at the end of December 1917 on 'the intervention of the Prime Minister' and returned to Derby. And, just over a year later, both Winnie and Alfred were allowed out too, again on 'the intervention of the Prime Minister'. But, no doubt as a result of having starved herself half to death, Alice was never able to work again. She may well have severely compromised her immune system too because she succumbed to the Spanish flu during the pandemic of the time and, on 21 February 1919, Alice died.

At her funeral, her friend, the prominent socialist and CO, John Smith Clarke, gave a eulogy in which he severely berated a certain 'incarnation… who in the midst of high affairs of state, went out of his way to pursue a poor obscure family…' for Alice's 'judicial murder'. Although he did not mention the 'incarnation' by name few were left in any doubt as to whom he was referring.

In the early 1920s, Alice's son, Willie, also a schoolteacher, left Derby for the emerging Soviet Union, but it seems that he found himself on the wrong side of the authorities there too, as he is understood to have been shot dead by the Stalinist regime, for some reason, during the 1930s. Exactly what happened to Alfred and Winnie remains unclear.

Looking back at the way this investigation and trial were carried out against the political backdrop of the time, history now appears to have judged that it is highly unlikely that Alice, Alfred and Winnie were plotting to murder politicians and were, therefore, treated unfairly. And I understand that, to this day, Alice's family continues to appeal the convictions.

A blue plaque now adorns the wall of Alice's former home and shop at 12, Pear Tree Road, Derby (now a jewellers). It reads simply: 'ALICE WHEELDON 1866–1919 Anti-war activist, socialist and suffragist…'.

*

Just prior to the official outbreak of war, along with several other Territorial units, the 4th Leicesters had been at their annual training camp, held that year in Bridlington. Having only arrived at around 4pm the previous day, they received the order to return home in the early hours of Monday 3 August. After a hasty meal had been dished out at around midday, they left and were back in Leicester by early evening. This would have been the first and only main peacetime training camp (such as it was) that Syd would attend as he had only enlisted the previous February. Frank, on the other hand, was a veteran of three previous camps, having joined the TF in November 1910. All held in the month of August, his first, in 1911, was at High Tor Farm near Whitwick – very close to home, since Whitwick is only some twelve miles north-west of Leicester. Frank's record clearly attests to his attendance at the training camp held the following year between the 4th and the 11th of August 1912 but I cannot, for the life of me, make out the name of its location. The record for the third location in 1913 is quite clear, though: Grantham. Interestingly neither Frank's nor Syd's training records confirm their attendance at Bridlington in 1914 but I strongly suspect that this was an omission due either to its almost non-existent nature or the confusion that the start of the war brought about, rather than them not having been there.

From the station in Leicester, guards directed the route to the Magazine and only the 'Terriers' were allowed inside, no doubt a little weary from the sudden change of events.

The Magazine, or Magazine Gateway (or Newarke Gateway: originally New Work or New Works) is an imposing sandstone building situated to the south-west of the old town, and dates back to the late Middle Ages. Richard III is understood to have ridden out through its arch on his way to Bosworth Field in 1485 after spending the previous night at the Blue Boar Inn, Leicester. Originally an ornate gateway into Leicester from the south, the Magazine had subsequently been used as a prison and then, in the Civil War, to store arms and ammunition – the reason behind its modern name. During the Victorian era, when it housed the Yeomanry, various additions were made to it, including stores, offices, a drill hall and a drill square. It was where the Leicester Territorial Force was formed in 1908 and was to become a focus for mobilisation throughout the Great War. Today the Magazine still stands, and I understand is undergoing further restorations. However, all its Victorian extensions are now gone and sitting, as it does, forlorn at the side of a main route through the city, it looks rather incongruous, not least because it 'stands up and shouts' at the very modern De Montfort University Law School building just next to it. For the Terriers that night, however, it was a hive of activity and when the commanding officer, Colonel W.A. Harrison, addressed the men he told them that, although they could go home that night, they were still under training and must report for drill in Western Park at 9am sharp the following morning.

It was late evening by the time Frank and Syd finally arrived back at Western Road but not one of the other family members who still lived there had gone to bed. As soon as they got in, they were met with a barrage of anxious questions and inferences.

"What have they said?" "How long 'ave *y'* got before…?" "Surely it'll be a bit before everything's organised, after all we're not even at war yet." "There's still a chance that Germany could pull out." "Not a chance," declared Richard. "They'll totally ignore us. By this time tomorrow we'll be at war, in fact we probably are already! No doubt in my mind at all about that."

"You're right, Dad, it's been obvious for some time, if truth be told.

But as far as what 'appens next, well, you've as good an idea as us," said Frank. "All we've been told is that we've to parade at Western Park first thing tomorrow so maybe we'll get more of an idea then."

Louisa did not say much, but her mind was racing and, as her eyes yet again misted over, she prayed to herself, *God keep them safe, please keep them safe.*

"I want to go too!" piped up Ernie. "You're too young," snapped Louisa. At only fifteen he was, but Louisa knew that if the war was to last a few years, and many were saying that it would, he too would likely become involved, and even Leonard (aged only twelve, always known as 'Joe') – *perish the thought*, she sighed to herself.

Incidentally, I don't know why Leonard was called Joe, it certainly was not his middle name as he didn't have one. I can only assume that it was because he was the youngest and, therefore, the smallest – 'Little Joe'?

Perhaps as well, then, that Louisa could not have envisaged that, as the war went on, many boys of such tender years would manage to trick their way into joining up, the youngest authenticated case being that of Sidney George Lewis, who enlisted at just twelve in 1915. He was to fight on the Somme in 1916 and thankfully survived the war, despite being almost a year Leonard's junior! With the introduction of conscription in 1916, Ernest was indeed called up in May 1917, shortly after his eighteenth birthday, but I can find no record of Leonard having served, which of course, on account of his age, is exactly as it should have been.

Whilst Dolly was sitting in the corner, not really understanding what was going on, Albert thought about what his own role would be in all this. He knew that, if the war dragged on, he would come under increasing pressure from certain quarters to join up and, although he knew none of that would come from his mother, he was not entirely sure about his father. For the time being he resolved to see how it went with Frank and Syd before 'doing anything rash'. In the event he volunteered in early 1915 and, although he survived the war (I would not be here otherwise), it was to be at some considerable cost.

As regards the other eligible sons, my understanding is that John (Jack) joined up and was wounded, but I do not know when or where. Arch, I believe, was already a regular in the Royal Marines and was to serve with them in Serbia. From what I can gather, he too was wounded. I must confess that I do not know anything at all about Fred's wartime service but there has never been any mention in my family of him having been a casualty.

And Richard's prediction was bang on; the Germans simply ignored the British ultimatum that required they undertake to leave Belgium, fiercely maintaining that they were merely defending themselves from invasion by France and had absolutely no intention of annexing Belgium. Thus war was now a reality and, for the Territorials, this meant full embodiment into the Army.

The Territorial Force (TF) had been set up by the then Secretary of State for War, Richard (later Viscount) Haldane, through the Territorial and Reserve Forces Act of 1907. Its effective purpose was to mitigate against a repeat of the shortage of military personnel on the home front which existed during the Second Boer War of 1899–1902 by incorporating various voluntary army auxiliaries including the Volunteer Force, the Yeomanry (essentially descended from the Cavalry) and the Militia, etc. into a new Special Reserve. It was to be, essentially, a local reserve force and men could not be automatically transferred to the Regular Army without their consent. Although they could be required to serve in any part of the UK, again they could not be sent abroad without their express consent. In times of severe threat, however, the Force could be embodied into the Regular Army, but this required a Royal Proclamation, and so, on that 4th of August 1914, King George V issued it. This enabled adjutants to issue the formal Territorial Force Embodiment Notice (Army Form E 635) which was sent out to all reservists informing them of where and when to attend and carrying the stern warning that, 'Should you not attend you will be liable to be proceeded against' [*sic*].

The day after the Bank Holiday, when Frank and Syd reported at Western Park, the arrangements were still a bit vague. After firearms training in the morning, they returned to the Magazine for further drilling and were told that they needed to continue to report for at least the next fifteen days. The *Leicester Daily Mercury* seemed to think that, with the outbreak of war, the 4th Battalion (and, by association, the 5th) would be going to Aldershot, but in reality this turned out not to be so. No doubt all part and parcel of the confusion and disinformation that arises in such times.

When the first reports of the Germans storming through Belgium and bombing France began to circulate, the Prime Minister, Herbert Asquith, announced to the House that 'unhappily, there is only one conclusion – war is certain!'. Not long afterwards rumours that the Germans had also intruded into the Netherlands started to come through. As a result, Belgium gave her permission for both Britain and France to enter her territory, in order to confront the advance.

At sea, British merchant ships were ordered to the nearest British port without delay, increasing anxieties over possible food shortages and also the effect that the loss of the reservists and volunteers would have on industry in general. Locally, activity in and around the Magazine increased, the police were preparing some elementary schools to serve as temporary barracks, and there were calls for St. John's Ambulance men to enlist with the Medical Corps.

As 11pm passed on Tuesday 4 August 1914, Britain, along with France, Russia, Belgium and Serbia, was officially at war with Germany and by circumstance, therefore, with Austria-Hungary. Soon after, Japan was to join with the Allies and Ottoman Turkey with the Central Powers. Whilst Italy, as previously stated, having originally supported the Central Powers, instead would join alongside the Allies in 1915, as would Romania in 1916, with Bulgaria joining the Central Powers that same year. But it would not be until 1917 that the United States finally came to the aid of the Allies.

As the first reports of border skirmishes began to filter through, so did the apocryphal rumours that the Germans were already being pushed back, no doubt giving foundation to the belief held by many at the time that 'it'll all be over by Christmas'. A headline in the *Leicester*

Daily Mercury on the 5th of August read: 'Rumours of Victory' but, in fairness, I think this related to an early engagement at sea, the details of which were just coming in. Much more worrying were the widespread rumours of German brutality that began to emerge, perhaps inevitable given the circumstances. But just how accurate were they? Was it fact or only propaganda?

As French was appointed Director-General of the forces, the King's appeal to the Empire was immediately met with assurances of commitment.

By Thursday 6 August the jingoism was being ratcheted up even more with one Reuters report headlined: 'Great Belgian Victory – German Army Corps in Retreat', relating to the result of the first confrontations at Liege. Allied losses were said to have been light whilst thousands of Germans were said to have been killed and very many wounded and/or taken prisoner. In reality, however, although Liege, being the first major city encountered in Belgium when entering from Germany, had been substantially reinforced since the German invasion in 1870 by the construction of no less than twelve surrounding forts, these forts were to prove no match for the tremendously destructive weaponry of industrialised warfare that could never have been fully appreciated when they were built.

*

During those first few days of the war, when that ironic period of excitement prevailed, it seemed like there was always something going on. Troops were everywhere and long queues began to form outside recruiting offices in response to the ever-increasing numbers of adverts and posters encouraging enlistment. It is probably as well then, that nobody can foresee the future, because, had they been able to, there would certainly not have been much to get excited about.

On the afternoon of Wednesday 12 August, under a blistering sun, with that feeling of adventure still very much in the air, the 4th Battalion, including Frank and Syd, assembled in full army marching order at the Magazine. After the Colour Party had laid up the Colours at nearby St. Martin's Church (now Leicester Cathedral), to a great send-off the soldiers paraded off down Newarke Street towards the Midland Station on London Road, led by a troop of Boy Scouts and with an increasing entourage of local young lads marching behind and alongside them. When they neared the station and a woman's voice rang out to the effect that, 'I'll be waiting 'ere for *y'* when *y'* get back, *me duck*', it must have felt to each and every one of those boys who heard it, as though it was meant for them.

The rest of the family could not get time off but Louisa and Dolly (whose school had been temporarily closed in order to make room for preparations) had gone along to bid Frank and Syd farewell. Having caught sight of both lads briefly at the start of the march, they had been unable to get close enough to hug them or even catch their eye. Then, as the parade moved on, they soon lost sight of them altogether, as they faded in with the rest of the column. Like everybody else, though, Louisa and Dolly had been buoyed up while all the cheering and waving was in full swing and, for a brief moment at least, the sheer excitement of it all had caused them to forget the full reality of the occasion. When it was over, however, and all the soldiers had gone, the sense of foreboding returned to haunt them. The stroll home was a sombre affair and, although the remains of that day were still fine and sunny, both Louisa's and Dolly's hearts were heavy as they walked back in silence. On the way they passed friends and neighbours who were all 'in the same boat': Mrs. Smith, whose only son had also been in the TF, Mr. and Mrs. Jones, whose lad was in the Navy and so on. Back at home the quiet, pensive mood continued. As Joe returned from school and, later on, the others from work, there still did not seem much to say, a quiescence which, apart from the odd word or two, would persist throughout the evening.

As the train left for Belper from platform one that day, it carried with it just a small part of the many that would follow in their wake. But for Richard and Louisa, the Warren family as a whole, and many other families for that matter, it was their flesh and blood, their sacrifice, their first down payment, not in cash but in heart, towards the great price that that so-called 'Great War for Civilisation' was, in the end, to exact.

Chapter 9

The Long Trail

'There's a long, long trail a-winding
Into the land of my dreams...'
Stoddard King

After the first Regulars and Terriers had left, as in other towns and cities across the nation, Leicester was still abuzz with activity. As recruitment continued the drilling of the first volunteers in places like Western Park, the Magazine Square and elsewhere was relentless. Albeit at first, dressed in 'civvies' and presenting wooden rifles, soon uniforms and proper weaponry began to appear.

Although recruiting in and around Leicester had, at first, been slower than in many other parts of the country, there was no shortage of candidates at the first recruiting meetings. One in the Market Place is said to have attracted 15,000 or so and another at the De Montfort Hall was over-attended, leaving some 2,000 unable to get in. But in spite of this, and all the rousing songs and patriotic regalia etc., designed to inspire the young men to join up, in his book, *The Last Great War*, Adrian Gregory recalls that the De Montfort Hall meeting raised only nine pledges and when only four out of these turned up to commit, two were found unfit!

In an attempt to increase the number of volunteers, as well as at the Magazine, recruitment centres soon sprang up at various other locations in and around Leicester, including one in the town hall. Recruitment officers also began to appear on street corners and women started to hand out the dreaded white feathers to any man not in uniform but whom they considered eligible. What with all this, along with gung-ho articles in the press and rousing, evocative music hall and cinema renditions, you would have thought it hard to hold out. There can be little doubt that this level of 'hawkishness' must have had something to do with the relatively large numbers of underage recruits who joined up or, at least, attempted to. With their fewer ties and greater naivety, set against the 'needs must' atmosphere of the time, it is understandable that a 'path of least resistance' arose and their claims about age, unless obviously ridiculous, would often be accepted at face value.

Another 'inducement' was the creation of the 'Pals Battalions', where groups who were associated by location or employment, etc. could join up together, on the understanding that they would serve together. Undoubtedly not fully appreciated at the time, there would be a sad consequence to this scheme, however, as whenever Pals Battalions went into action together, not just families, but entire streets, neighbourhoods or establishments could be left bereft as a result.

Not only were soldiers and sailors required but also others such as doctors, dentists, nurses along with other medical staff and, of course, vets, principally in order to treat the millions of horses that would become involved. All too soon it was beginning to look as though, for the first time in British history, the demands of this war would far outstrip the abilities of the regular forces alone. And this only served to reinforce the (perhaps inevitable) paranoia that was to follow. Alongside fears for husbands, sons and other relatives sent to the front, widespread obsessions about spies, agents and infiltrators at home also began to develop. It would not be long before so many rumours were flying around that everything seemed questionable and suspicions could arise at the drop of a hat, over the slightest thing. One of the more droll examples is said to have taken place when soldiers aboard a packed train from Scotland were asked where they had come from. Their reply, apparently taken to be 'Russia', was said to have caused some considerable concern. However, what they were really supposed to have said was 'Ross-shire'. Did this actually happen, or was it just made up? A joke perhaps? And why should the sight of Russians cause so much concern anyway? After all, they were on our side, weren't they?

*

Presided over by Strutt's Cotton Mill since the turn of the nineteenth century, Belper is a small town some eight miles north of Derby – just over thirty miles or the best part (in those days) of an hour's train ride from Leicester. By the time Frank and Syd's train arrived there, that warm August day had turned into a barmy August evening. After disembarking they gathered just outside the station to await further orders. During their official embodiment, which had taken place just a couple of days before, Frank had been promoted to lance corporal in recognition of his almost four years' previous service in the TF and was put in charge of a small group which did not include Syd. No doubt a chance arrangement, but I suppose that there is a possibility (unlikely because of the confusion surrounding all that was going on) that they could have been deliberately separated so as not to compromise either Frank's judgment or Syd's independence. Who knows?

Frank and his group were billeted in the Public Hall (later to become the Ritz Cinema) and Syd in a small school. While there they practised marching and drilling and when they were asked to confirm their wish to volunteer for service abroad, both readily did so. As usual, Frank had absolutely no qualms about all this. In fact, he felt that his job in the dull, hot, noisy factory was not real life, he only really lived for his weekends on manoeuvres in the open air and now this; this was what he'd been waiting for all his life. Syd, in truth and quite understandably, remained a little more apprehensive. To say he liked his job back home would be stretching things a bit but, unlike his brother, he did not hate it. Nevertheless, he was resolute enough not to show his reservations, especially in front of Frank.

Enjoined with the Lincolns as a brigade, after three days at Belper, the weather was still fine when, on the evening of Saturday 15 August, they set off to march to Derby. Said to be in fine fettle after all the exercise, they sang as they marched and were cheered on by those they passed along the way. Then, once in the town (as Derby then was), they were cheered even more loudly as they made their way towards the station.

Bound for further training at Luton, for some reason their train was not set to leave until very early the following morning, so they had to spend the intervening few hours in a nearby field. Kept warm by blankets and cups of tea provided by kindly locals, when they finally boarded and were able to rest, Syd's thoughts returned to his family. Unlike Frank, who had spent many periods away from home, this was already the longest time that Syd had been away. *How nice it will be,* he thought as he drifted off, *to get back on leave. I hope it's not too long before we can.*

When the train arrived at Luton, the dawn of that bright Sunday morning was just breaking. Somewhat bleary-eyed, the troops alighted and stood on the platform, smoking and chatting, surrounded by their kit. This time both Frank, along with his group, and Syd's group were billeted together – at Beech Hill School. Here the cold, hard stone floor made for an uncomfortable night's sleep but was more than compensated for by the warm, generous welcome they all received. As the days went on, it seemed as though each and every one of the town's inhabitants was going out of their way to be as accommodating as they could. One officer was so impressed that he was said to have buttonholed the mayor and told him that he should be proud that his town was such a hospitable place.

In the school hall the cry went out: 'Can anybody play the old

Joanna?' as an old upright piano was pulled out from a corner. Several shouted replies confirmed that many could and, from then on, full use would be made of the instrument accompanied, in the main, by rousing sing-alongs guaranteed to lift the spirit. Indeed, it would be a rare occasion if the piano was not being played and some jaunty rendition was not ringing out as you passed that hall, perhaps with a harmonica thrown in for good measure!

Army HQ was in the workhouse, a half a mile or so down the road from the school. Not having contained many residents at the outbreak of war, it had been a relatively easy job to rehouse them all nearby. The heating and cooking facilities, and particularly the baths there, came in very handy – especially after a long day's serious training and, for the attendants, like the other locals, nothing seemed to be too much trouble.

As autumn arrived and the training continued apace, the 'brass' started pressing for the whole North Midland Division to get to France at the earliest opportunity. During September both the King and Lord Kitchener made separate inspections at Luton Hoo, a large mansion with gardens landscaped by Capability Brown, situated some two or three miles south of the town. At the time this was the home of the 'well connected' Lady Alice Wernher (later Baroness Ludlow), the widow of Julius Wernher, whose diamond mining ventures in South Africa had made him one of the richest men in Britain. Still a haunt of the rich and well off, Luton Hoo is nowadays a luxury golfing and spa hotel. During Kitchener's inspection, however, he was apparently overheard expressing concerns that, should the Division be deployed too soon, there might not be a sufficient number of troops to replace it at home.

There seems little doubt that the lads greatly enjoyed their time at Luton, and it was there that, after less than three months as a 'lancejack', on the 21st of October 1914 Frank was made up to full corporal. But duty aside, at times things apparently started to get a little out of hand and, in some cases, the antics even necessitated disciplinary action. Although attempts were made to manage the situation, including the liberal issue of leave passes, etc., the problems associated with large groups of young men gathered together for any length of time, persisted, and in the end, the only way out would be to move them on. The issue did enable both Frank and Syd to get home on weekend passes during their time at Luton, though.

*

On 21 August 1914 a young reconnaissance cyclist, Pte. John Henry Parr, came across a German mounted patrol at Obourg on the outskirts of Mons, just a few miles inside the Belgian border from France. While John kept watch, another cyclist rode off to report the sighting but when British troops arrived and opened fire on the Germans, John was shot and killed instantly (possibly, it has to be said, as a result of so-called 'friendly fire'). But it was, sadly, in this way that John Parr became the first British soldier to die in World War I. (Not to be confused with Henry Hadley, who was the first British civilian to be killed. Hadley had lived in Germany and was shot by a German officer while on a train in the early hours of 5 August 1914.)

John Parr is buried in the St. Symphorien Military Cemetery near Mons and, coincidentally, his grave faces that of Pte. George Edward Ellison, who served throughout the war but was killed, again near Mons, just an hour and a half before the Armistice came into force on 11 November 1918, thus making him the *last* British soldier to die during the conflict. But Pte. Ellison was not to be the very last soldier to be killed prior to the Armistice. Although a Canadian soldier, George Lawrence Price, was killed at 10.58am on Armistice Day, that unfortunate distinction fell to Sgt. Henry Gunther, an American soldier, and it looks as though his death may have been totally avoidable too. I always like to think that, if I had been in charge of a unit, after it had become clear that the Armistice was about to be signed, I would do my level best to ensure that all my men and I kept our heads down for as long as it took. Also, if not attacked by the enemy first, I would certainly not have felt the need to attack them. For some reason, though, some American units did not see things this way and seemed to want to continue the belligerence right up to the last minute or, possibly in some cases, even beyond it! It could have been this, or the fact that Henry had become depressed after recently being demoted for apparently criticising conditions in the trenches, or perhaps a bit of both that made him do what he did next. Despite being told to hold the lines and stay put, for some reason he ignored the order and started to advance towards the German line. Both sides then looked on in bewilderment as, bayonet fixed, he suddenly started to rush a machine gun post, totally ignoring the desperate cries from both his comrades and the Germans not to. A brief rattle of machine gun fire rang out and Henry fell dead. The time – 10.59am – just one minute before the Armistice came into effect!

Even the Armistice did not put a complete end to the killing though. Sapper Ernest Wilber of the Royal Engineers, who had received the Military Medal for his bravery, was working clearing mines near the small town of Epehy between Cambrai and Saint-Quentin in Northern France when an explosion killed him and several others. It was 15 November – four days after the official end of hostilities. Although his family had moved to London when Ernest was quite young, he was born in Hinckley, some fourteen miles to the south-west of Leicester.

*

Returning to the start of the war, as it got underway the Battle of the Frontiers and the resulting 'Race for the Sea' began to define the location of the front line. Two days after John Parr's death, things really started to hot up when the British Expeditionary Force, along with the French Fifth Army, met head-on with the German First Army. It was to become known as the Battle of Mons.

In the initial stages the Germans incurred heavy losses and it began to look as though the Allies would succeed in holding the line at the Mons-Condé Canal. However, the Germans were quick to reinforce and when, later that day, the French, despite having mounted such fierce resistance, suddenly pulled back, the British were left with no alternative but to follow suit, thus enabling the Germans to cross the canal. Initially dubbed a 'tactical withdrawal', when the Germans became so tenacious in pressing their counterattack, it turned undeniably into a full-blown retreat. And it would be no less than two weeks later, after the British had been pushed back as far as the banks of the River Marne, almost at the edge of Paris, before the Allies would be able to mount a counteroffensive of their own.

By now, having pushed so far into France so quickly, the Germans had overextended themselves and were encircled, enabling the regrouped French and British forces to attack them from several sides. Although progress was slow, by mid-September the Germans had been pushed back some forty miles to the banks of the River Aisne, where they dug in, effectively beginning the 'trench stalemate' into which the war would turn. The Schlieffen Plan (Germany's intention to sweep through Belgium and Northern France and then swiftly capture Paris) was now dead in the water and General Moltke suicidal!

At the end of October Turkey officially declared war on the Allies and, back in Belgium, the First Battle of Ypres (a place that would suffer a series of encounters throughout the conflict) got underway. This 'first stage of the war' would last until the end of November 1914.

*

Although sad to leave Luton, the Battalion received orders early on Monday 16 November to march some twenty two miles east to Ware in Hertfordshire. With the start of winter this best part of a day's march over hills was made even more miserable by bad weather. And, in the event, Ware was just to be a stopover; after a day's rest there, the march recommenced eastwards to Bishop's Stortford where the next phase of training would begin. Here Frank and Syd were billeted in pubs, albeit different ones, which helped tremendously when it came to winding down, particularly as they were to spend Christmas there. As the New Year arrived many began to wonder whether they were ever going to make it to France but, by the end of February 1915, preparations would be in hand for their embarkation.

*

Of the myriad stories concerning life in the trenches, the most poignant and proclaimed must be that relating to the Christmas Truce of 1914. A sort of 'oasis in the desert', the war having been a reality for over four months, the carnage had begun, and it clearly was *not* going to be 'over by Christmas'.

Although it can be argued that war may bring out the worst in us, by accentuating some ancient animal instinct to kill, perhaps, psychopaths and cranks aside, the need to befriend is undeniably a natural human instinct too. After all, it brings with it companionship, a sense of security in numbers and, by reducing hostility, fosters survival, an instinct at the heart of all life. With the possible exception of bitter hatred over a previous unspeakable wrong or in self-defence, to encourage killing another human being has to be unnatural. Even though we know (or think we know) the reasons why we are fighting, whichever way you cut it, war is killing for political, not personal, reasons. In other words, you must kill somebody simply because they are 'the enemy'. You do not know them personally, who they are, and how they have lived their lives or anything at all about them. Those judgements have been made for you; they are essentially irrelevant. You are told that you must not hesitate in your 'duty', and should you run away, then your own country may very well kill you instead!

The debate as to exactly how much of the story is true, and how much is fanciful imagination goes on, but I would be very surprised if nothing along its lines took place at all. Christmas, being an evocative time of the year for many, based on peace and love, especially under the prevailing circumstances, must surely have aroused some emotions, even if only for a short period of time and in only a few places along the front. Although I believe that the prime purpose of any such abatements of hostility were much more likely to have been in order to collect and bury the dead, reinforce the trenches and/or stake out sniping positions etc. for when the fighting resumed, it is undeniable that some degree of cordiality must also have arisen as a result of these lulls.

The story goes that in one particular part of the line, near Armentières, as the light went down on the afternoon of Christmas Eve, the shooting stopped, and rows of small lighted Christmas trees could be made out along the German line. As it grew darker the sound of the Christmas carol, 'Silent Night', sung in German, could be heard to the accompaniment of a harmonica:

Stille Nacht, heilige Nacht,
Alles Schläft; einsam wacht,
Nur das traute hochheilige Paar.
Holder Knabe im lockigen Haar,
Schlaf in himmlisher Ruh!
Schlaf in himmlisher Ruh!

Stille Nacht, heilige Nacht...

This both fascinated the British soldiers and confused their officers in equal measure and, with all eyes fixed on them, a few British soldiers are said to have climbed over the parapet and started to walk slowly and quietly in the direction of the German trenches. Moments later some Germans came towards them and when they all met up in the middle of no-man's-land, instead of fighting, they shook hands and started to chat. Pronouncements of 'Merry Christmas' mixed with responses of '*Frohe Weihnachten*' – an opportunity to practise your German or, and perhaps more likely, to be impressed by how well the Germans spoke English. And with that the conviviality began to spread until, before long, both sides were mingling and singing together, and the singing grew louder. As the night passed more and more groups joined in and nationality and cause were forgotten. People became people again, people to be respected as people and even as friends. Somebody produced a football and the impromptu England v. Germany international was played – the result really irrelevant and, in any case, the score was unlikely to have been kept. Others exchanged hats, British cigarettes were swapped for German cigars and whisky for schnapps. As the party continued into the night, and a party it would have been, the craic turned: we're all blood brothers – after all weren't we all Saxons? Most of all, there was complete agreement on both sides: 'we won't start shooting again unless you do!'.

Despite the circumstances, there was certainly something of the spirit of Christmas in the air as the camaraderie continued well into the early hours. And, apparently, as it started to get light and the last of the stalwarts made their way back to their own trenches, heavy snow began to fall. Although sentries were posted, just in case, true to their word, no shots were said to have been fired that day.

There would have been gifts from friends and loved ones at home and, of course, the box from Princess Mary. All must have been a comfort but, for any soldier who experienced it, the unofficial truce must have been the best Christmas present of all.

When word got around as to what had happened, however, it 'put the wind up the brass big time'! In response to the dreadful atrocities that the start of the war had brought about, there had already been calls for a ceasefire from several influential quarters, including the pope, and the fear was that, on top of this, what had happened in the trenches that Christmas might make men refuse to fight or even lead to mutiny. Smith-Dorrien issued strict orders against any 'fraternising with the enemy' and the consequences of refusing to fight were spelt out in no uncertain terms. The result was that, although at least one smaller truce is understood to have taken place the following Christmas, nothing anywhere near so widespread ever happened again. And indeed, if it had, it would certainly not have been publicised. But was this just the result of the high command's draconian response, I wonder? Or was it more to do with the ill feeling towards the enemy that would naturally intensify as the war dragged on?

*

Although John Parr was the first British soldier killed at the front, the first to be killed on British soil had more local connections.

The morning of Wednesday 16 December 1914 saw one of the first sea bombardments of the war by the Imperial German Navy and took the life of Pte. Theophilus Jones who, up until just before, had been headmaster of Thringstone School. Thringstone is a village just a few miles north-west of Leicester but, of course, no shell could have carried anywhere near that far inland, and Theophilus was in the coastal town of Hartlepool at the time.

Born in East Terrace, Darlington in 1885 (an address that, as such, no longer exists), the first child (I believe) of John Jones, an oil merchant's clerk, and his wife, Lettie. Although not a great deal is known about Theo's early years, he seems to have moved around quite a lot with his family during his childhood. The Census of April 1891 finds him at Malpas Terrace, Northallerton, living with his mother and two younger brothers, Charles and Alfred. There is no mention of his father here and it seems that he may well have died by that time. However, as Lettie styles herself as 'wife', rather than 'widow', I suppose it is also possible that he could have been away temporarily, or they could have become estranged. With the combination of John as a very common first name and Jones being a very common surname it is hard to research definitively but Theo's father was certainly no longer around in 1893, as Lettie remarried that year in Thirsk, this time to a John Lowes. The 1901 Census records the newly formed family living at Newsham with Breckenbrough. Somewhat 'out in the sticks', this is a small settlement next to Kirby Wiske, near Thirsk, the remoteness perhaps not entirely surprising, since John Lowes was a gamekeeper. By then, Theo had a half-sister, Annie, Lettie having given birth to the child by Lowes in 1895. Having only just turned sixteen, Theo's occupation is recorded in this Census as 'Pupil Teacher' at his school near Thirsk. This term was usually used to denote a trusted and often clever pupil who stayed on at school to continue with their studies but also assisted the teacher and could even, at times, be left in complete and sole charge of a class. No doubt his ambitions having developed through this experience, in 1905, after the family appears to have moved to Hartlepool, he became an assistant teacher at St. Aidan's C of E School there.

It was while he was at St. Aidan's that Theo met Mary Baty; a fellow teacher. They were often seen out together and it is thought that, if things had been different, they may well have married. In the event, however, I understand that she never married at all. Incidentally, there is no mention of Theo's brother Charles in the 1901 Census. He would by then have been fourteen years old, but I have been unable to discover exactly what happened to him. Although it is conceivable that, by that age he could have left home, in view of the high rate of child mortality at the time, however, it is also possible that he may have died.

According to the 1911 Census the family were still in Hartlepool but now at Number 14, Dorset Street – a small, terraced house to the south of the town centre which still stands today. John Lowes must have died sometime between 1901 and 1911, since there is no mention of him, and Lettie is down as a 'widow'. She is also calling herself 'Jones' again, as is Annie, her daughter by John Lowes. Interestingly, Theo is listed in this Census as 'Head' [of the house] whereas Lettie is down as 'Mother'. Theo, I believe, was still at St. Aidan's School but now, at twenty-six years old, is a fully qualified 'Elementary School Teacher'. His younger brother, Alfred, now twenty-one, is working as a 'Timber Merchant's Clerk' and Annie, now sixteen, is a 'Grocer's Assistant'.

Theo landed the job of headmaster at Thringstone Church School some time during 1913, apparently through his contact with the local vicar, the Reverend Cheverton Shrewsbury, who had previously been the curate at St. Aidan's Church (the church associated with Theo's old school). Taking up this new post on 1 October that year, by all accounts, Theo was a very popular and industrious all-rounder. He soon warmed to the village and, having been a member of a choir in Hartlepool, took on the mantle of church choirmaster. He was also a keen sportsman, having played cricket, football and swum in his time, and so was soon roped in to playing rugby for the nearby Coalville Rugby Club as well.

Unfortunately, a year or so later, Theo's career was suddenly cut short by the outbreak of war. In October 1914 he volunteered to join the Pals Battalion of the Durham Light Infantry and so returned to the North-East. At his farewell celebration at Thringstone School, after he was presented with a prayer book, he vowed that he would keep in touch. In the event, however, there would just be a grim telegram, carrying the news of Theo's death, which found its way back to Thringstone only a few weeks later.

Although intelligence had indicated the possibility of attacks from the North Sea, when they came, their ferocity was a resounding shock to all concerned. The morning routine of Hartlepool was shattered at just after eight o'clock on the morning of Wednesday 16 December 1914 when the cruisers *Blücher*, *Moltke* and *Seydlitz* opened fire on it from three miles out, after emerging through the sea mist. In less than an hour several buildings were reduced to ruins, hundreds of people had been wounded and Theo, along with over a hundred others, lay dead.

The full flotilla had consisted of more ships, some having broken from the group en route in order to attack Scarborough and Whitby, but Hartlepool was the main target because of its docks and factories, and it was Hartlepool that sustained the most damage. In Scarborough, however, the deaths included a baby, which inevitably reignited the then already legendary stories of German atrocities in Belgium. Churchill, it is said, raged about 'the baby-killers of Scarborough' and much was made of the tragedy for propaganda purposes and in order to boost recruitment.

Fire was returned from the large guns of the Heugh Gun Battery situated on the Headland which juts out into the North Sea just north-west of Hartlepool. The Battery had originally been built in the

1860s to defend the growing port from any threat that the French might still pose following the Napoleonic Wars. And by the end of the nineteenth century, although that particular anxiety had subsided, the Battery had been upgraded, this time with the new threat posed by Germany in mind. Following the outbreak of war, the position was regularly manned and Theo, having now trained as a gunner, had been on duty there at the time of the attack.

It was to become a popular saying as the war progressed that 'somewhere out there was a bullet [or shell] with your name on it' and sadly, the one marked 'Theophilus Jones' was aboard one of the attacking German ships because, at some time during the bombardment, a fragment from that shell hit him in the chest and killed him outright. His cause of death is recorded as simply 'killed in action'. The prayer book presented to him by Thringstone School was found in his breast pocket. It had also been hit and pierced almost through, by either another fragment of shell or the one that killed him.

At the time of his death, Theo was living at 44, Ash Grove Avenue, Hartlepool, presumably back with his mother, Lettie. Although not far from Dorset Street, it looks a somewhat larger dwelling so, when he had started his new (and presumably better paid) job at Thringstone, maybe Theo had decided to use some of the extra money to embellish his mother's lifestyle a little too. The house would probably have been rented but if, after Theo's death, the opportunity ever arose for Lettie to purchase it, the £150 that he left her in his will would certainly have gone a long way towards the cost of such a house in those days.

The following Saturday the life of Theophilus Jones was celebrated before a large congregation at his beloved St. Aidan's Church, Hartlepool, which is only yards from both Ash Grove Avenue and his previous home in Dorset Street. He was given a full military funeral and the Reverend Shrewsbury returned there to pay his tributes. Afterwards the brave soldier and highly respected teacher was laid to rest in Stanton Cemetery beneath a rifle salute and to the strain of the Last Post. Today a large headstone in the shape of a cross marks his grave.

The Reverend Shrewsbury brought the damaged prayer book back to Thringstone with him for the commemorative service that took place at St. Andrews Church the following day. Legend has it that the fragment of shell had left a mark under the words 'Thy will be done', which, I suppose, adds a sort of 'kismet' to the whole tragedy. Later the book was returned to Theo's mother.

Amongst the several memorials to Theophilus Jones is a stained-glass window built into St. Andrews Church, Thringstone, which, in a comparison to Theo's circumstances, depicts St. Alban, Britain's first Christian martyr. There is also a memorial plaque on which Theophilus Jones is the first name. But, as history would have it, another twenty-six names of local men lost to that bloody conflict would be added by the time the guns fell silent, among them sadly, Theo's younger brother, Alfred.

*

When, in early 1915, the pace of life in Bishop's Stortford began to accelerate, it became clear that full deployment could not be too far off. The King inspected the now well-drilled North Midland Division as part of a parade of 33,000 troops which took place in the grounds of nearby Hallingbury Park during February. (Another great stately mansion with grounds landscaped by Capability Brown, then owned by the Houblon family, who were descended from Sir John Houblon (1632–1712), the first Governor of the Bank of England and whose picture was once portrayed on the reverse of the £50 note. Sadly, the mansion was demolished shortly after the war, as there was an insufficiency of funds available to maintain it.)

With a clear chain of command now established and reinforced by some additional men from the 2/4th Leicestershire Regiment, on the cold, damp morning of Saturday 27 February, the Battalion marched towards Bishop's Stortford railway station. Although Louisa would have dearly loved to have gone down to see her boys off, Richard had decided that they could not afford for both to go and, as somebody who had rarely left Leicester, let alone the county, she could not countenance the thought of undertaking such a long journey on her own. Just the same, that quiet unease, that had prevailed when Frank and Syd first left in the previous August, would once again descend upon the Warren household, this time, no doubt, exacerbated by the ever-increasing number of reports detailing the full horror that the war was now turning into.

In contrast the atmosphere at the station had been far from downhearted and, on the outside at least, the troops gave the impression that they were pleased, at last, to be 'getting on with the job'. When the train pulled out and moved off down the line it was to the strains of 'Goodbye Dolly Gray' and 'Belgium Put the Kibosh on the Kaiser'! However, the singing abruptly petered out when a troop train carrying wounded soldiers back from the front passed in the opposite direction.

After three nights' rest in Southampton the orders arrived to embark for France and so, on the afternoon of Tuesday 2 March, half the Battalion was divided between the paddle steamers HMS *Golden Eagle* and HMS *Queen Empress* bound for Le Havre. Under the cover of darkness, both ships then weighed anchor and set sail across a calm English Channel, the remaining half of the Battalion following on a couple of days later aboard a third steamer, the *City of Dunkirk*. And so it was, that on the bright spring morning of the 3rd of March 1915 the first 4th Leicesters would, at last, set foot on French soil.

With foreign travel a novelty to almost all concerned, the newcomers soon became intrigued by the contrast to home: keeping to the right, the cacophony that was the French language, the different ways and customs of the people, and so on, as they marched towards No.6 Infantry Rest Camp at Graville, some four or five miles east of Le Havre. Although the weather turned much colder and wetter during their stay, the couple of days at the Camp allowed for a bit of catching up. Constantly subject to the regular readings out of general instructions, to which the consequences of desertion or falling asleep on duty, etc., were appended in no uncertain terms, they could at least have a wash. Here also, the first letters home were written, while, to stave off the chill, thick socks and goatskin coats (met with an inevitable chorus of bleating) were handed out.

Incidentally, Graville sits next to Harfleur, which had been besieged by Henry V just prior to the Battle of Agincourt almost exactly 500 years earlier; then, of course, fought against the French – same place, different time…

On 5 March, after the *City of Dunkirk* had pulled into Le Havre and the Battalion was once again reunited, all gathered at the station bound for an undisclosed destination. In the early hours of the morning, after being supplied with food and drink by British women volunteers, they boarded the train and, whilst the officers were seated in passenger carriages, the men were all loaded into cattle trucks. "At least the straw's clean!" somebody was heard to say. He was still to realise that there would be plenty more straw to come and nothing like as clean.

Mid-morning the following day, the train pulled into Cassel (Flemish: 'Kassel') in the drizzling rain. Cassel is in the area traditionally known as French Flanders; although still in France, it is only a few miles from the Belgian border. At the time the French were planning a spring offensive at Neuve-Chapelle, which is only about ten miles south-east of Cassel, and it would be in this direction that the boys were to head next. But, with everything that was going on, things had started to get a bit muddled and at first it was unclear where they would be staying that night. Even though everybody did find somewhere to kip in the end, almost all were yet to realise that this first upheaval was to be just the start of many. Hopping about from one place to another, over the border into Belgium, then back and forth there and then back into France again – 'We're 'ere because we're 'ere because we're 'ere because we're 'ere…'. There were to be many 'long periods of boredom' to come before the inevitable punctuations of sheer terror.

As the following day was a Sunday it was Church Parade at 10am. Then they marched a couple of miles or so west to Zuytpeene, where they stayed in farmers' barns, the discomfort not helped by a smattering of snow. However, the mood lightened a bit when some soldiers of the Leicestershire Yeomanry, who were stationed nearby, dropped in.

The next leg was a march to Strazeele, some four miles south-east. Along one stretch of the way Gen. Smith-Dorrien turned out to watch them all march past. On arrival, the quartering was in barns again but they were now only about twelve miles north of Neuve-Chapelle, within earshot of the noise of battle. And, as if to underpin what was expected in the way of discipline, it was apparently here that some poor devil, who had overstepped the mark, was made an example of by being manacled to a wagon wheel for a couple of hours. With the Duke of Wellington's passing, flogging for misdemeanours in the military had been banned in 1881 and replaced by 'Field Punishments'. Basically, Field Punishment No.1 (FP1) was where you were tied to something solid which was considered particularly demeaning, whereas FP2 was where you were just shackled. They could be handed out for a variety of reasons, such as drunkenness, not taking care of kit or even being 'improperly dressed'. "Never mind, lad, we'll be in the thick of it tomorrow or at any rate, within a day or two," the sergeant would remind the unfortunate recipient.

Although everybody was by now 'psyched up for battle', naturally, beneath the surface there were mixed feelings, especially after a couple of days of reflection. Would I still be alive next week? Yet, when new orders did come through, they were all set – perhaps relieved that the waiting was over.

They were to march twelve miles further south-east to Sailly-sur-la-Lys, just five miles north of Neuve-Chapelle. On poor roads and with full pack, progress was slow but by early evening, although sore-footed, they had made it. With this increased level of activity, it was looking more and more likely that they would be directly facing the enemy before too much longer. On this occasion, however, although within shelling distance of the front and being able to hear sniper fire in the distance, they merely replaced the rear position held by the 1st Canadian Division, who then did go into action. At first there was rumour of a breakthrough and that the Germans had been overrun but, although there was some ground taken, the attack had been halted and, in the end, the advance only amounted to about a mile and a half along a three-mile stretch of the front.

After Church Parade on Sunday 14 March they were again on the march, but this time, only to Bac-Saint-Maur, a mile or so east. While they were there, the Germans began a concerted attack a few miles across the Belgian border at Saint-Éloi (also called 'Sint-Elooi') and it was touch and go as to whether the North Midland Division would be called on for support. As it turned out they were not required and were instead moved to various farms around Steenwerck a couple of miles to the north. The several days spent here mostly involved training in weaponry, tactics, trench digging, fag smoking, playing football and yet more of the seemingly incessant marching. Before too much longer, however, although it would be a bit 'in at the shallow end' to start with, they were indeed to experience the real thing.

Over the next few days, the weather turned very cold; firstly, sleet fell and then, the following weekend, there was a covering of snow. It was still cold and grey on the afternoon of Friday 26 March when the Battalion set out for Le Bizet on the outskirts of Armentières and right on the Belgian border. As they marched it is hard to imagine that the rendering of a certain song did not ring out at some stage. Around since the nineteenth century, with the focus now on Flanders, it had recently been revived in the music halls and although it may have been new to Frank and Syd, they would get to know all the verses and all the variants of this song *par coeur* as the year went on:

Mademoiselle from Armentières, Parlez-vous?
Mademoiselle from Armentières, Parlez-vous?
Mademoiselle from Armentières,
Hasn't been kissed for forty years,
Inky, dinky, parlez-vous.

Mademoiselle from Armentières... (and so on).

Versions varied and I'm not sure whether the word 'kissed' was always sung or another word substituted now and again. And then, of course, there was that other old favourite: 'It's a Long Way to Tipperary' (or was that 'tickle Mary' I heard?). But, whatever, it spurred them on their way.

Taken shortly after the outbreak of war, Armentières would remain a stronghold of the British until 1918. Although less than a mile from the German line, the robust nature of the Allied front here meant that attacks on it were rare and so it was a relatively quiet section of the trenches. As a result, although far from a 'safe place to be' on account of sniper fire, the odd whizz-bang, gas shell or piece of unexploded ordnance, it is probably fair to say that most of the day-to-day duties there were fairly perfunctory. The tots of rum, now and then, came in handy too. One unfortunate incident did occur on Monday 29 March 1915, however, when one Pte. Preston was killed after he went to examine an unexploded grenade. Apparently, after poking it with a knife, it went off and blew him to pieces. The explosion also injured two other soldiers.

The Leicesters were housed in a disused factory, and even though it was a large building, the numbers meant that it was still a bit of a squeeze at times. All were well received by the Regulars and regaled with many a story, both gruesome and humorous, about life at the front. Each did a twenty-four-hour stint in the trench, during which time you 'learned the ropes', particularly to keep your head down, especially at night when a Very light went up. The Terriers spent their time at Le Bizet digging out some of the reserve trenches there, but also managing to attract some enemy shelling in the process. Thankfully, although there were a few narrow misses, none of the Leicesters was hit but there was continued fighting up ahead and some of the wounded from other battalions on the front had to be conducted through, in order to receive treatment.

After five days the 4th Leicesters were on the march again, back to Steenwerck but, by now, having acquired a much more 'warrior-like' confidence. They had been at the front, the very purpose for which they had trained and the essence of why they were there. Many a spirited letter dropped on the floor behind the front doors of Leicester, and around the county, as a result of that 'baptism of fire'. In reality, however, still more nights in smelly barns lay ahead.

In 1915 Easter directly followed April Fools' Day, in that Good Friday fell on 2 April and, on Saturday the 3rd, the Battalion marched to Dranouter (or Dranoutre) just inside the Belgian border. Church Parade that Easter Sunday took place in a field and followed another night spent in a barn. Although just as uncomfortable as before, some could not help but feel that they may have been a little too quick to complain at first, now that they were able to compare first-hand the warmth of a barn to conditions in the trenches. But back to the trenches they were bound and that evening marched the three miles or so to the HQ of the 1st Monmouths at One Tree Farm, just to the east of Kemmel, in order to replace them on the front at Spanbroekmolen (Spanbroek Mill, a strange name for a mill if you look it up but, in any case, by this time there wasn't much left of it).

The fighting line at that point faced Wytschaete (a.k.a. Wijtschate or, as the British called it, 'White Sheet') on the Messines Ridge, about six miles south of Ypres. The Germans needed to be kept in check after having taken the high ground during the First Battle of Ypres as part of that 'Race to the Sea' the previous autumn, the objective would be to maintain and reinforce the British opposition there. Unfortunately, the shortage of weaponry and ammunition, which had resulted from Britain's failure to prepare adequately for war, was, by now, beginning to bite and this 'reinforcement' was, very much one of manpower rather than the much-needed materiel.

Although only yards from the Germans (with their advantage of the higher ground) the Leicesters found things relatively quiet, due, not least, to the very wet weather, which had led to run-off from the Ridge waterlogging some of the trenches and disrupting communications. To make matters worse, as a result of the heavy fighting that had gone on beforehand, there were dead bodies everywhere. Only three weeks before, a young subaltern of the Royal

Engineers, Lt. Cyril Martin, had won the VC by leading a successful attack on the German line despite having been wounded. Obviously made of some 'strong stuff', he would go on to attain the rank of Brigadier, survive both World Wars and live on until 1980, well into his 89th year.

At first light that Easter Monday, the 'newcomers' gazed out on a dismal scene. The landscape of no man's land, not long since green and lush, was now a dull, foreboding wasteland. The British side of the front there consisted of a sandbag barricade from which ran several small trenches, and it was essentially a case of 'holding the line' while supporting mining operations towards the Ridge. The Germans too were mining from their positions and sometimes opposing excavations would get so close to each other that you could hear the Germans talking in their tunnel from inside a British one.

The rotting corpses, some completely buried, some partially buried and others just lying on the bare earth, caused an almighty stench, and this attracted rats that grew fatter by the day on this 'bumper harvest'. The reluctance of the French to bury their dead made the problem particularly bad in their sector to the left of the British. The only way to control this was, where at all possible, to cover exposed corpses with lime, which, as a result, was in constant demand, but sadly, also in very limited supply. The sobriquet, 'Hell's Kitchen' that this place had acquired was certainly not without justification.

As dawn broke on the following Friday, the 4th Leicesters were relieved by the 5th Lincs. and were able to fall back again to One Tree Farm under the cover of the early morning mist. Although exhausted, they were then ordered to march back to Dranoutre but, on arrival, were still not so weary as to prevent a resounding song or two before collapsing in the (now not so unpleasant) barns. Fortunately, this stint in the trenches had only cost the 4ths a relatively small number of casualties but, unfortunately, one soldier had been killed by accident. Apparently, a shell fired by the Staffordshires had landed short of its target and fell straight into the British trench. The blast injured another two soldiers, one losing an arm.

In total, the Leicesters spent almost three months doing stints at the Spanbroekmolen Front, moving from their billets at Dranoutre in late May to an encampment at Kemmel Hill, as the weather improved. During their time there the skirmishes continued, as on one night when a patrol of German soldiers had managed to get close enough to bomb a section of their trench. Although repulsed under Very lights it cost three lives; two British and one German. One British private had gone missing during the raid and there were fears that the Germans might have captured him and extracted details of mining operations from him. The fact that, shortly afterwards, the Germans could be heard mining nearer and nearer and then, ten days later, blew up part of the British line, would appear to have confirmed this. Regretfully, despite a frantic struggle to dig out those buried by the explosions, there were numerous casualties, many of whom died.

It was during this period that a letter of thanks, written by Syd, found its way to the offices and then the columns of the *Leicester Chronicle* newspaper. It appears that the good people of Leicester had contributed to a parcel of gifts sent out to the troops, the contents of which had obviously been most gratefully received. It read:

> Signaller Sydney Warren writes on behalf of the Signallers of the 4th Leicestershire Territorials from "Somewhere in Belgium":—
>
> We have just received your gift of a packet of tobacco, which was fully appreciated by all, so we write these few lines thanking you so much for your thoughtful generosity. I do not think that you could have sent a more useful present than the writing pads, which came in very useful for all. I believe that when they were received, every man wrote one or more letters home. It shows that by these presents we are not forgotten and are always in the thoughts of the citizens of Leicester, to whom we also send our sincere thanks. Hoping you accept our thanks.

Very moving to think that such simple gifts, under such circumstances, meant so much.

Towards the end of May, the poor health of Lt. Col. T.T. Gresson forced his replacement as commanding officer of the 4th Leicesters by the newly promoted Lt. Col. R.E. Martin. Hitherto second in command of the 5th Leicesters, Martin had a reputation for being 'firm but fair'. I do not think that he was in any way related to Cyril Martin (who won the VC), by the way. From then on, the North Midland Division, of which the 4th Leicesters were part, would be known as the '46th (North Midland) Division'.

With the onset of summer, an air of (almost) contentment prevailed at Spanbroekmolen; the mining and shelling had abated somewhat and the results of all the hard work were beginning to show. The trenches had dried out and were boarded, the barricades reinforced and many of the exposed dead had been recovered and buried.

When the time came to pull out, though, probably even worse than handling the corpses was the dreaded filling in of the old trench latrines and digging new ones before the incomers arrived.

*

At around the time that war broke out, Albert, my granddad, had met Marion Blyth, my grandma, a Scottish girl whose family had moved down to Leicester from Leith, near Edinburgh, just after the turn of the twentieth century. Her father, David Blyth, had lost his wife, Margaret, in 1900 and, possibly in the hope of making a new start, he had obtained a job operating the new electric trams that started to appear on Leicester's streets during 1904. Marion's family lived in Haddon Street – about a mile and a half's trek across Leicester from Western Road. The house belonged to her cousin, William Blyth, who had also moved down from Scotland and married a girl from Burton upon Trent, Edith. As well as her widowed father, Marion's younger brother, Charles, and William's and Edith's sons, William and Thomas, also shared the house.

I do not know exactly how or where they met, since Marion worked in the 'boot and shoe' at the time and Albert on the railway, but it must have been an intimate affair from the start because, although she may not have fully realised it, around the middle of December 1914 Marion must have been in the initial stages of pregnancy. Could it have been that, with the war now well underway and the call for every able-bodied young man to join up, Albert had finally made his mind up that he could not put off enlisting any longer and had resolved to do 'what was expected of him'? With this in mind, could their relationship have grown much more intense than under different circumstances; at the thought of Albert's imminent departure into danger? Perhaps they felt an imperative to make that Christmas together (what may have been their first and last) truly unforgettable. Whatever, just into the New Year Albert signed up with the 9th Leicesters.

Attitudes towards pregnancy outside of marriage have changed so much in the intervening years that it is now nigh on impossible to appreciate fully the level of social stigma that surrounded it in those days. Like today, though, as well as being 'star-crossed lovers' there were, of course, myriad other reasons for it arising, not least the casual liaisons, often after a drink or two and perhaps in particular, between a local girl and a serviceman temporarily billeted nearby; a circumstance obviously typical at that time. But whatever the cause, when pregnancy did arise out of wedlock, back then it was almost always met with something of a 'hoo-ha' within the family.

Albert and Marion were clearly in love, though, and May Day 1915 saw them married in the parish church of St. John the Divine on South Albion Street; just down the road from Dunkirk Street, where they were both now living together. By the time baby Gwendoline May (the middle name no doubt an allusion to the date of the wedding) was born on the 25th of September, however, Albert would be away fighting in France.

Incidentally, Marion's father, David, who by then would have been well into his forties, is down on the marriage certificate as 'soldier' so, presumably, he too had joined up, despite being over what I understand was the maximum age limit of forty-one.

*

Shortly before Gwen's conception, at Leicester Prison another life had ended, or rather had been ended; through judicial hanging! I cannot be absolutely sure, but I cannot find any evidence that I am in any way related to Arnold Warren and sincerely hope that I am not. But with him living so near to the extended family that the Leicester Warrens at that time were, I can never be totally sure.

By all accounts Arnold, an engineer by trade, was both a heavy drinker and a heavy gambler and was not averse to knocking both his wife, Edith, and his two-year-old son, James, about while under the influence or when his luck ran out, which was of course, quite often the case. On one occasion he beat his wife so badly that she left him and subsequently successfully prosecuted him for assault. In court the judge ordered Arnold to pay her ten shillings a week in order to support herself and James. Predictably this did not go down at all well with Arnold.

The matter came to a head during July, when Arnold happened on his wife in the street. After ranting to her that he had now lost his job, he added that he had just placed one last big bet and, if the horse did not come in, he was going to poison himself. At the time Edith, having heard this sort of thing from Arnold so many times before, thought little of it and was glad just to get away from him.

As you may well have expected, the horse did not win and early that evening Arnold, in a fit of pique, made his way to the Fosse recreation ground; a place where he knew his toddler son was often taken at around that time of day by a young girl who regularly took care of the boy. When Arnold saw the girl with James, he is said to have sent her away with a note to Edith begging her for money, but when the girl returned both Arnold and James were nowhere to be seen.

Later that evening a couple came across them lying side by side. Arnold, still clutching a bottle that had contained laudanum (essentially opium) in his hand, was unconscious, but James was dead, his throat having been viciously ripped open by a cut-throat razor.

A policeman, summoned to the scene, managed to revive Arnold, who then began to complain bitterly about not having been simply left to die.

Shortly afterwards a doctor arrived on the scene and certified James's death. Arnold was arrested and remanded until the committal proceedings later that month.

At his first court appearance Arnold represented himself and, for some reason, subjected the young girl who had taken James to the recreation ground to an intense cross-examination. The police evidence was damning, however, and included what amounted to his complete confession, so the case was sent to trial.

When the full trial began in October, this time Arnold was represented and pleaded not guilty; essentially citing lack of intent and an unsound mind. However, apart from seeming to suggest that his former employer was to blame (for sacking him) and his mother giving evidence that a bout of typhoid, when he was younger, had altered his personality for the worse, the evidence against him, in particular that from the police, including his confession, was overwhelming and it took the jury just twenty minutes to find him guilty of murder. They did, however, add a plea for mercy in view of the circumstances.

Despite acknowledging the plea and assuring the jury that it would be duly considered, the judge had little hesitation in sentencing Arnold to death. And if the plea were indeed taken any notice of at all, it must have been summarily dismissed, as on 12 November 1914 at Leicester Prison, Arnold Warren was duly hanged.

*

As 1915 got underway, reports of the war's progress were everywhere and continued to vary widely in accuracy. One of the biggest stories to hit the papers in May that year, however, was about the sinking of the passenger ship *Lusitania* by the German submarine U20 in the Celtic Sea off Southern Ireland.

At the turn of the twentieth century, work had begun on two large passenger ships for the Anglo-American Cunard Line: RMS *Lusitania* and her sister ship, RMS *Mauretania*. They were named after the two Roman provinces that are now Portugal and Northern Morocco/Algeria respectively and 'Mauretania' (spelt with an 'e') should not be confused with modern 'Mauritania' which is situated further south. *Lusitania* was built by John Brown & Co. on the Clyde and *Mauretania* by Swan Hunter on Tyneside. *Lusitania* was launched in May 1906 and was, at the time, the largest passenger liner in the world; however, when *Mauretania* slid into the Tyne the following September, she took the title and would keep it until 1911, when the yet larger British liner, RMS *Olympic*, was launched.

In order to fund the project, Cunard had secured a very advantageous deal with the British Government involving a substantial loan at a very good rate of interest, subsidies on future running costs and a very lucrative mail contract. The quid pro quo, however (and there always is one under such circumstances) was that, due to the mounting threat perceived from Germany, who were also building bigger and better ships, both *Lusitania* and *Mauretania* must be of such a design as to be easily converted into fully armed battleships, should the need arise.

By early 1915 the war at sea had already claimed many battleships on both sides, but the first British merchantman to go down was SS *Glitra*, which was boarded and scuttled by the crew of U-boat 17 off the Norwegian coast in October 1914. At this very early stage in the war, however, the Germans were still respecting the so-called 'Cruiser Rules' or 'Prize Rules' which harked back to the days of piracy. Essentially, they required that an unarmed merchantman be given warning before being attacked and that steps be taken to preserve life. In the *Glitra*'s case only fuel and materials were being transported and there were no passengers, but the crew were allowed to escape in lifeboats. Fortunately, they survived and were subsequently rescued by a neutral Norwegian naval vessel.

As far as British passenger ships were concerned, although *Lusitania* is the more renowned, she was not the first to be sunk by enemy action during World War I. Although a much smaller vessel than *Lusitania*, RMS *Falaba* had gone down just over a month before, also off the south coast of Ireland but a little further east, while on her way from Liverpool to West Africa. By then the Kaiser had declared the Channel and surrounding waters a war zone and, therefore, that any shipping from anywhere, found there, was 'fair game'. Nevertheless, a warning had been issued, but the commander of the U-boat then fired a torpedo before allowing anything like enough time to evacuate the ship. Having received a direct hit, the Falaba sank in minutes with the loss of over a hundred lives.

Yet another reason why the Germans began to ignore the Cruiser Rules may well have been the British realisation that these Rules could be manipulated in order to increase the vulnerability of German shipping, especially submarines, by the deployment of the so-called Q-ships. These were armed vessels masquerading as innocent passenger ships that could quickly reveal themselves and open fire once a belligerent vessel had been lured close enough and attentions had been turned towards issuing warnings etc.

In any event, the sinking of the *Falaba* had come very close to drawing the United States into the war, since one of the victims, Leon Thrasher, was a US citizen and he is, in fact, generally considered to be the first American to be killed during World War I. However, although America was initially outraged, the issue was to become somewhat clouded over arguments as to whether the rules were or were not correctly followed. Then, when it came to light that the

Falaba had been carrying a considerable quantity of high explosives, President Woodrow Wilson relented.

Lusitania, or 'Lucy' as she was affectionately known, set sail on one of her regular voyages from New York to Liverpool on the same day that Albert and Marion had married in Leicester; that bright May Day of 1915. She was one of the most luxurious liners of her time and, as the passengers boarded, the dockside was crowded with friends, relatives and onlookers cheering and waving their goodbyes. The event was filmed and, according to one reel, a passenger was apparently heard to say, "I will see this picture in London." Whether he ever did or not, I have absolutely no idea.

Before long *Lusitania* pulled out of New York harbour, with many on board who would never see dry land again enthusiastically waving. And that was the last that America would ever see of her too.

Due to the activities of German U-boats off the south coast of Ireland, not least the recent sinking of the *Falaba* there, the British authorities had issued warnings to avoid the area if at all possible. However, for some reason, Captain Turner chose to ignore them. It could have been because the voyage was running late as, although *Lusitania* was due to arrive in Liverpool on Thursday 6 May, on the bright early afternoon of Friday the 7th she was still only off the south coast of Ireland and this is where she first drew the attention of Walther Schwieger, the commander of U-boat 20. Due south of Cork, eleven miles off Kinsale, there was no warning given this time and a single torpedo was enough to take out one of *Lusitania's* boilers. This caused the ship to list heavily and meant that lifeboats could only be launched from one side. She was to sink within twenty minutes. Perhaps surprisingly, there are no exact figures, but only some 760 (including Captain Turner) out of the estimated total of around 1,960 passengers and crew on board, were spared.

Predictably the downright audacity of sinking a passenger liner like this caused public outrage, not only in Britain but around the world and, yet again, particularly within the United States, whose citizens had made up a significant proportion of those killed. The Germans argued vehemently that, not only had they made it crystal clear to all concerned that every kind of shipping in the Channel was open to their attack, but that *Lusitania* had been adapted for war service and was also carrying armaments for the war effort, which, in all fairness, she had and was. Afterwards, however, the Germans managed to make themselves look a bit foolish when they decided to cast a medallion commemorating the event. Not only did they get the date of *Lusitania*'s sinking wrong (the date of the sinking read, '5th May' rather than '7th May') but, rather than rousing German support as intended, it increased British recruitment and went on to be widely used as a propaganda tool aimed at encouraging the United States into the conflict alongside the Allies. Later that year, however, Germany appeared to change its policy yet again, by agreeing to respect neutrality and not to attack passenger ships without warning. If the truth be known, this decision was probably more out of a desire to ward off the American threat than through remorse, though, and it would be the best part of another two long years, by which time German attacks on merchant shipping had resurged, before America did enter the war. When she finally did, in April 1917, the straw that broke the camel's back was the so-called Zimmerman Telegram issued by the German Foreign Ministry, which proposed an alliance between Germany and Mexico and effectively encouraged Mexico to declare war on the US. Nevertheless, America would maintain that the sinking of the *Lusitania* had been part and parcel of her reasoning for going to war all along, especially as Germany, despite her assurances after the sinking, had repeatedly failed to live up to them. As for Mexico, in the event she did not declare war and would remain neutral throughout the conflict.

*

In Europe, by early 1915, thoughts were turning towards how to 'kick-start' the stalemate that was developing on the Western Front, prompting the then First Lord of the Admiralty, Winston Churchill, to consider attacking from another direction – the Dardanelles. This narrow strait directly connects the Mediterranean, via the Aegean Sea, to the Sea of Marmora and Istanbul (Constantinople – the capital of Ottoman Turkey as it then was). The idea was to take the Ottoman Empire out of the war by hitting it at its very heart and securing the sea route to the Russian Caucasus where the Turks were heavily engaged against the Russians.

The first naval bombardments began from a distance in February 1915 but, as the ships began to move in, as well as finding that the waters had been heavily mined, they came under blistering fire from the coast. As a result, by mid-March a significant number of ships had been lost. Nevertheless, in April British, French and ANZAC (Australia and New Zealand Army Corps) troops did manage to land on the Gallipoli Peninsula to the west of the strait, but it was then the difficult terrain that hindered progress. The Turks, occupying the higher ground, had the advantage of being able to fire down onto their invaders and despite their very brave efforts, heavy Allied losses were incurred. Although beachheads were established, the Allies were, of course, much less able to resupply and reinforce than the Turks and then, when summer came, the heat and insects (exacerbated by the rotting dead) became unbearable and started to spread disease. Although a further separate landing was made in early August which did progress for a time, sadly, the mess and confusion into which the invasion had sunk, had, by then, gone too far.

By the autumn, despite all the heroics and in the face of mounting losses, it started to become obvious that the offensive could not continue and in December the growing belief that it would be in the best interests of the Allies to pull out was finally accepted, despite the realisation that the withdrawal, in itself, was bound to incur a significant number of additional casualties.

Many would hold Churchill responsible for the disaster that Gallipoli was, not least Churchill himself who, as a result, decided to quit the Government in order to serve in person as a soldier in France. An old Roman saying resurrected by John F. Kennedy during the 'Bay of Pigs' crisis, probably sums up the situation best:

'Victory has a thousand fathers, but defeat is an orphan'.

In other words, defeat is a lonely place, particularly in politics, where popularity (if that's the right word), even by mere association, can make or break a career. But in all fairness, although the Government approved his plan, he was given neither the number of troops nor ships that he had asked for and anyway, when things went wrong, who else would be the obvious scapegoat? Would more troops and ships have made a difference?

Who knows? Not perfect (who is?), but we do know that Churchill returned to politics and there is little doubt, in my mind at least, that his leadership during the Second World War led, in no small part, to our conclusive victory in 1945.

*

Apart from obtaining some of his hospital records, I have not been anything like as successful in tracking my grandfather's war service as that of my great-uncles, Frank and Syd. I strongly suspect, as previously mentioned, that this is because many of his records were among those destroyed when the Arnside Street Repository in London was blitzed in 1940. What little I have managed to discover is that he was a machine gunner, and I understand that, after basic training, in late July 1915, while the Gallipoli Campaign was raging, he arrived in France and was initially stationed near Saint-Omer, about sixty-five miles south-east of Calais. It would be just under a year later, however, on the fields near to the River Somme that his very survival (and, consequently, my father's future life and indeed mine) would hang in the balance.

Back on the Messines Ridge, however, a pleasantly warm June was breaking and looking down from the hill, with a light breeze blowing through the trees, it was almost possible, if only for a moment, to forget that there was a war on. On such days, if one had some free time, stopping by at Tina's tea shop in Bailleul, by all accounts, was a very nice way to spend it. Something of a legend in its time, pitted and cratered all around as a result of the shelling, the flower garden there was said to be like an 'oasis in the desert'. Everybody was made to feel quite at home and, perhaps allowing for the modicum of licence that war necessitates, great effort went into serving tea 'British style' and 'with all the trimmings'.

Very pretty and friendly, Tina was known affectionately to the troops as 'little sister' and considering that she was only a teenager at the time, her resilience under the circumstances seems to have been remarkable. So it must have been sad for her, each time she lost yet another of the many friends she had made, to the war. And what happened to her in 1918, when the tide turned and Bailleul was overrun by the Germans, is unclear. There were rumours that she may have been captured as a spy and even shot as one, but nobody really seems to know. I sincerely hope not and wish that she (as they say) 'lived happily ever after' because there can be no doubt that she deserved to.

Syd, at least, had other things on his mind, as he had been given five days' leave, allowing him just enough time to get back home for two or three days. It was both a time of rest and a time to catch up on things. He was shocked to hear that Flo's husband, Sam, had gone AWOL and had been briefly detained in prison as a result. Naturally everyone wanted to know how things were going at the front and there would have been no shortage of advice and political criticism about how the war was being prosecuted. At times, no doubt like Paul Bäumer in *All Quiet on the Western Front*, this rhetoric would become so preposterous and over-simplistic that Syd must have just had to let it 'wash over him'. Nevertheless, he would have been glad to be home again, if only for a short time, as were Richard, Louisa, Flo, Doll and all the other members of the family and friends to see him. The problem with short periods of leave, though, is that, before long, you have to go back and the pain of saying goodbye again comes around all too soon. To the family it must have seemed that, although he was now leaving, Syd had only just arrived. It was a heavy-hearted Richard, with Louisa by his side, trying desperately to hold back her tears, who stood waving as the train pulled out of the station to take their son away from them again, back to that dreadful turmoil!

As the warm summer progressed, soldiering on the Ridge became a comparatively 'steady job'. A sort of equilibrium had developed and, perhaps as some sort of acknowledgement of the warm, fine weather, the German line was now adorned by a gaily coloured parapet. The continual necessity to venture into no man's land for observational purposes could still be a bit 'hairy', though. The sudden brightness of a Very light as it started to burn and fall, seemingly slowly, from the sky meant that if you didn't dive quickly to the ground there was a very real risk of you being caught in the sights of a sniper's rifle. And it was not only the sights of a German sniper's rifle, either. Being silhouetted against the glow could also attract fire from your own side on account of the shooter being unsure as to exactly who you were or what you were doing. It remained a sad fact that a number of soldiers would be wounded or killed in this way, rather than by the enemy. Also, as may well be the case in peacetime too, even mere day-to-day routines can be dangerous, especially when dealing with explosives, as witness Lt. Brice who was killed around this time when a type of grenade that he was demonstrating unexpectedly went off.

This relative calm just couldn't last, though, and with the heavy fighting at Ypres, which was not far away, it did not take a genius to work out where they were likely to be headed next. And so it was that on 18 June (the hundredth anniversary of that famous Battle at Waterloo which had taken place only some seventy miles to the east of them) the 4th Battalion were on the move again. Then, of course, the shoe had been on the other foot, with the British fighting alongside the Prussians against the French! What a difference a hundred years can make.

The very name Ypres, or 'Wipers' as the Tommies called it, with its much-targeted Cloth Hall, has become emblematic of the futility of World War I. The medieval town had been a pinch point from the very start, when the British and French had met with the invading German Army and stemmed its progress there in the earliest stages of the war. And then it was to become the focus of continued bitter campaigns throughout the duration of the conflict with the result that very little, if anything, was left of the town by 1918. Today the Menin Gate Memorial, which bears the names of almost 55,000 dead, stands witness to that bloodiest of times. On it is inscribed '*Pro Patria*', though I'm not sure that Wilfred Owen would see the logic.

First, though, there was further training at Ouderdom, to the north of Kemmel, including instruction on hand-to-hand fighting which would, no doubt, have done nothing to ease the apprehension over what was to come. The weather was gloriously hot to begin with and, although a torrential storm later flooded the camp, the period spent here would remain a relatively easy one. Quite convivially there was a nice little *estaminet* just down the road called '*Les Trois Amis*' where, as the weather improved, there might well have been a moment or two to sit in the garden and enjoy a refreshing glass of (what passed for) beer or perhaps even a glass (or more) of 'plonk'. To those perhaps inclined to 'over relax', however, the occasional shelling and the sounds of heavy artillery in the distance would remain constant reminders of reality. That caveat was poignantly brought home when a bandleader, Sgt. Stevenson, tuned up one day along with other reinforcements. Apparently, he was a cheery old chap who had raised many a spirit in his time. It was a sad affair indeed then, when, only shortly afterwards, he was killed by shellfire.

The evening of the 29th of June saw the Battalion march off down the dusty Kruisstaat road that led past Zillebeke Lake, in sight of the infamous Hill 60, to Sanctuary Wood south-east of Ypres, where they relieved the Sherwood Foresters. The Wood had been heavily cratered as a result of intense shelling which made the contrast to Kemmel immediately obvious from the start. Five would be killed and twelve injured before the Leicesters were relieved by the Staffords a week later. Mournful and exhausted, they marched back to Ouderdom in groups. Grub up and then a slug of something, once settled, most were soon fast off.

Exhaustion, at the best of times, is a wretched feeling and can render sufferers totally incapable. We have all heard stories of soldiers 'sleeping while marching'. I personally can't imagine how this works, save to say that, on rare occasions, I have been so tired as to have entered a sort of trance-like state myself. So much so that I sometimes cannot remember what I have done when so affected. (Not always through drink, I hasten to add.) Whereas, in ordinary life, these incapacities may be fleeting and fairly inconsequential, at the front, if not taken into account, can lead to disaster. In Ouderdom that day the leadership must have been good as the men were given six days' rest. There was to be no 'lazing about', however, and parades and drills continued, a support line was dug and even a route march was thrown in for good measure. Nevertheless spirits were raised and, above all, you were away from the fighting.

As with all good things, though, this period came to an end when the Battalion was called upon to relieve the 1st Dorsets on the 13th of July. This time the job was to guard the railway line to Comines, between Kruisstaat and Zillebeke Lake. They were told to keep as low a profile as possible, the Germans having not, as yet, seen fit to focus much of their attention here. As a result, the task turned out to be a fairly perfunctory one, with only the occasional shell or whizz-bang to dodge. Nevertheless, it was a dangerous place to be, especially since one end of the railway line ran towards the enemy line and the whole area was overlooked by the Germans from Hill 60 – a mound created when the line had been excavated. The extent of this exposure would be brought home a few days later when Lt. Frank Tarr, a very popular officer, was killed by the shrapnel from an all too accurately targeted bomb.

On the 19th of July the 4th Leicesters were moved again, not far though, but certainly not for the better, as this time they found themselves alongside the 5th Leicesters in trenches directly facing Hill 60. The area had been heavily laced with underground mines laid by both sides, and on the early evening of the 23rd the British succeeded in blowing up part of the German line, with subsequent very accurate artillery fire finishing off many a Boche not killed by the explosion. In retaliation, however, later that evening, the Germans detonated a mine under the 5th Leicesters' section. The 4ths immediately went to their aid but the scene was one of carnage and both the 4ths and 5ths spent the rest of the night digging out the dead and wounded under heavy fire. With the injured evacuated, work began over the following two nights to reinforce the badly damaged part of the trench. They were hindered by bright moonlight, though, and a mortar delivered from the German line found its way and cost yet another life whilst leaving another soldier wounded.

At the end of July the 4th Leicesters were back in the dugouts near Zillebeke Lake when, just to the north-east of them, at Hooge, the Germans broke through part of the British line using flamethrowers. Still never having been in direct face-to-face combat, they must have thought that this was it when they were suddenly ordered to stand to with a view to reinforcing the line there. Although the crack was jocular and upbeat that summer's night, under the surface, tensions must have been raised, even more so when they readied to march and could see both the flashes and hear the noise of the battle that raged in front of them. But they need not have worried because, just as they were about to set off, the flashes slowly subsided and the noise died down. At the very last minute they were stood down and instead of marching into hell, they were able to slope back to the comparative luxury of the dugouts. For that night, at least, they were out of it but not for much longer.

Chapter 10

Into the Fray

'Dulce et decorum est
Pro patria mori'.

Horace (Odes III.2.13) and
Wilfred Owen's 'old lie'

As with fleas, the human body louse (*Pediculus humanus humanus* or *P. h. corporis*) can turn up wherever large numbers of people are in close contact in dirty conditions, so how it must have loved the trenches of the Western Front and indeed, few soldiers there would have escaped its attention. Attracted by body heat, the adult lice bite into the skin and feed on blood. At first the damaged skin becomes irritated with a red, raised rash that starts to itch intensely and then, with time, starts to thicken and darken.

Once a colony infests the body the females lay their eggs (or 'nits') inside trouser waistbands and seams, etc. The eggs are often referred to as 'crumbs' because they resemble breadcrumbs at a glance and, like the term 'lousy' – literally meaning 'infested with lice' but also meaning 'something that is no good', 'crummy' (or 'crumby'), a term probably less used today but similar in meaning – also comes from the louse infestations of the trenches. Thus, the tedious act of picking out lice eggs, immatures and adults, one by one from clothing, was dubbed, 'crumming' (or 'crumbing').

Another common army slang word used for being infested with lice was 'cooty'. Not of Scottish origin, as you may have first thought, but more likely from the Malay word '*kutu*' for 'lice' or bugs in general – most probably passed on from service undertaken down the years in the Far East.

The adult lice were called 'chats' and so the act of getting rid of them was 'chatting'. Improvised methods included running a candle flame quickly along infested seams, soaking clothes in naphthalene or even, when possible, boiling them. These methods all afforded some temporary respite but, as more eggs hatched, the infestation would very soon return.

The classic chemical treatment was known as 'Keating's Powder': a preparation made from ground-up chrysanthemum flowers which contain the natural insecticides, pyrethrins. The preparation was originally called 'Persian Powder' as the first extracts were produced from certain species of chrysanthemums native to Persia (modern-day Iran) which are particularly strong in pyrethrins. Pyrethrins make efficient and relatively safe treatments because the doses effective against lice are unlikely to affect humans. Because of their efficacy many artificial derivatives known as 'pyrethroids' have since been synthesised; essentially they all work by interfering with the normal functioning of the insects' nervous systems.

At less than a millimetre long, the tiny eggs have a light, shiny hue but, hidden in the folds of uniforms, can remain unnoticed until they emerge as nymphs (immatures) and start to infest the waist and groin areas of the body. The nymphs turn into adults within a few days and the females then lay more eggs, either on the same host or after having crawled onto somebody else nearby. Thus their life cycle is completed, while at the same time spreading the infestation together with all the infections that lice may carry.

The immature nymphs are slightly smaller than the adults but can still be seen with the naked eye. The adults, like the nymphs, are light brown in colour and, at three to four millimetres long, are quite easy to spot. They are significantly thinner and longer than adults of the sexually transmitted pubic lice and, although both species are insects, pubic lice are somewhat more crustacean-like in appearance, hence the term, 'having a dose of the crabs', being often attributed to those infected with pubic lice.

As well as causing generalised irritation, the infections that body lice can carry include: *Bartonella* (formerly *Rochalimaea* or *Rickettsia*... those taxonomists!) *quintana* which causes trench fever, along with other *Rickettsia* spp. which can cause typhus (jail fever) and *Borrelia* spp. which can cause 'relapsing fever'. (As the name would suggest, this condition can recur many times after the initial symptoms have apparently subsided.) Some also believe that lice can spread bubonic plague.

Not to be confused with 'trench foot'; a non-communicable foot rot that arises through prolonged exposure of the feet to the damp, dirty, cold conditions of a trench. Trench fever is more prevalent in warmer climates, and so was more likely the further south along the line you were. However, many cases were to arise along the entire length of the front as the war progressed. Sufferers initially present with a flu-like illness and, because the association with lice was not fully appreciated at the time, the first reported cases tended to be met with some scepticism as to whether they were real illnesses or just malingering. Although not usually fatal, the effects of a serious louse-borne infection can be quite debilitating but the paucity of scientific knowledge and understanding of all the possible health consequences back then meant that the Army could do little, if anything, to tackle the problem. Nowadays such infections are easily treated with antibiotics but, of course, there was no such thing in 1915 and nor would there be until several years after the war had ended. Even then it would take until the Second World War before they were widely available, when there is little doubt that they saved a great number of lives in that conflict that would probably have been lost if similarly affected during World War I.

But even where lice infestations do not give rise to infections the profound irritation and itching that they can cause provoke a constant desire to scratch which, in turn, creates more irritation and damage to the skin and things just get worse and worse. In some cases, it could only take the putrid, stale smell that results from all this, especially in the confined space of a trench and in the face of everything else that was going on, to make life unbearable.

*

After a month in the dugouts, it was hardly surprising then, that when Frank, Syd and the rest of the 4th Leicesters arrived back at Ouderdom, as well as being exhausted, with blistered feet, they were also well and truly 'lousy'. Even though they had not yet 'gone over the top' they certainly were, by this point, battle-weary. Having lost comrades to the shelling and sniping and been on iron rations of just bully beef and biscuits, these infestations had only served to make matters worse. Nevertheless, the rest could only do them good, or so they thought…

Throughout the remainder of August and most of September the 4ths continued to cover the support trenches near Hill 60. Some of the time it would be relatively quiet but, from time to time, flare-ups would arise on one side or the other. On occasions a 'sausage bomb' would hurtle over; these lethal concoctions of the Devil were about three feet long and would spin about in the air before exploding loudly on impact with the ground, leaving anybody in the vicinity riddled with deadly fragments.

In contrast the weather turned gracefully autumnal and, as if mimicking the way of all flesh, the sunsets, pink at first, gradually turned blood red before the descent of the dark night. Neither the sausage bombs nor the sunsets affected Frank during August, though, as he had been granted a month's leave. As with Syd, a month or two before, Richard, Louisa and all his family and friends were as delighted to see him again as Frank was to see them. If truth be known, Frank had needed this relatively long break from the front for some time as, by now, the pressure was really starting to tell on him. In fact, he had worried his senior officers so much that he had been offered a posting behind the lines which, at first, he had almost been tempted to accept. Having adjusted well during his leave, however, when the time came to go back, Frank was determined that he would return to the firing line. Furthermore, following the 'sweet sorrow' of leaving once more for the front and the long journey back, Frank so impressed his seniors with his renewed courage and determination that he was made up to acting sergeant. Shortly afterwards Syd, who was now an experienced signaller, was promoted too – to lance corporal. Now both were NCOs and equally proud to be.

Regardless, from a general perspective the situation at the front was not getting any easier. With the war now entering its second year, a political standpoint began to emerge that something really needed to be done to break the stalemate that had developed. As a result, during September the levels of shelling and attacks on both sides were heightened. Predictably, this was to raise the death toll significantly, not least due to a failed assault on the Germans at nearby Bellewaerde. Also, the 4th Leicesters began to hear the first rumblings of something going on some distance to the south and, although they would not yet have realised it, they were shortly to become much more acquainted with these rumblings. The reality was that they were destined to get very up close and personal with what was to be the first major set piece battle of the Great War.

On 26 September, at first thankful to be relieved by the 5th Lincolns, the 4ths were just preparing to pull out when shelling and rifle fire, from the German side, suddenly flared up. For a while, they were uncertain as to whether they might have to stay and lend a hand. But fortuitously, just as at Zillebeke two months earlier, every bit as quickly as things had escalated, they began to quieten and the feared follow-through attack never materialised. So, by the evening the Battalion was yet again able to wind down to the prospect of another 'six-dayer', this time in a place known as the Dickebusch Huts – about halfway between Kruisstaat and Ouderdom. Fair to say not quite as far back from the line as before, but still just far enough west to be away from the thick of it, thank God.

Wednesday 1 September had been Syd's 19th birthday but the conditions he was under meant that there would be little time for celebration. Frank had made a point of coming over to congratulate his brother, which turned into a bit of a chat over a mug of tea about how everyone was, what might or might not be going on at home and what they might all do as and when they got back. Although (no doubt deliberately) the conversation did not extend to what their immediate futures might hold, there was now little doubt that the previous week's increases in the rumblings to the south were down to the rumoured escalations at Loos. This, and with all leave cancelled, in the back of their minds they must have been pretty sure that Loos was where the 4th Leicesters would be bound for next.

The following day General Allenby arrived to discuss tactics with the commanding officer, Col. Martin, and early on the wet afternoon of 2 October the Battalion set out to march to Abele, some twelve miles or so westwards, on the Belgian border, where they boarded a southbound train back into France. In John Milne's excellent book, *Footprints of the 1/4th Leicestershire Regiment*, it says that the train was bound for 'Fonquevillers, near Bethune' but I am left wondering whether this is a mistranscription of 'Fouquereuil'. The reason being that this similar-sounding venue is next to Bethune, whereas Fonquevillers is getting on for thirty miles south of it – the other side of Arras, in fact. As Fouquereuil does have a station and the passage goes on to say that the Battalion was billeted at Gonnehem that night, which is just to the north of Fouquereuil, I think that this can be the only explanation.

Whatever, it must now have been clear to all concerned that the eruptions at Loos were where they were headed next.

*

Although the first recorded instance of the use of poison as a weapon of war dates back to ancient Greece, when the water supply to the besieged city of Kirrha (Kirra or Chirra) was deliberately adulterated with poisonous plants, the use of chlorine gas in such a way was not seriously considered until the American Civil War of the early 1860s. Despite the various treaties that followed, designed to prevent chemical warfare – principally the Hague Convention – sadly World War I was infamously to become the first major conflict to incorporate its use.

Deployed by the French virtually from the start of the war, tear gas had been developed shortly before, in order to control riots etc. Unsurprisingly, the Germans soon began to retaliate, at first with tear gas against the Russians in January 1915, and then with halogen-based gases. Their first use of pure chlorine was against the French at Gravenstafel Ridge at the start of the Second Battle of Ypres on 22 April 1915. Its effectiveness soon became clear as large numbers of casualties began to writhe, blindly choking and spluttering, as the greenish-yellow cloud of gas drifted over them, many of whom died as a result.

The proponent of chlorine gas production in Germany, and indeed, often referred to as 'The Father of Chemical Warfare', was Fritz Haber, the chemist who had also developed the Haber process (or Haber-Bosch Process, to give its co-creator, Carl Bosch, his due), an efficient way of producing ammonia; a major component of artificial fertilisers. This development would significantly increase food production worldwide and lead to Haber receiving the Noble Prize for Chemistry in 1918. There was a sort of double paradox to all this, however, as firstly, ammonia is also a common ingredient of explosives and secondly, Haber was Jewish. Nevertheless, he was, as were many German Jews of the time, a staunch supporter of the Great War and was prepared to do his best to help it succeed.

Chlorine gas is produced by the Castner-Kellner process; essentially the electrolysis of (introducing an electric current to) brine which releases the chlorine as gas (Cl_2) from the salt (sodium chloride – NaCl) in the solution. Hydrogen gas (H_2) and caustic soda (or sodium hydroxide – NaOH) are also produced by the process. Alternatively, potassium chloride (KCl) solution may be used which would give caustic potash (or potassium hydroxide – KOH) instead of caustic soda. The method was developed by the American chemist, Hamilton Castner, and his Austrian business partner, Carl Kellner, in the 1890s, following which they began its commercial production in the UK at their plant near Runcorn, Cheshire in the mid-1900s.

Chlorine serves many beneficial functions, including its use in industrial processes, medical treatments, and sanitation. The most obvious is probably its addition to swimming pool water in order to prevent the transmission of disease through communal bathing and, in so doing, giving rise to that 'bleachy' smell that comes from the chlorine reacting with fluids on the surface of the skin. But it is also a deadly poison and, being a gas at normal temperatures, can easily be dispatched towards the enemy by its release into an airstream moving in the right direction. Once enveloped, a victim finds it impossible to avoid breathing it in, instilling it through the eyes and even ingesting it. Almost instantly the gas reacts with bodily fluids forming acids to which the body responds by producing yet more fluid, presumably in an attempt to dilute the acids to more acceptable levels. Thus the lungs fill with liquid (pulmonary oedema), severely affecting breathing, acidic tears irritate the eyes and irritation in the gut leads to stomach ache and resultant vomiting and diarrhoea, often containing blood. The skin blisters and, in high concentrations, chlorine can also be absorbed directly through the skin, affecting blood flow and causing yet more widespread damage to the general physiology. There is no antidote, and the only treatment is to get anyone affected as far away from the gas as possible and support their breathing. Much easier said than done in a war scenario but continued exposure is very likely to lead to what must be a very painful death.

Even where those affected survive, the damage done can often be permanent. People of my age may still recall from childhood old men who had been gassed during the First World War and who still seemed to have difficulty breathing some fifty years later!

Since the consequences of chemical warfare are so barbaric, it was initially considered that such forms of weaponry would never be deployed, but of course they were, giving rise to the need for some sort of protection. The first gas masks were developed by the Scottish doctor John Scott Haldane, which, although better than nothing at all, it is probably fair to say, were pretty basic. Consisting simply of a cloth surround with transparent eyepieces that were prone to misting up, they contained cotton wool soaked in sodium thiosulphate ($Na_2S_2O_3$) which reacts with chlorine and neutralises it. However, if these first masks were a bit crude, they were at least an improvement on the ad hoc procedure that went before. In the early days, as word of a gas attack went around, anybody likely to be affected would often urinate onto a handkerchief or cap and then hold the soaked item over their face. Although only affording minimal protection, if any at all, there was something to it since urine contains ammonia (NH_3) which can react with chlorine (Cl_2) to produce ammonium chloride (NH_4Cl) which is relatively harmless, along with nitrogen. The production of small vials of ammonia would later provide for a more hygienic variation on this method, although anybody who has ever inhaled ammonia will tell you that that, in itself, is not a particularly pleasant experience.

As the war progressed, other more lethal substances would be used as weapons, including cyanide, phosgene, and the dreaded mustard gas, to devastating effect. The number of casualties, as a result of these more potent chemicals, from July 1917 until the Armistice, far outweighing the number of those affected during the entire previous part of the war.

After 1918, when the full horror of employing these terrible tactics had been fully realised, efforts were redoubled to try to ban the use of chemical weaponry and with some measure of success, since none was used on European battlefields during World War II. Sadly, however, it did not prevent their use by the Germans in the cruel mass murder of the Jews during the Holocaust and even today, their continued use by some despotic regimes against their perceived 'enemies'. Although it is an absolute certainty that there will come a day when man will no longer use chemical weapons, I can only hope that it dawns before the human race itself is gone.

The Battle of Loos was part of a combined British and French attempt to break though the enemy line and cut the Germans off in Northern France and, although a previous attempt to take the town during May 1915 had failed, this time it was hoped that things would be different. So, with this in mind, it began with several days of intense bombardment, mainly by the standard British Army eighteen-pounder heavy artillery, along with aerial bombardments. As well as breaking up much of the barbed wire, this wreaked serious disruption on the enemy's trenches. Also redoubts and observation points were destroyed and many buildings were significantly damaged. Then, early on 25 September, the infantry assault began. It was to be the first time that the British, themselves, had deployed the poison gas chlorine as a weapon of war, Haig apparently fearing that the offensive would surely fail without it. Even so, it turned out to be quite an exercise in logistics and tied up a large contingent of men in order to put in place the 5,500 canisters containing the 150 tons or so of chlorine considered sufficient enough to be effective. Unfortunately, probably due to lack of experience, it turned into something of a fiasco. At first, when the gas was released early that morning, it drifted as planned towards the German lines, but then the wind changed and blew the cloud back again. Over 2,500 attacking British soldiers were left choking in the fumes and many who emerged from the fog were immediately gunned down by the Germans. Also, some cylinders started to leak and since, in addition to being poisonous, chlorine gas is corrosive to gun metals especially in damp conditions, it was feared that the ability to fire on the enemy might be compromised. Despite a high casualty rate, the British did make something of a breakthrough and within about ninety minutes, the town of Loos itself was secured. Sadly, however, the cost was high and, due to a lack of reinforcements and a shortage of ordnance, the attack could not be properly followed through. It was simply yet another direct result of the shortage of men and materiel that was beginning to tell as the war entered its second year, exacerbated not least by the extra pull that the Gallipoli Campaign had placed on resources. That same day, a little further up the line, the 9th Scottish Division was decimated trying to take the notorious Hohenzollern Redoubt. In this case, subsequent analysis generally concluded that poor military planning was to blame and that, had the initial assault been more successful, the future course of the war may well have been very different. Nevertheless, the Redoubt was taken the following day, but it would not remain in British hands for long.

A redoubt is a built-up fortification generally protruding towards the enemy that forms a hub of defence along a battlefront. Both the Allies and the Germans built them, their purpose being to allow snipers, bombers and machine gunners a wide overview of the enemy line, enabling them to react swiftly to an attack, not only one directly towards them but also oblique approaches, from either side. Although the area was dotted with other redoubts, naming this particular one after the German Royal family – the Kaiser's surname, I presume, was intended to inject its threatening profile yet further into the psyche and it was generally considered to be one of the strongest fortifications of its type. Located a mile or so due south of Auchy-les-Mines (known at the time as Auchy-lez-La-Bassée), a small mining village in the Pas-de-Calais *département* of France and about three miles due north of Loos-en-Gohelle itself, its prime purpose was to guard a strategic high mound of coal slag (or *crassier*) known as 'The Dump' as part of the measures to reinforce the Western Front ordered by General von Falkenhayn in early 1915. In comparison to what it must have looked like during the war, though, standing there now, as I have, you could be forgiven for doubting that the Hohenzollern Redoubt ever existed. Today it is simply a small mound surrounded by farmers' fields where only a slightly higher frequency of chalky fragments betrays its dark past.

Although Frank and Syd may not have initially appreciated that this redoubt was the very reason why they were being moved, firstly to Gonnehem, near Béthune and then just down the road to Hesdigneul in early October, for further intensive training and practice in the skills of warfare, then they soon would. As the preparations unfolded so did the realisation that this time there was to be little, if any, doubt about it. They had been selected to do a job and they were about to 'go over the top'.

On Tuesday 12 October the Battalion marched east to Vermelles and as they passed the men coming out of the trenches and asked, "What's it like up there?" the response was at least consistent: "Bloody awful!", or words to that effect. Having been fed and watered en route, at Sailly-Labourse, when they reached the front they relieved the Guards just to the south-west of Auchy and the Hohenzollern Redoubt. All along the way and into that evening Frank and Syd had chatted as and when they could. Although it is fair to say that they must have been apprehensive after coming so far, could there yet have been some small spark of excitement to it as well? After all, this was what they had volunteered for and what their training had been all about. Would it all work out? Would they be heroes? Maybe just to survive would be enough… but for now, there were letters home to write.

*

Earlier that very day a forty-nine-year-old dedicated British nurse had been hauled before a German firing squad on a rifle range on the eastern outskirts of Brussels and executed, on the basis that she had assisted Allied soldiers to escape.

Born in 1865, Edith Cavell was the eldest child of an East Anglican clergyman and (no doubt encouraged by her father, who is said to have had something of a pious reputation) had started her working life as a governess. Quite popular at the time, the job entailed caring for and teaching the children of well-to-do families and, in Edith's case, included a period of several years looking after the children of a Belgian lawyer in Brussels. In 1895, Edith's father became quite seriously ill and she returned home for a brief while in order to care for him. He survived the ordeal and, possibly as a result of this experience, she subsequently applied for and was accepted as a nursing assistant at the Fountain Fever Hospital in London. By this time, though, she had turned thirty and so was perhaps then, as now, a little older than the average age for embarking on such a career.

Eager to progress, Edith then applied for and was accepted as a student nurse at Tredegar House – the London Hospital's innovative nurse training school of the time, created and run by Matron Eva Lückes, who was a friend and great follower of the ways of the legendary Florence Nightingale. During the years that followed, through sheer hard work and devotion, and in spite of the many medical challenges thrown up at the end of the nineteenth century, Edith qualified, and in her subsequent career went on to devote herself unswervingly to the care of others.

In early 1901 she took up the position of night superintendent at the St. Pancras Hospital. Operating under the Poor Law, with limited staff, it proved even more demanding, and was said to have tested even Edith's capacity to the limit. Nevertheless, she stuck at it for almost three years before acquiring the post of assistant matron at Shoreditch Infirmary (later St. Leonard's Hospital). Here she became involved in the teaching of student nurses and made several applications for the position of matron, all sadly unsuccessful.

By 1906 Edith was exhausted and needed to rest. After a long holiday she returned briefly to her childhood home at Swardeston, near Norwich, before taking up a position in Manchester. Here, at what was known as the Queens District Home, when the matron fell ill, Edith agreed to stand in for her, at the same time continuing both to teach her student nurses and pursue her search for a post as full-time matron in her own right.

The search was to prove fruitful as, within a year or so, Edith was introduced to the eminent Brussels surgeon, Dr. Antoine Depage, by the Belgian lawyer to whose children she had previously been governess. Depage was in the process of setting up a nursing school and had been impressed to hear about Edith's qualities, her training as a nurse and how she had 'risen through the ranks'. Since she was also fluent in French, the surgeon grew as eager to take her on as she was to accept, and so Edith came to be put in charge of L'Ecole Belge d'Infirmières Diplômée (The Belgian Graduate Nursing School). Part of the Berkendael Medical Institute, it was situated on Rue de la Culture (now Rue Franz Merjay) in the Ixelles district of Brussels. Here Edith was soon to realise that the ways of nursing in Belgium were well behind those of the time in Britain, in particular regarding hygiene. The relationship between 'asepsis' as it is known (the removal of infective agents such as bacteria) and recovery, obviously not, there and then, so clearly understood. The improvement of cleanliness, that most 'matronly' of endeavours, must have worked wonders, though, because her esteem and respect continued to flourish in the eyes of her colleagues, especially in those of her students, and she was said to have taken standards to an exemplary level.

In 1910 a large new hospital was opened in the neighbouring St. Gilles district of Brussels and Edith would become its first matron. By now the number of student nurses under her supervision had risen greatly and with the extra resources that the new hospital afforded, Edith's influence had reached its zenith. By 1912 plans were in place for yet more new premises to be built just to the south in the Rue de Bruxelles (now Rue Edith Cavell). This later became the Edith Cavell Clinic which stands there to this day. Additionally, her name lives on in an even wider form within the 'CHIREC' (Centre Hospitalier Interrégional Edith Cavell) group of hospitals located in various parts of Belgium, of which the Edith Cavell Clinic in Brussels is just one.

In August 1914, when Belgium was invaded, Edith was on holiday back in Norwich, but she returned immediately to the Institute on hearing the news, and on the 20th of August she describes in the *Nursing Mirror* how the Germans marched into Brussels 'with much pomp and circumstance of war'. Although she could have been repatriated under a scheme negotiated by the American representatives, Edith, together with many other British nurses, chose to stay. At first there was not a great deal to do, but from the way the German invaders were behaving and the inevitable battles to come, there would soon be a steady supply of injured to be treated and Edith ensured that all, regardless of nationality or allegiance, would receive the best care possible.

November, however, saw the first in a series of events that would carry with them catastrophic consequences, when two wounded British soldiers retreating from Mons, Lt. Col. Dudley Boger and Sgt. Frederick Meachin, turned up at the hospital in civilian clothes. After being admitted and treated, Edith then arranged for their escape to neutral Holland. Although Boger was captured, Meachin got away and in so doing, established 'a route home' along which so many more would follow.

As the occupation continued, this 'route' was consolidated through a network of facilitators covertly headed by the influential Belgian aristocrat, Prince Reginald de Croy and, unfortunately, Edith's connection to the syndicate began to get noticed by the Germans. She did herself no favours either when writing to her cousin in early 1915 that, although she was not overworked, 'I am helping in ways I may not describe here'. Then, in addition to the regular, unannounced searches of the hospital, a group of 'workmen' appeared just in front of the building. Although ostensibly there to attend to the road surface, in practice they seemed to be achieving very little in that respect, instead showing a great deal more interest in the daily comings and goings at the hospital.

It finally became obvious that the Germans had strong suspicions about what was going on when a stranger (believed to be Georges Gaston Quien) turned up at the hospital claiming to be a French intelligence agent but who was almost certainly spying on behalf of the Germans. Although the hospital's initial response was to send him away and report him to the German Authorities, the surveillance continued until the end of July 1915 when the leader of the escape network, Philippe Baucq, was arrested. Edith herself was then arrested a few days later.

After the war the so-called French agent, Quien, was arrested in France and tried as a collaborator. Initially sentenced to death, on appeal he managed to convince the Public Prosecutor that it was not he who had betrayed Edith and, although his death sentence was withdrawn, he was still sentenced to twenty years in prison on other counts. Despite hardly anyone ever believing him, he continued throughout his life to protest his innocence.

During her interrogation the Germans tricked Edith by saying that they knew everything and that she could only save her friends by co-operating fully. Edith took this at face value and, believing that she was merely confirming what was already known, confessed to assisting the escape of Allied prisoners, unwittingly mentioning many of her associates in the matter by name.

On 10 August Edith was thrown into a squalid cell at St. Gilles Prison, only a stone's throw from the Berkendael Institute, along with other members of her network, while awaiting trial for 'war treason'. She was allowed pastoral visits and some contact and advice through the offices of the American Legation who continued to do their very best throughout to help her. Meanwhile there was a heartfelt appeal lodged by a group of fellow nurses to the German Governor General. But, despite all this, on 7 October 1915, the case was put before a German military tribunal and Edith was effectively court-martialled.

At the time it was quite common for nurses to wear their uniforms when off duty but Edith chose to wear civilian clothes while giving evidence. It has been suggested that, in so doing, even under such dire circumstances, she was keen not to be seen as currying any possible sympathetic advantage that the wearing of her uniform may have carried. Although she was obviously under pressure, her evidence was delivered clearly and she admitted unequivocally to assisting some 200 escapees, adding that it was purely and simply in order to save their lives. Had she not, she reasoned, they would almost certainly have been shot.

It has strongly been suggested since, that the number was an underestimation and that as many as 1,000 may have benefited by her actions.

After the trial the members of the court martial retired to decide the verdict and sentence in private. But, in view of the admissions and all the attention that Edith's case had drawn, there was now little doubt that, in line with all the other brutal acts that they had inflicted on Belgium, the Germans were determined to make her an example to others who might be contemplating doing the same. That verdict and sentence were arrived at on 9 October but Edith was not informed until two days later. Despite some of the accused being sent to prison, Edith and several others, including Baucq, considered the 'ringleaders', were condemned to death.

Now resigned to her fate, Edith refused to appeal, turning her attention instead to preparing final farewell letters in which she declared her love and devotion to her fellow nurses.

Under pressure to conclude things, the Germans wasted no time and early on the morning of Tuesday 12 October 1915 Edith was fetched from St. Gilles Prison to the Tir National Rifle Range on the other side of Brussels where, at 7am, dignified to the end, she was summarily executed, alongside Baucq.

Initially buried nearby, Edith's remains were brought back to England shortly after the war had ended and, following an elaborate ceremony at Westminster Abbey, she was finally laid to rest in the grounds of Norwich Cathedral.

Although technically, in protecting their interests, the Germans clearly had a case against Edith Cavell, the execution of a dedicated nurse was always going to attract criticism. And it did, not only in Britain and Belgium but around the world, not least with the Americans, whose dismay was palpable after having done so much to help her. Although immeasurable, this affair must also have had some bearing on their decision to join the Allied war effort some eighteen months later. It also served to re-emphasise the cause of the Suffragette Movement that had been 'put on hold' in Britain for the duration, as a clear demonstration to people of just how brave and courageous a woman could be. Even the Kaiser was so moved as to declare that no more women were to be executed without his say-so.

Among the many memorials to this great woman stands a raised statue in St. Martin's Place, London, beneath which are inscribed the poignant words she used after realising that her fate was sealed. After all that she had endured, they stand as an exemplar to all:

'PATRIOTISM IS NOT ENOUGH
I MUST HAVE NO HATRED OR
BITTERNESS FOR ANYONE'

*

Because it was the date of the first organised assault of the Battle of Loos, Saturday 25 September is obviously taken as its start date. For some reason or other though, the date it is considered to have ended differs widely in different accounts. I have heard the Battle of Loos being alluded to as 'the Forgotten Battle' so maybe this has some bearing on things, but some accounts have it ending as early as 28 September, whilst others as late as 19 October. I must confess that I am not at all sure why this should be so, and certainly understand even less why some accounts do not regard the assault on the Hohenzollern Redoubt of 13 October as part of the Battle at all. Perhaps it could just be because the Redoubt was a 'bit up the road' from Loos. With this in mind, in his excellent book, *The Battle of Loos*, Philip Warner, on his map labelled 'Loos 1915; the Stages of the Battle', cites the period from 25 September to 14 October. Furthermore, the account of the Battle, under 'The Long, Long Trail' on the Internet, takes it to the 19th of October, so if those time frames are good enough for them, then they're good enough for me.

At the time it was fought, Loos was the biggest battle ever to have taken place on European soil. Overall, it cost some 60,000 British casualties with something like a third of these killed. A lamentable toll indeed, especially since this is a similar number to the total British losses incurred throughout the entire Second Boer War! But as the Great War went on, of course, things would only get worse, with the Battle of the Somme, under a year later, claiming a similar number on its first day! In comparison, the first day at Loos saw some 8,500 killed, many of whom were never found. Also, probably because it was relatively early in this new type of conflict, when battles were more 'led from the front', the proportion of casualties among officers was significantly higher than would come to be expected as the war continued.

The overall outcome was to be a clear victory for the Germans, who sustained only about half as many casualties.

Among the more widely known who lost their lives during the Battle of Loos were John Kipling; the only son of the writer and poet Rudyard Kipling, who called him 'Jack', Fergus Bowes-Lyon; the brother of the Queen Mother and Charles Hamilton Sorley; the Scottish poet.

The story of John Kipling is detailed in the play and television film *My Boy Jack* (the title derived from a poem penned by Kipling about the loss of his son) which tells how the young Jack's attempts to enlist in the Navy at the outbreak of war were thwarted by his poor eyesight. Seeing that his son remained as determined as ever to enlist, however, Kipling presses the authorities and finally ends up securing his son a commission with the Irish Guards. This takes Jack to France and by September 1915 the Irish Guards are fighting at Loos. On 27 September, in an attempt to build on the initial assault that had begun two days earlier, the Scots and Irish Guards were ordered to sweep across no man's land to a point just north of Loos. As they neared the German line, just in front of Bois Hugo (Hugo Wood), they came under heavy fire, and evidently it was here that Jack, who had lost his glasses in the confusion, was mown down, while fumbling about on the ground for them.

Rudyard Kipling was never really to get over Jack's death, not least I suppose, because he had moved heaven and earth to enable his son to fight, in spite of strong objections by other members of his family. He was so affected by it all that he began to question his faith in the very way the war had been conducted and, because there was no report of Jack's body ever having been recovered, he became even further obsessed about whether his son might still be alive. For years afterwards Kipling would relentlessly try to track down anybody who might have some idea as to exactly what had happened to him. Whether it eased the pain at all nobody can say, but it does appear that Jack's remains may well have been located after all.

Despite all his efforts, when Kipling died in 1936, he had never realised that, shortly after the end of the war, the body of an Irish Guards officer was recovered from near where Jack had last been seen and had then been reinterred in an unmarked grave in the St. Mary's ADS (Advanced Dressing Station) Cemetery just north of Loos. In 1992 the War Graves Commission declared that it believed these remains were, indeed, those of John Kipling and erected a headstone over the grave to that effect. And mercifully, although doubts still persist, others who have looked into the matter in detail would appear to agree.

*

In September 1915 the late Queen Mother was only a girl of fifteen; Lady Elizabeth Bowes-Lyon, the ninth of ten children born to Claude, the Rt. Hon. Earl of Strathmore and Kinghorne, and his wife, Lady Cecilia. As we all know, she married Prince Albert, the then Duke of York, later to become King George VI, as a result of his brother's (Edward VIII's) abdication, and thus she became Queen Consort and the mother of Queen Elizabeth II. Her older brother, the Hon. Fergus Bowes-Lyon, was eleven years her senior. On the outbreak of war, at the age of twenty-five and shortly after marrying, Fergus joined the newly formed 8th Battalion of the Black Watch and arrived in France a couple of months after Frank and Syd. Like theirs, as the summer of 1915 began to draw to a close, the progress of his war brought him to the Loos area, albeit slightly earlier. Like Frank, Fergus had been on leave shortly before the Battle of Loos, but on the 27th of September (the same day that Jack Kipling was killed) Captain Bowes-Lyon led his men into battle in order to protect the then precariously British-held Hohenzollern Redoubt against persistent German attempts to retake it. During the assault it is understood that he was hit by machine gun fire after having received severe wounds from a nearby blast of heavy artillery. Although he lived long enough to be evacuated from the battlefield, he died shortly afterwards. His remains were buried in a mass grave and so were never identified but a stone in the Quarry Cemetery, near Vermelles (just a couple of miles north of John Kipling's stone) commemorates that he is 'buried near this spot'.

As in all such cases, the family was devastated when they heard. They had another son at the front and two others wounded. Fergus's mother was particularly affected and totally withdrew into herself. Rarely seen for some considerable time afterwards, she would only emerge and, to some extent at least, re-engage, when her daughter married the Duke of York in 1923 – nearly five years after the war had ended.

*

There were also several VCs won at Loos, including that of Daniel Logan Laidlaw, the 'Piper of Loos'. He had been a regular soldier who had served in India but, by the start of the war, he had left the Army. Nevertheless, eager to do his bit, he rejoined shortly after war broke out and was made up to acting corporal. Clearly 'a bit of a lad' though, shortly after arriving in France he was reduced back down to the ranks for being drunk.

On 25 September 1915, Laidlaw, a piper of the King's Own Scottish Borderers, was involved in the attack on Hill 70, just to the south-east of Loos when, at forty-one years of age, he was not exactly in the first flush of youth. Apparently, after the shouts and whistles rang out to advance towards the enemy positions, there was a thick cloud of gas in the air and, instead of racing over the top, the troops seemed reluctant to move, some even looking as though they might refuse. After a tense moment or two, an officer, probably out of sheer instinct, was heard to shout out, "Laidlaw, *ferr* God's sake do something wi' *yerr* pipes!" Upon which Laidlaw, without any thought for himself, scrambled out of the trench and began piping loudly. This hearty rendering of 'The Blue Bonnets', a uniquely Scottish sound, was said to have spurred the men on and instantaneously resolved the contumacy. Unfortunately, after a while Laidlaw was wounded by shrapnel, but even then, continued to play on. He was to survive the battle, though, and would luckily be among the relatively small proportion of pipers who fought at Loos to survive the war.

It was his actions that day that earned him the Victoria Cross and it was personally presented to him by King George V at Buckingham Palace the following year. He must have been a very brave chap too, because, before the end of the war, he went on to receive the French *Croix de Guerre* medal as well.

Daniel Laidlaw was eventually demobbed in 1919, having regained his NCO status and ultimately risen to the rank of sergeant, afterwards working on the land and later for the postal service in and around the Scottish Borders. He also got to play himself in a couple of films made about the Great War: *The Guns of Loos* in the late 1920s and *Forgotten Men* in the early 1930s. He lived to the age of seventy-five and died in Northumberland in 1950.

*

Another soldier to win the VC was Lance Naik (equivalent to lance corporal) Kulbir Thapa, a Gurkha. He was, in fact, the very first native Gurkha ever to win a VC and, indeed, one of only two Gurkhas to win the award in the whole of the Great War. Although he was part of the same push as that in which Daniel Laidlaw was involved on 25 September, Kulbir's group had mounted a diversionary attack about ten miles north of Loos, near Fauquissart, alongside some Leicesters (not involving Frank's and Syd's group). Despite being badly shot up himself, he did reach the German trenches where he came across an injured soldier, thought to have been Bill Keightley from Melton Mowbray, who was drifting in and out of consciousness. Like so many other assaults during that battle, the attack had been a disaster, with almost everybody taken out. However, in spite of being urged to save himself, the brave Gurkha (their motto being, 'Better to die than live a coward') stayed with Bill and comforted him for the rest of that day and night.

When dawn broke, under the cover of the mist, Kulbir was able to move Bill to relative safety and then, after rescuing two other wounded Gurkhas, returned to carry him away. Whilst initially attracting heavy fire, when the Germans realised what he was achieving they stopped shooting and began to cheer him on.

Both Kulbir Thapa and Bill Keightley survived the war, but Bill would lose both his legs as a result of the ordeal. Both died in 1956.

Legend also has it that Kulbir Thapa 'set the record straight' for another act of bravery which had taken place earlier in the war at Neuve-Chapelle where, this time, one of the Leicesters would win the VC for saving a Gurkha. Although born in Bedford, Private William Buckingham had lived in a children's home in Countesthorpe, Leicestershire since he was six. His early years were quite fraught in that his natural father, also William, died of TB not long after the boy's birth, leaving his mother struggling to raise both the young William and his brother Frederick. This led to him spending a period in the workhouse, but he was to be reunited with his mother and brother after she had remarried to a Joseph Buckingham and they had moved to Leicester. Both boys took Buckingham's name but, unfortunately, this new family continued to struggle and William had to be separated from them yet again, this time ending up in the children's home in Countesthorpe.

When he was old enough, William joined the Regular Army and served in India but after the outbreak of war he was sent to France. At Neuve-Chapelle, amid the fierce fighting over the two-day period between the 10th and 12th of March 1915, he managed to recover several wounded soldiers, one of whom turned out to be a Gurkha. As the battle had left him with arm and chest wounds, however, he was sent home to recover where, for his heroism, he too was awarded the VC.

Leicester was so proud of William that, in addition, he was presented with £100 and a purse of gold! While at home he was stationed at Glen Parva Barracks, near Leicester and promoted to lance corporal but on his return to France in 1916 he declined the promotion, preferring to remain a private soldier. Sadly, he was killed towards the end of the Battle of the Somme near Thiepval. His body was one of the many never identified but he is commemorated on the Thiepval Memorial and Buckingham Road, in Countesthorpe, was named after him.

*

Yet another hero of the Battle of Loos was a Frenchwoman by the name of Émilienne Moreau, also known as the Lady of Loos. Born not far away, she and her family moved to Loos-en-Gohelle just before the war where her father, a former coal miner, ran a shop. At first things went well and even when the war began, she could never have anticipated the scale of the horrors to come. At first her brother was sent to fight at the front. Then the arrival of the Germans saw her father arrested and sadly, like so many others who had been similarly treated, he was never to recover from his ordeal.

Early in 1915 Émilienne, intending to become a teacher, had set up a small school in her house to look after some of the many children in the area who, mainly as a result of the invasion, had lost a parent or, in many cases, both.

When the Battle of Loos began, she was just seventeen, and after the way her father had been treated, Émilienne was very eager to do whatever she could to help. Because of his former job, the family had the right to collect *gaillettes* (small cobbles of coal) from the nearby *crassiers* (slag heaps) from where she was able to gaze down on the

German soldiers and record their exact locations and activities in some detail. When she then passed this intelligence on to the Black Watch contingent in the area, of particular importance were details about the German strategic fortification at Pit 15 which the Watch were preparing to overrun. The information that she provided helped enormously, not only with the progress of the attack but also in reducing casualties.

When the Germans reattacked, in order to protect a nearby British soldier who was under fire, she apparently asked for and was given a couple of hand grenades which she threw at the Germans, managing to blow some to smithereens! Then, when more German soldiers arrived, she bagged a gun and wildly started to shoot at them killing and/or wounding several in the process. The Germans, needless to say, returned fire and it almost cost her her life when one bullet only narrowly missed her.

As if these heroics had not been enough, as the war went on, she managed to help set up and run a Red Cross first aid station too!

On account of her outstanding bravery, Émilienne received many decorations including the British Military Medal and, for her care of the wounded, the Royal Red Cross Medal, as well as the British Red Cross Venerable Order of Saint John of Jerusalem. The French also awarded her the *Croix de Guerre* and the *Croix de Combatant* and she became a national and international hero when she was invited to meet with both the French President, Poincaré, and King George V.

Towards the end of the war, she fulfilled her ambition to train as a teacher and took up a teaching post in Paris. However, she subsequently returned to live in Lens, just south-east of Loos, where she met and married the social activist, Just Evrard.

When the Second World War broke out her reputation went before her and the occupying Germans, worried that she would cause more trouble for them, briefly detained her. Despite this, her bravery never deserted her and as soon as she could, alongside her husband, she joined the French Resistance. For this she would be awarded the *Ordre de la Libération* – a rare honour, only ever awarded to the bravest of the brave who fought to liberate France.

After the end of the Second World War Émilienne and her husband were eventually able to settle down to life in peacetime but still remained active in local politics. She died in early 1971 and is buried in Lens Cemetery but it is highly unlikely that the people of France, especially those in Loos-en-Gohelle, will ever forget her.

*

It is the stuff of legends and comic books, but when the cries and whistles went up on 25 September, somewhere along the trenches occupied by the London Irish Rifles a half-inflated football shot out.

After the paranoia generated by the unofficial truce at Christmas, when the British and Germans were said to have played football with each other, the mere possession of a football was enough to raise an officer's eyebrows and could even lead to a court martial. But perhaps predictably this threat was nowhere near enough to put off hardened fans of the game and many still did own a football. In any case, not really wishing punishment to result from such a trivial matter, in general an officer would merely puncture any footballs he found, either with a bayonet or by shooting them through with his service revolver, and that would be the end of the matter.

This time it was Rifleman Frank Edwards of the London Irish Rifles who was the man behind the ball. He had always said that he would do it and now there he was, dribbling a football through no man's land towards the enemy. Perhaps some might ask why he would have wanted to. What was going on in his mind? Could it not have hijacked his concentration; making him less aware of the danger and therefore more vulnerable to being shot? Would it not focus more enemy attention on him? On the other hand, maybe there is something to be said for having your attention diverted somewhat when going into hell and there could well be something about racing towards the enemy, dribbling a football, that makes it seem more intimidating. Whatever, despite the rules, like others had before and would do again, he did it and his comrades joined in, shouting and passing the ball as the attack gathered momentum. Somewhere in the gas cloud, however, the ball got caught up in the barbed wire and was lost.

Unlike so many of his comrades, although wounded in the thigh and badly gassed, Frank Edwards did survive to tell the tale and, despite a relentless German response to their attack, the London Irish were able to hold their advance for several days. No action was taken against him, and he was sent home to recuperate but, although the wound healed, he never fully got over being gassed. He was able to work, however, and following the war became a military policeman and, after that, an NSPCC inspector.

Following the death of his second wife in 1956, Frank Edwards was looked after by his daughter. He died in 1964.

But what happened to the football? Well, apparently it was recovered from the barbed wire after the battle and put on display at the London Irish Rifles' Museum in Camberwell. Albeit having been considerably restored at the beginning of the twenty-first century, when it had started to deteriorate considerably, the ball can still be seen there to this day.

*

As the struggle at Loos continued into the last days of September and the first days of October 1915, the tide began to turn against the Allies. The reasonably good weather at the start of the battle deteriorated and low cloud began to hamper the aerial bombardment. Whilst the Germans were reinforcing, Allied supplies of ammunition were becoming strained, and although the night of 25 September had seen the best part of the Hohenzollern Redoubt area in Allied hands, the Germans had managed to recapture it on 3 October. Balanced against this was the symbolic name, its strategic position and the losses that it had already cost. As a result, its recapture seemed to be turning into something of a military obsession. In other words, whatever it took, it appeared that Haig was determined to recapture the Redoubt.

Chapter 11

That Ill News

'I wis, in all the Senate,
There was no heart so bold,
But sore it ached, and fast it beat,
When that ill news was told...'

'Horatius at the Bridge'
– Thomas Babington Macaulay

The autumn sun shone brightly down as dawn broke in the trenches near Vermelles on the morning of Wednesday 13 October 1915. Having arrived late the previous evening, this was the first that Frank and Syd had seen of the area and indeed the first time ever that they had been right on the front line, preparing to go into direct action against the enemy. Against the German 6th Army to be precise, under the command of Crown Prince Rupprecht of Bavaria, who now held the dreaded Hohenzollern Redoubt that stood only a few hundred yards in front of them. Not that you would have wanted to spend too much time with your head above the parapet, but the Redoubt would have been clearly visible from the British position, as would the slag heap, known as the Dump at Fosse 8, behind it. Although not quite yet the classic no man's land of later battles, with their muddy and often water-filled craters, copious entanglements of barbed wire and spikes of dead trees, etc., the terrain was, by now, beginning to look a bit battle-worn. However, if you looked hard enough, you could still make out some patches of green between the barricades and shell holes. As a result, soldiers attacking here would not have been anything like as bogged down as those who were to fight, say, at Passchendaele in 1917, where endless rain, after some two further years of constant pounding, had turned the land to sludge. In fact, the going was firm that day but, sadly, this was only to make what was to follow take place much more quickly and much more decisively than might otherwise have been the case.

Despite being tired from the previous day's journey, on account of their situation, the seemingly continuous sniper fire and in anticipation of the events to come, nobody had really slept well the night before. The trench had been dark, but some had managed to scribble notes, mostly short ones (intended for the nearest and dearest, in the event that this was to be the one from which they did not return). I have absolutely no idea as to whether Frank or Syd wrote anything along these lines but, if they did, the messages would then have been collected, along with any valuables and personal possessions, before the assault, with the intention of sending them to their next of kin should the worst, indeed, come to the worst.

As the final details of the planned assault were decided the morning turned into a waiting game and naturally, as they all sat around and smoked, in between conversations they began to reflect. Understandably, given the circumstances, the more they thought, the more it became difficult not to linger on the worst-case scenario, this moroseness ironically lifting in an instant on hearing the officer's whistle when the need for full focus forces the adrenaline to kick in.

So it was that heartbeats quickened at midday when the first bombardments of Allied heavy artillery rang out, but something did not seem quite right. No doubt down to the shortage of ammunition that was by now beginning to tell, the bombardment did not seem nearly heavy enough nor last nearly long enough. An hour later gas and smoke were released, and although initially the cloud drifted towards the German line as planned, just as it had proved unpredictable on the first day of the battle back in September, before long it came to a standstill and failed to reach its target. When the emissions were stopped after some fifty minutes, a dense fug hung in the air over no man's land and what had been intended to aid the assault turned into yet another obstacle. And, as if that were not enough, the enemy sniping had now begun in earnest.

At two o'clock, after generous rum rations had been handed out, Frank, Syd, their men and the rest of the first run were all set to go. Then, when the whistles sounded and the assault began, their minds raced: this was it, this was what they had trained for all this time, and after all, this was the whole point of having been there all along. Any fear of failure or death evaporated, such an outcome would be impossible; unthinkable.

Almost instinctively the lads scrambled up the trench ladders *en masse* and charged across the flat plane into hell, nobody really noticing or acknowledging anybody else – there was a job to get on with and it had begun. A shout of "*En avant, mes braves*!" rang out as they continued towards the enemy. By now, though, the German response had reached its crescendo and, not least because this completely new type of warfare still lacked scrutiny and analysis, many bunched in the confusion and so more and more of the Leicesters began to fall to the ground, having been hit either by bullets or shrapnel or both. Of those who did manage to make it through the fog, many were cut down mercilessly when they emerged the other side.

Not that it would have really made much difference in this case but, despite having been in common use as head armour down the ages, there were no British 'tin hats' at Loos. Despite re-enactments in films or on book covers often portraying British troops at this time in the classic 'Tommy's steel helmet' (more specifically called the Brodie helmet after its inventor), although they began to be distributed towards the end of 1915, they were not widely worn until 1916. Both the French and the Germans were wearing some form of helmet by

1915, however, even though the French *Adrian* steel helmet, on account of its thin gauge, really only offered very limited protection. And the German *Pickelhaube* (the one with the spike or knob sticking out at the top), despite its menacing appearance, probably offered even less protection, as the earlier versions, at least, were made of leather. The standard British army headgear of the time was simply the cloth trench cap and practically all the British soldiers that went forth that day had never gone into battle wearing any form of protective headgear. And those who did not return, of course, never would. Perhaps in line with British eccentricity, in many of the hellish assaults that took place in the Gallipoli campaign that lasted for most of 1915 and into early 1916, pith helmets were often the preferred option.

In the end only a relatively few reached the Redoubt and, in spite of a follow-up by the Sherwoods and 5th Leicesters, the support had become so strained that, sadly, it became quite impossible to adequately secure the advance. And, although some Germans were finished off with bayonets, it soon became clear that the offensive was unsustainable.

In the aftermath, no man's land lay carpeted with dead, dying and wounded soldiers. The whole thing had been a complete disaster! As the day passed the full horror of what had happened in this initial (and, for many, their last) direct assault, served again to underline that, lacking artillery fire and inadequate Mills bombs apart, this new type of combat really was a colossally more powerful manner of warfare than anything else that had ever gone before. The days of those magnificent mounted charges into battle were well and truly a thing of the past, the technology had seen to that and, because such technology had never been known before, nobody could have ever been fully trained to deal with it. It was now undeniable that victory was as far away as ever and that the swift solution, initially predicted, had just been wishful thinking. Possibly for the first time, in very many cases, from the ranks and the officers to the generals and the politicians alike, the true scale of this monumental task was finally beginning to sink in. This 'war to end wars' was not going to be over any time soon!

Exactly how, where or when Frank and Syd were killed can never be precisely known. It would appear, though, that like so many that day, not very long after leaving their trench, they must have been very badly cut up by machine gun fire and/or explosions to the extent that they were unrecognisable, since neither of their bodies was ever knowingly recovered. Whatever, I believe and hope that the end was swift for them and that they did not suffer needlessly. But the tragic loss of life at such a young age – just twenty-three and nineteen respectively – and in such a way, really does bring home the full cost of war. At times it must make even the most ardent supporter of military solutions question whether it is all really worth it.

Their bones could well still lie in the soil over which I have walked, or they could have been recovered and buried under a headstone marked 'A SOLDIER OF THE GREAT WAR KNOWN UNTO GOD', who can say? They are, of course, both commemorated on the wall tablets at the Loos Memorial:

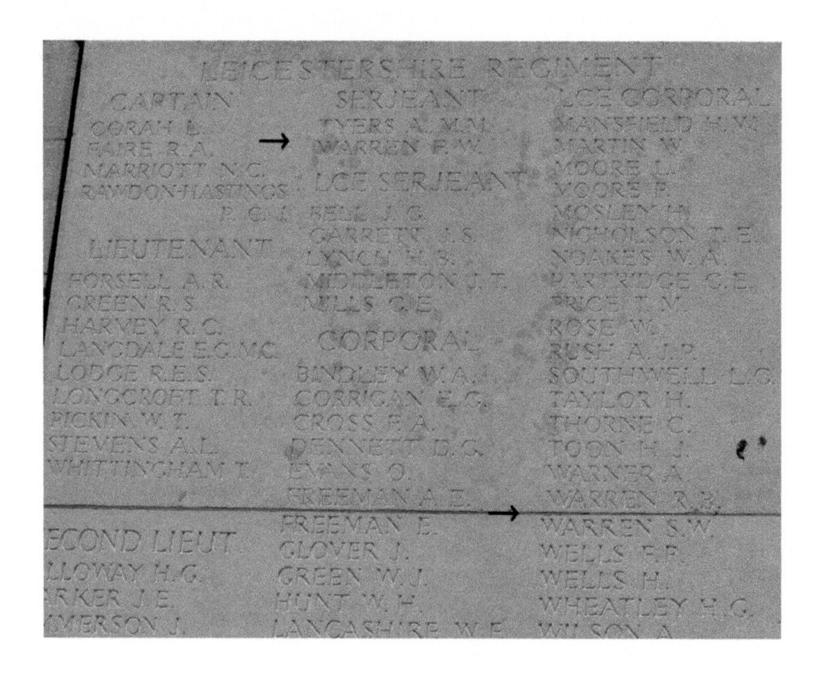

(Interestingly Syd's initials have been reversed, presumably because he was always known as Syd, rather than Walter.)

Although what remained of the Leicesters just managed to hold some of the areas in and around the Redoubt, that was as far as it went. The following day, having been relieved by the Sherwood Foresters, they were able to return to the relative safety of the Lancs' trench near Vermelles. Every single one of their officers involved in the assault had been either killed or wounded. The commanding officer, Lt. Col. R.E. Martin, despite his wounds, was said to have bravely continued to direct operations for almost twenty-four hours, only after then retiring to the dressing station in order to receive treatment.

In all the 1/4th Leicesters lost twenty officers and 453 other ranks. Only 188 soldiers answered roll-call on the 14th and on the 15th these were taken back behind the lines to Hesdigneul, where they had been while en route to Vermelles from Gonnehem, just the previous week. The commanding officer wrote a Congratulatory Order to the Battalion on the 'excellent work done by them in the attack of Oct. 13th', but nobody really felt like celebrating and the Germans were very soon to be back in full control of the Redoubt anyway. It would become an oft-repeated sentiment that the Leicesters were never the same again after that fateful day.

At an international level, as had been anticipated for some time, the Kingdom of Bulgaria (as it was then), having sat on the sidelines for so long, chose October to enter the war on the side of the Central Powers. Bulgaria's subsequent invasion of Macedonia and then Northern Greece would frustrate Allied efforts in the region until September 1918, when she finally threw in the towel and pulled out of the war.

*

It was also on 13 October 1915 that the up-and-coming twenty-year-old Scottish poet, Charles Hamilton Sorley, lost his life.

Although born in Aberdeen, he moved down to Cambridge as a child when his father, who taught at Aberdeen University, obtained a professorship at Cambridge. His love of verse no doubt stemmed from his mother who, when Charles, his sister and twin brother were very young, would eagerly encourage them to read and write poetry.

After a relatively brief period of study at Oxford University, he went on to enrol at the University in Jena, Germany, but as the outbreak of war became more and more inevitable, he wanted to return home. Briefly detained by the German authorities when he first tried to leave, he eventually made it back and joined up. Originally commissioned as a second lieutenant in the Suffolks, he had reached the rank of captain just prior to the Battle of Loos. He is understood to have been shot in the head by sniper fire but, just as with Frank and Syd, he completely disappeared in the melee that day and his remains, too, were never identified.

In spite of his young age, Sorley was considered a fine poet by many, including Robert Graves who, following the war, went on to write his moving wartime autobiography *Goodbye to All That* in which he praises Sorley and his work.

In all, Sorley's death was not only sad in itself but widely considered a great loss to the literary arts. His last poem, found among his possessions after his death, was untitled and it appears to suggest that mourning for dead soldiers is futile. Although it must have been written beforehand, it would appear to capture the aftermath of that assault on the Hohenzollern Redoubt pretty accurately, don't you think?

> When you see millions of the mouthless dead
> Across your dreams in pale battalions go,
> Say not soft things as other men have said,
> That you'll remember. For you need not so.
> Give them not praise. For, deaf, how should they know
> It is not curses heaped on each gashed head?
> Nor tears. Their blind eyes see not your tears flow.
> Nor honour. It is easy to be dead.
> Say only this, 'They are dead.' Then add thereto,
> 'Yet many a better one has died before.'

Then, scanning all the o'ercrowded mass, should you
Perceive one face that you loved heretofore,
It is a spook. None wears the face you knew.
Great death has made all his for evermore.

*

In the mixed fortunes that war brings, another young Scotsman who found himself among the same chaotic and confused scenario as Sorley, would, that same day, win the Victoria Cross through his outstanding heroism.

Cpl. James Lennox Dawson was one of the Royal Engineers who had been involved in setting up the gas canisters. The story goes that some British soldiers were placed at serious risk of being gassed when three of the canisters began to leak into their nearby trench. On realising, despite putting himself at great risk from enemy fire, Dawson directed his men to roll the affected canisters away. They then shot holes in them so that the gas could escape at a safe distance, so averting the catastrophe that several men being gassed by their own side would have been.

James received his VC from King George V at Buckingham Palace in December 1915. The following year he was promoted but then, just prior to the Battle of the Somme, was wounded. And although he continued to serve, from then on it would only be in a non-combative way.

He married in 1917 and, after leaving the Army at the end of hostilities, was finally able to complete the degree at Glasgow University that he had begun before the start of the war. Following this he became a schoolteacher but later rejoined the Army, this time to teach in the Education Corps. During World War II he transferred to the Indian Army Ordnance Corps with whom he served in Africa.

By the time James Dawson retired around 1950, he had acquired many more medals to go with his VC and had risen to the rank of colonel. He died at his home in Eastbourne in February 1967, aged seventy-five.

Heroics must have been a family trait because James Dawson's cousin, James Pollock, had also been awarded the VC in the early stages of the Battle of Loos through his courageous defence of Little Willie Trench – a trench which ran to the north of the Hohenzollern Redoubt. As part of the Germans' frantic attempts to retake the Redoubt after its initial loss at the start of battle on the 27th of September, they launched a concerted bombardment along this trench. In spite of the obvious dangers, James Pollock's response was to crawl along the trench edge and when he came to where the Germans were, he simply threw grenades down on top of them. Having put himself at such considerable risk James was lucky to survive with just a gunshot wound to his arm yet, through his bravery, he had succeeded in considerably frustrating the German attack. Although he was later to lose an eye in the conflict, like his cousin, he survived the war, and also went on to serve in World War II.

In the early 1950s James Pollock would move to Leicester, in order to take up the directorship of one of its many hosiery works. He died in 1958, shortly after being suddenly taken ill in Ayr, where he is buried.

Yet another hero, Charles Geoffrey Vickers turned twenty-one on 13 October 1915, but it would be the following day that he too won the VC at the Hohenzollern Redoubt. He was born in Nottingham, but his parents had married in Leicester in 1882. He had studied at Oxford University and was commissioned on joining up with the Sherwood Foresters in September 1914. In the struggle to retain at least some advantage following the assault of the previous day, while under constant fire resulting in heavy losses, he and two others succeeded in maintaining a temporary barrier across one of the trenches that the Germans were pounding with grenades. This enabled the construction of a much stronger barrier behind him but unfortunately left him isolated between the two barriers and, although able to hold his position, Charles was badly wounded in the process and had to be repatriated for treatment. The much coveted 'Blighty wound' one might say, but even this was not enough to keep him out of the war for good.

Charles Vickers also received his medal from the King at Buckingham Palace while he was still recuperating, and when he had recovered sufficiently, was able to complete another two stints in France. Firstly, between late 1916 and early 1917 and then again in early 1918 until the Armistice, getting married and commanding a company at the Officer Cadet Battalion, Pirbright, in between. In June 1918 he was awarded the *Croix de Guerre* for his actions defending the Marne, presumably just prior to the Second Battle of the Marne which, in the event, turned out to be the final major German offensive of the war.

After the war, Charles returned to Oxford to continue his studies, which included law, and in 1923 he became a solicitor. At the same time, however, ever the military man, he continued to serve in the Territorial Force which included a couple of years with the 4th Leicesters in the early 1920s.

After divorcing his first wife and remarrying in the 1930s, Charles would go on to serve in World War II; mainly in intelligence and, after receiving other decorations including the American Medal of Freedom with Gold Palm, in recognition of all his achievements, he was knighted in 1946. In later life he wrote a number of books on various subjects, many concerning social systems. He died in Oxfordshire during March 1982, aged eighty-seven.

As far as winning the Victoria Cross during the Great War goes, though, Captain Noel Chavasse's record would have been a tough act to follow. He won two! And he remains the only man to have achieved this between 1914 and 1918. The recipient also of the Military Medal, he must have been a very brave man indeed. An army doctor, his first valiant act was at Guillemont on the Somme during August 1916, where, very near to the German lines and under intense shellfire, he continued to treat wounded soldiers all day long, only to go on searching for more wounded well into the evening. The following day, he was wounded while retrieving a casualty, but nevertheless, alongside others, went out yet again that evening to rescue even more casualties – some twenty in all.

He acted in exactly the same manner a year later, at Wieltje, near Ypres, Belgium, during the Battle of Passchendaele. Despite this time being very badly wounded, in true fashion he insisted on continuing to venture out into no man's land to rescue the wounded. This won him his second VC (bar) but sadly he would not live long enough to receive it as, shortly afterwards, he succumbed to his wounds and died.

Only two other people have ever won the VC twice since the award was created by Queen Victoria in 1856 to honour heroes of the Crimean War. One was Captain Arthur Martin-Leake, another medic. After winning his first VC in the Boer War, he won his bar in 1914 near Zonnebeke, during the First Battle of Ypres, by rescuing several wounded soldiers under heavy enemy fire. At the time he was the first person ever to have received the award twice. Capt. Martin-Leake did survive the war and lived on to the age of seventy-nine.

The only other double recipient of the VC was Captain Charles Upham, a New Zealand soldier during the Second World War; firstly in Greece and then in Egypt, in both cases because of his outstanding bravery in the face of the enemy. Despite being wounded, he too survived, but only after having been taken prisoner of war. On liberation he returned to New Zealand where he lived to the age of eighty-six.

*

After the glorious victory at El Alamein in 1942, Churchill declared that: "This is not the end, it is not even the beginning of the end. But it is, perhaps, the end of the beginning [of the Second World War]." And, although the Battle of Loos was far from a victory, it too was (arguably) the end of the beginning of the First World War. The might with which a heavily fortified war trench system could defend itself against a powerfully armed attack was now clear, as was the full consequence of trying to break the stalemate. All future strategies would simply have to be reviewed accordingly.

Just as with Churchill over Gallipoli, however, whilst the leader takes the credit for success so must they be ultimately responsible for failure and, owing largely to his responsibility for the lack of resources considered pivotal to this operation, this particular misadventure was to cost Sir John French (who, it is fair to say, had not hitherto enjoyed great popularity) his position as commander in France, however, not before having mulishly planned, yet again, to try to retake the Redoubt. In the end it would be the weather that decided what happened next and when the cold winter began to set in early, his ambitions had, mercifully, to be abandoned.

*

Winter was setting in at home, too. In fact, the winter of 1915–16 was to turn into one of the coldest and wettest on record, and it was on a particularly cold morning in early November that a young man in a peaked cap and dark uniform cycled towards 192, Western Road in Leicester. There suddenly seemed to be a lot more of these lads about than there had been before, and they had all been quite busy of late. You dreaded the messages they carried but even more, you dreaded them stopping anywhere near your house. Most of all, you were terrified at even the thought of them knocking on your door!

Louisa was busy washing the laundry in the copper at the back of the house that day and so did not at first feel that sickening welling up that the very sight of a telegram boy could set off within anyone who had loved ones at the front. For her it all started with a knock at the door. *Who's this?* she thought, as she wiped her hands and made to the front room. But when she opened the door and was bluntly confronted by the scenario she had dreaded and had had nightmares about, her heart sank. And, with five sons involved in the war, she had good reason to be worried. The anxiety made her head spin, and at one stage she thought her legs would give way. The boy just stood there, his arm outstretched towards her, holding the telegram. "Mrs. Warren?" he asked.

"Yes," Louisa mumbled, slowly reaching out for the telegram. Without another word she took it and, as she pushed the door to, thought she heard the boy asking if there would be any reply. She did not respond and when the catch clicked into place, her back against the door, Louisa slowly and silently sank to the floor.

The telegram boy, to whom this reaction had started to become all too common, lowered his eyes, got back on his bike and rode off to his next delivery – only a street or two away.

As she felt the cold, hard tiles beneath her, Louisa's mind began to lose track of everything else that was going on that day as she cast back a few weeks to a strange feeling she had experienced around the middle of October. A disquiet that, at the time, she could not put her finger on, but she knew, she just knew that something was wrong. The only way she had been able to describe it was a sort of dismal desolation, as though she had lost part of herself, and that whatever it was that was lost, would never return. Naturally, the possibility that it may have been to do with the loss of one of her sons did occur to her but, without anything else to go on, she had been able to put that fear out of her mind. Now, though, unless it was a dreadful nightmare from which she would soon wake, if this was indeed the reality, Louisa feared that she might not be able to find the strength to carry on.

The hand that clutched the telegram was still damp from the washing and, despite the cold outside, her palm had now begun to sweat a little. As she raised both her hands to her mouth the moisture that had already soaked into the telegram mixed with her tears. The thing was, she had a damn good idea what the telegram said, she didn't even need to open it. *What on earth would have been the point in replying to it*? she thought.

After a few minutes she came round a little. Perhaps things were not as bad as she feared. Was she overreacting? Could somebody have just been injured? They might be on their way home, home for good… no need to go back to the war… she picked herself up and sat on the sofa; that same sofa on which baby Richard Walter had lain all those years ago, in the room that, apart from special occasions, was hardly ever used. The seat felt cold and hard as she continued to stare at the scrap of paper, still not yet daring to open it. *Perhaps leave it until Richard gets back*, she thought, and quickly got up, lodging it behind a vase on the mantelpiece. *Now where was I?* She moved to go back to her washing but, for some reason, could not get past the lounge door. Whatever it was in that telegram, she could not change it. It would read the same whether she opened it now, waited for Richard or threw it on the fire. Back she went and, standing by the mantelpiece, tore it open.

It was, of course, as she had feared; the worst. The perfunctory note read:

POST OFFICE TELEGRAPHS

I certify that this Telegram is sent on the service of the

WAR OFFICE

Deeply
| ^ Regret | to | inform | you | that |

[Though the word 'Deeply' had been written above a caret before 'Regret', the other words above were printed. In order to save time? The note then went on:]

L-Cpl. Walter Sydney Warren killed in action on October 13th. Lord Kitchener expresses his sympathy.

From { Secretary, War Office

It was just as she had suspected, no sigh of relief, no homecoming to look forward to, no hope. And what of her other sons?

The tears had by now soaked the paper. As she threw back her head Louisa's cries of anguish could be heard in the street, and even though anybody passing would likely have guessed why, they would probably have still continued on their way, not wishing to intrude on the grief.

Louisa was still lying on the sofa in the front room when Joe and Dolly came home from school. The washing now abandoned, she had simply curled up on the cold settee and cried herself to sleep, not bothering about nor even wanting to wake up again. At first, they thought she was dead, but then realised that she was breathing and thought that she must be ill. They did not notice the telegram, which was by now a crumpled, soggy mass in Louisa's clenched fist. Thinking that when their dad got home he would know what to do, they covered her with a blanket and sat by her until he returned.

Richard knew what it was all about as soon as he saw the state that Louisa was in. He knew full well that she was clutching a telegram and what it meant. If truth be known he had also had those same feelings a few weeks before but he, like Louisa, had not mentioned them.

As Louisa stirred, Richard embraced her. No words were spoken and with both now in the grip of grief, their embrace continued in silence for several minutes. When Richard eventually gently pulled himself away, he got up and did the only thing he could think of – make a cup of tea. As he did so he heard Louisa climbing the stairs and when he went back into the front room, the telegram, now in tatters, lay in the middle of the sofa. Although the children were staring up at him, he could not see them, only that piece of paper held his focus. As he picked it up, slowly unscrewed it and stared at those dreadful words that he had hoped against hope he would never have to read, he too broke down.

"This bloody war! This *bloody* war..." he sobbed. "'Aven't we gone through enough God?" By now the kids, increasingly picking up on all the emotions, had also begun to understand what it might all be about. Although they did not yet know to whom exactly the telegram referred, they realised that it could only be to do with one of their brothers and so began to weep too.

Ernest arrived home to a deathly silence. It was quite obvious to him that something was seriously wrong and, although he had a good idea of what it might be, not daring to suggest the worst, he whispered to his father, "What's wrong, Dad?" Trying desperately to control his emotions, Richard then explained everything to him, Joe and Dolly. As he did so Ernest's eyes filled with tears as he slumped into a chair, his head back and his eyes closed, in an attempt to take it all in. Having overheard all this, when she felt able, Louisa returned to the room, walked over to her children, and huddled them all together around her. Richard, normally not a tactile person, also joined in, and for a couple of minutes they all hugged each other tightly before gently releasing their hold and pulling apart. After that, save for an occasional sob, the cold, reflective silence resumed. Nobody ate much of anything that night, nor did anybody do much of anything except get up now and again, mainly just to poke or restack the fire or to step outside briefly for a breath of fresh air.

When Louisa woke the following morning, Richard was gone but had left no message, so it was not clear whether he had gone to work. She had half-expected this and prayed that he would not disappear this time, as he so often would in response to such tribulation. But if he did disappear, she hoped desperately that he would not stay away too long, because now, as much as anything, she needed his support and felt that she simply could not go on without it. Stirring to get up, the whole awful realisation flooded back to her like a torrent of cold water and her strength completely deserted her. All she could do was whimper, "My baby, my baby," under her breath as she sank back on the bed, all thoughts of rising now forsaken. It was simply too much of an effort. What was the point in continuing to engage with this stupid world anyway? She could not care less whether the kids were fed, got up for school or anything. As seconds turned to minutes and minutes to hours, she ended up staying in bed all that morning, drifting off between bouts of deep thought and others of trying not to think at all. Since the younger kids felt the same, they also stayed in bed all morning; school that day would have been out of the question anyway.

Ernest, having thought that something like this might happen, felt it best not to disturb his mother. He did not really want to go to work, either, but fearing that he might lose his job and knowing that the house was going to be an altogether dreary place that day, he felt he should. Although he arrived late, when he explained the situation to his boss, he was not penalised. It was even suggested that he leave early that afternoon, but Ernest declined the offer. There was more than enough to keep him occupied all that day at work and perhaps he just thought it best not to dwell. At that age, of course, he may well have been unable yet to take in the full extent of the situation.

At around midday, Joe, worried about his mother and by now beginning to feel a bit hungry, got up, put the kettle on and took her a cup of tea. Louisa was awake when he opened the bedroom door and managed a forced half-smile before sitting up and taking a sip. Again, nothing was said as the tea was drunk and, after she had put her cup down, Louisa hugged Joe as if she would never let him go. *Please make this bloody war be over before he's old enough to go*, she thought, *please God.*

By Saturday life at home had returned to as near normal as possible, given the circumstances. All the other members of the family who were not on active service were now aware of the tragedy and, despite being sick with grief, they had all rallied round to lend their support. Richard had indeed gone to work the day after the news and, as Louisa had hoped, had returned again that night. But although they could all now talk a bit more freely about what had happened, there still remained a thick air of melancholy in the house. They could not have known exactly where 1/4th Leicesters were at the time Syd had been killed but, in scanning every relevant newspaper report in the search for further information, the increase in the concentration of fighting around the Loos area seemed to suggest that this was where it may have happened. The main reservation being, that almost all of these reports were pretty gung-ho and spoke of 'a great victory' and the like, which did little to help them come to terms with how Syd had died. Also, they knew from Frank's recent spell of leave that he and Syd were still together, so now everybody was desperately worried about Frank and, since the telegram had arrived, Louisa had prayed for him constantly.

But then it came – another knock on the door!

This time it was Richard who answered it. The thought that it might be another telegram never entered his head until he opened the door and was faced with the telegram boy. Now feeling every bit as sick as Louisa had before; *surely not*, he thought to himself, *please God, surely not...* it was a different telegram boy to the one who had called before, but this one too had delivered enough telegrams to bereaved families to realise their effect on them. "Mr. Warren?" he asked in a quiet voice, averting his gaze. Richard nodded and took the telegram. The boy could sense the tension and after a slight hesitation, stuttered, "Sh-shall I wait?" He need not have bothered as, by this time, the door was slowly being closed and, with the final click of the latch, he had his answer.

Overhearing the brief conversation, by now other members of the family had gathered in the front room and, as Richard slowly turned towards them, his eyes filled with tears. That other telegram in his hand could only mean one thing. Soon everybody was crying as they again gathered together and hugged each other. A few quiet minutes followed when only the occasional sob could be heard; the 'calm before the storm'?

When they sank apart again Richard nervously opened the telegram. The same perfunctory note, almost identical to the one before but this time referring to Frank.

"The same day," mouthed Richard.

"Together," whispered Louisa. "They lived together, they did the same things together, they liked the same things and now they've died together. I'm not sure whether that makes it more or less bearable." *Oh God, I just want them back!* thought Louisa; a sentiment that she would retain for the rest of her long life.

The next few weeks were pretty miserable, to say the least. But although different people react differently to grief, there was much more of a 'stiff upper lip' attitude in those days, especially among the men. And with Richard, from my experience of the men in my family, albeit those of later generations, together with what I have been told about him, I have little doubt that he would soon have found some way to hide his emotions. That said, depression can sometimes linger below the surface and lead to outbursts of temper, resultant arguments, or sulks and the like. So I expect that such subconscious reactions would have continued to haunt the family for some considerable time after having lost those two dear sons, together, on that fateful day.

I do not know whether Richard and Louisa ever received any of those small bundles of personal effects, often containing a scribbled note starting, 'If you are reading this…' during the following weeks, and although many bereaved parents received compassionate letters from the officers in charge of their loved ones who had been killed, in this case, since all the officers had also been either killed or wounded, it seems unlikely. On 15 November 1915, however, the *Leicester Daily Mercury* carried the following report:

LOCAL CASUALTIES.

LEICESTER BROTHERS KILLED.

Sergeant FRANK WARREN and Lance-Corporal SYD WARREN both of the 1st.4th. Leicesters, sons of Mr. and Mrs. Warren, of 192 Western road were killed in the famous charge in October last. Sergeant Frank Warren was recently home on a month's leave and it was optional whether he returned to the firing line but he did so. Previous to going back he was a corporal in the 1st.4th. Leicesters but on his return was made sergeant. He was employed by Messrs I. and R. Morley, Oxford street. Lance-corporal Syd Warren was a

> signaller in the same company. Mr. and Mrs. Warren have two other sons in the Army, one being in Serbia and the other in France.

The son in France must have been my grandfather, Albert, and the one in Serbia I can only assume was my great-uncle Arch, whom I believe was in the Royal Marines; the Marines being in Serbia at the time, helping to mount the so-called 'defence of Belgrade'. At first, I thought that the omission of any reference to Jack in the report was a bit strange, but I know from my father that he was wounded at some time and so, if this happened very early on in the war, by now he could already have been discharged. I have no idea why Fred is not referred to.

In the days that followed, Frank and Syd were included in several of the long lists of casualties that both the Battle of Loos itself and all the various assaults on the Hohenzollern Redoubt had produced. Also, their photographs, along with tributes, were printed on separate subsequent days in the 'Fallen Leicesters' section of the *Leicester Daily Mercury*.

Their commemorations in the Leicester War Memorial Book (Vol.5) both carry very brief outlines of the assault and, apart from the names, of course, are virtually identical.

If they were not directly next to each other when they died, they were certainly in close proximity, and who knows? Their souls will hopefully have found each other and, if souls do indeed ascend, then I hope that theirs would have done so together. Like Sorley did for the situation at the front, Woodbine Willie, the legendary World War I priest, comforter and poet, pretty eloquently summed up the situation at home following such an occurrence with his poem, 'Pictures in the Fire':

> There's a soul in the Eternal,
> Standing stiff before the King.
> There's a little English maiden Sorrowing.
> There's a proud and tearless woman,

Seeing pictures in the fire.
There's a broken battered body
On the wire.

*

There have been reports recently of developments proposed for the land at Loos over which the battle was fought, including, believe it or not, turning it into a rubbish dump! I understand that this proposal was summarily dismissed and, in my view at least, quite rightly so. Latterly there has been a proposal to turn it into a wind farm, which I suppose would serve a purpose to this ever-hotter planet and certainly be less disrespectful.

I personally have very mixed feelings about this sort of thing. On the one hand, on account of what happened there, it is of considerable historical significance and remains a war cemetery. On the other, it is a stretch of land that needs to be used and maintained and political correctness in some quarters now suggests that reminders of wars may be inappropriate. Perhaps less specifically, though, the proposals made me wonder about how short memories can be. 'Lest we forget' it says on the war memorials, but what does that really mean? Politics of some sort or another lies behind all wars and, as Harold Wilson famously said, a week is a long time in politics. If a week is a long time, then how long is a century? Different attitudes (some say 'more modern', some say 'better', some speak the truth), different values and different times can alter the way in which we assess the past. And what of 'freedom'? What of 'sovereignty'? Are we to let the sacrifice of those who bravely stood up to tyranny be limited by changing values?

So how long should we wait before sites of former battles can respectfully be developed? At the turn of the twenty-first century complaints were made when the construction of a new motorway near the Spanish city of Talavera, some seventy miles south-west of Madrid, unearthed bones believed to have been those of soldiers killed in Wellington's famous battle there of 1809, during the Peninsula War.

So might there be complaints, if a similar thing happened to victims of battles that took place even earlier than 200 years ago? And if so, how much earlier? Well, not long ago I read of proposals to build holiday homes near to the site of the Battle of Bosworth Field, which took place over 500 years ago. To me the tone of this article seemed to suggest that the passage of half a century after the event may be more acceptable. I suppose that, as with other questions of morality, it is a matter of consensus.

To me war is failure; a failure of the skills of politics to prevent it. But then we are all only human and humans have always made mistakes and, since making mistakes is a human trait, we will continue to make them for as long as the human race survives. But if we do not, or cannot, learn from those mistakes, then we will keep on making the same mistakes over and over again, and thus the repetition of war is inevitable – an absolute certainty in fact. At the very least we must always try to find ways to avoid it.

That said, I cannot help but concede that the avoidance of war in the face of any future violations on the scale of the invasion of Belgium in World War I or that of Poland in World War II, would require the Wisdom of Solomon.

Chapter 12

The Somme

'War does not determine who is right,
only who is left'.

Bertrand Russell (among others)

If Loos had been a bloody tragedy, then (as if it were possible) there was far worse to come. The first day of the Battle of the Somme is one of bloodiest ever in history!

By the end of 1915 it was clear that the technology, the likes of which had never been seen before; principally the combination of powerful machine guns (based on those first used in the Russo-Japanese War of 1904–5), improved heavy artillery that could fire high explosives over long distances, and airpower, was pretty evenly matched on both sides. So much so that attempts to storm though enemy lines would prove extremely costly in lives and seemed doomed to failure. In short it had become a stalemate, and the only way forward would be to find some method of breaking the impasse.

During July 1915 Allied delegates had gathered to discuss the progress of the war at General Joffre's French Army HQ (*Grand Quartier Général*) in Chantilly, just north of Paris, and it was here that they decided to gather again towards the end of the year, with the intention of creating some sort of common solution. Although at the end of his role as British Commander-in-Chief, not least as a result of the criticisms levelled at him over what went wrong at Loos, Sir John French was still in post at the time and he, together with the Chief of the Imperial General Staff, Sir Archibald Murray, represented Britain alongside delegates from Russia, Serbia and Italy.

The underlying thread of the proposals was that the Allies should attack simultaneously over an extended area, in an attempt to prevent the enemy replenishing reserves as they had been able to between the more isolated attacks that had gone before. As far as the Western Front was concerned, after considering launching another major assault in Belgium, near Ypres, they decided it more strategic to attack further south, by the banks of the River Somme. To be led by the French, the strike was originally planned for August 1916, but the Germans had ideas of their own and on 21 February 1916 Von Falkenhayn launched his massive assault on Verdun. This was to turn into the longest battle of the entire war and draw heavily on both materiel and manpower (particularly French manpower, as Verdun was in their sector). In the bitter end, however, after some ten months of bloody struggle, the French managed to hold out, but it rather altered the priorities of the Allies' original plan.

By then, with Haig having replaced French as British Commander-in-Chief and Sir William Robertson having replaced Murray as Chief of the Imperial General Staff, it was felt that in view of Verdun, British rather than French forces should lead on the Somme (although the French would still play a major role) and that the offensive should be brought forward by some six weeks.

The first day of the Battle of the Somme (1 July 1916) has gone down in the annals of history as the bloodiest day of all and for no small reason, as it cost almost 60,000 British casualties, a third of whom lay dead. After an excruciating week-long artillery bombardment, the assault took place across a wide section of the front; the British aiming for the town of Bapaume and the French, a few miles further south, aiming for Péronne, directly on the banks of the river. If successful, the next intention was to consolidate the area in between these two towns.

As well as causing disruption in the enemy lines, one of the main purposes of the shelling had been to break up the barbed wire barricades in no man's land in order to facilitate the subsequent assault. Despite an intense and prolonged bombardment, however, the effect on the wire was disappointing. Aside from there being a vast area to shell, problems with the quality of the ordnance continued to arise. This was mainly a result of its over-rapid production in the face of ever-increasing demand but meant that up to a third of shells could turn out to be duds. Recces towards the end of June revealed that, rather than having broken up the wire as intended, the shelling had merely moved it about a bit. And it was because of this, together with the arrival of a spell of unseasonal wet weather, that it was decided to postpone the date of the push from the originally planned 29 June, to allow for an extra two days of shelling.

The bright summer's day that dawned that Saturday 1st of July 1916 was tempered by the anticipation of what was to come. At first the heavy artillery renewed its pounding of no man's land and the enemy lines, while preparations were made to ignite the massive amounts of high explosives that had been laid in tunnels dug directly beneath the German trenches.

Shortly after the last great showers of earth had been flung high into the air by the blasts, the officers' whistles sounded, and the lads began to scramble over the top. There was no gas or smoke this time to hamper progress, just a mass outburst of German machine gun fire. Carrying heavy equipment, as the attacking soldiers did, it would have been difficult for them to move with any great speed or agility. In fact, they had been told to walk rather than run, as the generals were expecting the Germans to have been all but wiped out by the prolonged shelling. But they had not been, and in the clear light of day, the slow-moving attacking Allies were 'sitting ducks'. In addition, despite the extra shelling, large sections of the barbed wire barriers still remained uncut and the German gunners were quickly and easily able to pick off those British and French soldiers unfortunate enough to become entangled in them.

At the end of the day, British accomplishments were, to say the least, disappointing. The furthest they got was about a mile; as far as the villages of Montauban and Mametz. The French, to the south, had done much better, however, and achieved virtually all they had set out to do.

As night fell on that first day of the battle, carnage such as the world had never seen before, lay spread out on the vast area over which the attack had taken place. Anybody who witnessed it must have feared that it might be the beginning of the end of humanity. How on earth could this war continue to be fought with so many being killed and wounded in a single day?

Nevertheless, when dawn broke the following day, it did go on and Haig was determined to build on whatever progress had been made. Fortunately, where they had broken through, the British were able to fend off the inevitable German counter-attacks and hold their positions while the French were able to continue their advance towards Péronne. Moreover, with the enemy also having suffered severely, one of the original objectives had been fulfilled in that the Germans had drawn reinforcements from Verdun.

As the fighting continued, the British began to concentrate on the wooded areas near to Mametz, but after intensifications here in the middle of the month things started to stagnate. If the advance was to continue, the high ground around Pozières had to be taken, but all attempts so far had been met with such fierce resistance that they became less and less worthwhile. Towards the end of July, however, it was decided that there was no alternative but to face the problem head-on and mount a once and for all offensive.

The attack was launched on the night of 22 July by the 48th (South Midland) Division, along with Australian Reserves under Lt. Gen. Gough and, despite fierce resistance, they were able to secure most of the Pozières area within two days. The Germans remained stubborn, however, and continued to counter-attack. By early August, although the Allies had managed to stand their ground, it was not without a cost, the Australians especially having suffered very heavy casualties.

As August passed the French continued to make further headway and, by mid-September, had consolidated all the area around Maurepas. Unfortunately, these gains were beginning to risk the formation of a bulge into German-held territory which could lead to repercussions from three sides; a situation very difficult to defend.

Soon, when little if any further progress was being made, it was beginning to look as though the task would take for ever and the efficacy of the plan began to be drawn into question. In response, no doubt with the newly invented tanks in mind, Haig insisted that another push would finish the job and attention was turned north to the high ground around Thiepval; now the site of the famous Thiepval Memorial but then an area stubbornly held onto by the Germans.

As at Loos, the front here included several redoubts and, although still difficult to attack, it was hoped that these fortifications would pose much less of a problem against tanks. Originally called 'landships', when loaded onto train wagons and sheeted over, they could easily be taken for water tanks or the like. Since this term also helped to keep their existence a secret, it was encouraged and so the name stuck.

As part of this push then, on 15 September 1916 at Flers-Courcelette, just to the east of Thiepval and Pozières, the very first tanks ever were deployed in battle. They must have appeared unstoppable, the tracked wheel design enabling them to negotiate virtually any sort of terrain, be it wet, rocky or afforested, and they could even pass over the narrower trenches. It was said that when the Germans first saw the lumbering but resolute monsters moving towards them spitting fire, they thought that the Devil himself was coming for them. Accounts talk of whole groups running for their lives! But just how much of this jingoism was truth and how much was exaggerated for public consumption is not clear. Whatever, the Germans must surely have been worried. Like every new invention, however, the first untried and untested tanks were not without their problems. As well as being prone to mechanical failure, the Germans soon realised that they could be relatively easily disabled by blowing their tracks off with grenades. But, although these early versions did not fulfil all expectations, they did prove effective, and by the end of September, the Allies had managed to advance a further five miles or so east of Pozières.

Unfortunately, at this point the advance was brought to a rather abrupt halt when heavy and persistent rain began to turn the ground into a thick sludge. There is a term for it, 'Somme mud', bringing to mind that classic image of the First World War with trucks and wheeled artillery having to be pushed out of ruts with wheels spinning and everybody covered in filth. Maintaining supplies and removing the wounded became nigh impossible and, in addition to hindering progress, the hiatus began to have a significant effect on morale and the psyche in general, with a notable rise in the number of cases of shell shock reported.

Although the Allies continued to apply pressure throughout October and into November, the gains started to become relatively small in comparison to ever-increasing losses. The British were able to consolidate their positions around Thiepval and the French their positions south of Péronne, but the weather continued to deteriorate to such an extent that, by mid-November, the prospect of any further progress seemed unrealistic, and it was becoming clear that the battle had reached its end.

To this day the situation on the Somme during 1916 has come to symbolise the very essence of The First World War: its mass slaughter, its seemingly impossible struggle, its stalemate, its weather, and the toll of over half a million Allied casualties, which does seem rather high for just a few square miles of land. It is perhaps not too surprising then, that history has come to judge those in charge, particularly Haig, with some severity.

On the other hand, although clearly somewhat pyrrhic in nature, the Battle of the Somme was an Allied success, in that it did result in some progress, it did afford some relief to the situation at Verdun, and it also cost Germany dearly in manpower (they lost a similar number to that of the Allies). And, looking at it impartially, I suppose that it is difficult to see how progress of any sort could have otherwise been achieved, in the face of this completely new type of warfare.

*

Shell shock, or neurasthenia (as it was also called) was first thought to be the result of physical damage to the brain caused by exploding artillery. However, post-traumatic stress disorder (PTSD), as it is known today, we now realise, is a disorder of the mind resulting from exposure to traumatic events. The symptoms can vary from individual to individual, and, although some can cope with or manage the effects, others are so badly affected that they become totally debilitated by them. One of the most common signs, though, is absurdly irrational overreactions to ordinary everyday events. Hardly surprising, if you had seen your best friend blown to smithereens or watched him slowly die of his wounds to a background of constant pounding artillery fire that may have gone on for days and nights, that a spark from the fire or a book falling onto a wooden floor would make you jump out of your skin. You come round but you feel dizzy, but you are safe… aren't you? It's silent again, like when you were on guard duty that night and were suddenly attacked from behind! *Oh, this has got to stop, I'm going mad. Or is it just my overactive imagination..? What was that?!*

Sufferers often relive their worst ordeals in nightmares or through flashbacks and hallucinations. Robert Graves, in *Goodbye to All That* speaks of visions of corpses lying in the streets of London, while home on leave. Anger may never be far from the surface and calmness one minute may not mean calmness the next. And who, having seen the horrible footage of the worst affected, writhing, contorting and shaking uncontrollably, can claim that the condition cannot be devastating? Sleep disturbance, tension and anxiety are also common symptoms.

The consequences can be long-term: feelings of depression, apathy and withdrawal can affect the ability to work and earn a living, as well as the ability to enjoy social activities. In truth, there are probably few aspects of life that would not be affected. Left ignored or untreated or, more likely in those days, misunderstood, the consequences can be disastrous and even fatal. Self-harm, substance abuse, self-neglect, even putting oneself in deliberate danger or the ultimate: suicide, to name but a few. With the large number of such cases that the Great War produced set against the poor understanding of the condition, many of those affected received little if any sympathy and instead were often pronounced fit to serve again far too soon. Probably the saddest and most regrettable consequence, however, was when this sort of thing was mistaken for cowardice and the sufferer (because that is what they would have been) was then shot by their own side.

I remember once, as a child of six or seven years old, being sent to 'stand under the clock' for some misdemeanour in class. The dreaded 'clock' stood in the school corridor and when, as always eventually happened, Mr. Morris, the headmaster, passed by, he knew that anybody standing under it was there for only one reason and his priorities would immediately be diverted towards the 'necessary castigations emendation'. As in this case, it usually entailed being taken to his office, which was a shed in the playground, so that he could enquire as to the nature of the transgression and decide on an appropriate punishment. The outcome was almost always a slap on the wrist and the recipient would be asked to place their hand on his outstretched palm. Mr. Morris would then raise his other hand high in the air and bring it down with sufficient force to cause a sharp sting. On this occasion I am ashamed to say that, just before his hand reached the back of mine, I pulled my hand away. I had not thought about it, it was not planned, it was just an impulse – the instinct to avoid pain, just as if my hand had been in danger of being burned. But the look on Mr. Morris's face said it all. Not one of anger but of abject disappointment. He was clearly disgusted that I had not been brave enough to 'take my punishment'. At that moment, if I could have substituted my head for my hand I would have done and if a train had been passing, I may well have thrown myself underneath it. I was ashamed of myself, and Mr. Morris knew it. Instead of grabbing my hand and trying again, though, he just left it at that and ordered me out. From what must have been my expression he had realised that what I had done had affected me much more than any slap on the wrist could have. So I often wonder, given all that I have read and been told about the myriad hell on earth situations that arose during the First World War (sometimes it is even hard to imagine Hell itself being quite so bad in comparison) whether I would have been able to hold my nerve under such pressure. As the bombs exploded around me and the rifles and machine guns spat towards me, the bullets whistled past me and my comrades were falling like flies all around, not to mention the hand-to-hand fighting to come, would I be able to keep going? Or would something snap inside me and would I turn and run? I'd like to think not, but I have no doubt that braver men than I have. Surely, it's only natural – adrenaline kicks in – fight or flight and all that. Logically, I suppose that the prospect of being shot at dawn was meant to put you off, but if the war had made you mentally ill, you would not be thinking logically. If you were, you would not be mentally ill. Think about it.

A former work client of mine, Tom Stones, found out when he was researching his family history quite late in life, that a relative of his, his great-uncle, had been shot at dawn for so-called 'cowardice'. It is a truly strange and incomprehensible story and seems, on the face of it at least, to be a gross miscarriage of justice. See what you think.

Joseph William Stones, known as 'Will', was a coal miner from Crook, County Durham, a small market town just a few miles south-west of Durham. He was born around 1890 and by the time war broke in 1914, had married and was living with his wife, Elizabeth, and their small family. Soon afterwards, eager to do his bit, Joseph tried to join up, but was initially rejected on account of his small stature; he was only 5 ft 2 inches – an inch short of the then minimum height, despite being of solid build. The height restriction was most probably used as a bit of a political tool at the time, in that it tended to control the steady flow of recruits through the system and (or so it was thought) would ensure that the 'more able' would be enlisted first. To this end the first few months of the war saw the minimum height shifted about a bit: first being raised to 5 ft 6 inches and then falling back again to 5 ft 3 inches when the demand for more volunteers increased. However, as the war got underway, the height restrictions began to come in for increasing criticism, not least from within the mining community, where being 'a bit short' was a distinct advantage. Also, at about the same time, although mining was a reserved occupation, there arose a much greater demand for miners at the front, in order to tunnel under no man's land to lay mines and blow up the enemy from beneath their trenches. Prompted mainly by these issues, one campaigner, Cheshire MP Alfred Bigland, formed the first of what were called 'Bantam Battalions' in Birkenhead in November 1914. These battalions, named after the small but feisty breed of poultry, enabled men below 5 ft 3 inches to enlist and, in early 1915, the formation of a Bantam Battalion of the Durham Light Infantry meant that Will could finally join up.

After his initial training, Pte. Stones embarked for France in early 1916 and within a few months he was fighting on the Somme. He was clearly a willing soldier, as during this time, in addition to having earned several commendations for bravery, Will was swiftly promoted through the ranks to lance (acting) sergeant.

After surviving the horrors of the initial stages of the battle, he fought bravely on right into late November, until an event said to have occurred on the front line near Arras on the night of 25/26 November was to seal his fate.

Accounts vary widely, in that some describe L/Sgt. Stones's group being attacked by a German raiding party, when his senior officer, a Lt. Munday, was fatally wounded, whereas others claim that Sgt. Stones and the officer were attacking the Germans when this happened. Yet another account suggests that a ferocious rumour had arisen (later proving to have been false) that the British were just about to be attacked and a sergeant had ordered them to withdraw. Whatever, that part of the line had been considered vulnerable by the Germans for some time and was renowned for being raided on a fairly regular basis, so everybody must have been a bit jumpy, to say the least. What also remains unclear is exactly why Sgt. Stones, along with two lance corporals, McDonald and Goggins, then fell back behind the lines, leaving their rifles behind. When found by military police, they were said to be in a terrible state, but it was the reasons why they were unarmed that would form the crux of the case against them.

Among the several grounds under which you could have been shot by your own side including desertion, falling asleep on guard duty or disobeying orders, was the 'casting away of arms', as it was called, i.e., abandoning arms or ammunition rather than fighting. So, at his court martial, which took place on Christmas Eve 1916, L/Sgt. Stones was officially charged with 'shamefully casting away his arms in the presence of the enemy'. Although not allowed to speak up for himself, his written statement went that Lt. Munday, after having been seriously wounded, ordered him to go for help. He maintained that the loss of his rifle was down to a problem with its mechanism that had prevented him from being able to fire it and so he had instead jammed it across the trench in the hope that it might at least hamper the German advance.

Despite this, and the support of his 'Prisoner's Friend' (another soldier allowed to speak in the prisoner's defence) together with Will's former commendations and statements from officers, including his commanding officer, to the effect that he was indeed a brave man and entirely incapable of cowardice, L/Sgt. Stones was summarily sentenced to death by firing squad. It seemed as though the obvious stress that would have affected the men who went through the full terrors of the Somme campaign, counted for nothing. The two lance corporals were also sentenced to death, in their cases for quitting their posts.

In spite of all the doubts, the so-called subsequent reviews of the case, including one by Haig himself, whilst upholding the verdicts on Stones, McDonald and Goggins, reprieved several others who had also been sentenced to death for desertion through the very same incident. Was it that these three were to be the scapegoats, the 'examples'?

The executions were set for dawn on Thursday 18 January 1917 in woods a few miles to the west of Arras. Accounts tell of how the three arrived in a field ambulance and were led, 'manacled and blindfolded', to three posts that had been driven into the ground and were surrounded by straw. An envelope was then pinned on each man's chest, over the position of the heart, to act as a target. After a brief speech, "Ready," the thirty-six soldiers of the firing squad drew their rifles (twelve per prisoner), "Aim," then, after a moment's silence, the officer in charge yanks his stick down; "Fire!"

Although tradition holds that at least one man in each squad would often have been given a rifle containing a blank cartridge in order to enable the possibility that any one of them may not have been the one who had killed the prisoner, what happened next is another source of controversy. Despite almost all other accounts implying that the prisoners were shot and killed outright by the firing squad, both Gary Miller, in his song, 'The Ballad of Lance Sergeant William Stones' and Peter Drake in his play and book, *The Prisoner's Friend*, suggest that the members of the firing squad aimed away (implicitly through conscience because they disagreed with the matter) and it was left to the officer in charge to finish the execution with his pistol. If so, it is not difficult to see why this particular aspect would have been suppressed at the time.

There was no report of any resistance, and all three men went to meet their maker in the most dignified of ways. Indeed, a chaplain, with whom they had earlier prayed, said that he had never met braver men.

I understand that Will had three young daughters, one of which had sadly died of measles shortly after he had left for the front. But it is understood that when a British military policeman picked up and read a letter taken from Will's tunic after he had been killed, and which was headed 'Dear Daddy', it reduced him to tears.

Unfortunately, the cold, hard official version of events more often prevails over the full details, and it was no doubt due to the shame of Will Stones's alleged cowardice that his family rarely spoke about him and indeed, were loath to hold on to any reminder that he ever even existed. When he was only a young man, Tom Stones himself said that he had been confused when he came across an old Bible in which his Great-Uncle Joseph's name had been written, as he had never heard of such a relation. It was only in later life, when further research led him to the Regimental Museum at Durham and the curator explained it all to him, that Tom fully began to understand why. Subsequently he was able to add further detail when a large number of previously secret war documents were released for public review.

There was to be a particularly disturbing aspect to this whole affair that would befall Will's wife, whom he called Lizzie, and her two small daughters, when they were denied both a war pension and any of the medals due to him for the campaigns in which he had previously so bravely fought. Having initially been told that he had been 'killed in action', her application for the pension is said to have been met with the callous, dismissive response, 'We don't give pensions to cowards' widows'! Additionally, it was decided that Will's name would be excluded from all the war memorials that were subsequently erected.

His final resting place is in the St. Pol Communal Cemetery Extension at Saint-Pol-sur-Ternoise, which is situated not far from where he was executed.

Other nations also executed some of their own soldiers for various acts of 'disobedience' during World War I, with France thought to have executed more than any other! Germany is understood to have executed only twenty or so but it should be added that during World War II, under Hitler, the number was said to have been in the thousands. As for Russia, who can say?

To put things in proportion, there were many thousands of Allied courts martial held during the course of World War I, many of which resulted in convictions for matters that could, in theory at least, have resulted in summary execution. In the vast majority of cases, however, these sentences were commuted, and the 346 who were actually executed, although a sad number, makes for a very low proportion.

The British Labour Government of the 1930s; the second term under Ramsey MacDonald, abolished the death penalty for desertion and no British soldiers were officially executed for this offence during World War II. With all the weaponry available, however, as to whether any were unofficially executed can only be guessed. Ironically, although the United States did not officially execute any of their soldiers during their involvement in World War I, just one, Edward Donald Slovik, was executed for desertion during World War II. Apparently, despite being given no end of opportunities simply to return to combat, he had insisted on facing a court martial, so could this also have been largely down to mental instability as well?

So moved by his discovery, Tom Stones spent the last years of his life on a crusade against what he saw as the grossly unjust way in which his great-uncle, and over 300 other British and Commonwealth combatants (the vast majority being British in either France or Belgium), had been dealt with during World War I. Through his organisation, SAD, short for 'Shot at Dawn', in the year 2000 he was able to overturn the ban on the relatives of those who had died this way from attending Armistice Day parades at the Cenotaph in London, proudly standing shoulder to shoulder with them at the event that year. He also managed to get Will's name added to the town's war memorial in Crook. Unfortunately, Tom died from cancer at the relatively young age of sixty early in 2001 and so did not live to see the opening of the National Memorial Arboretum near Alrewas in Staffordshire later that year. The Memorial is sited not too far from where Tom used to live, and incorporates a statue of a young, blindfolded soldier with his hands tied behind his back; a commemoration to all those British and Commonwealth combatants who were shot for, what was more than likely, an unavoidable and perfectly natural and understandable breakdown, brought on by the relentless nightmare in which they found themselves.

In 2006, Tom, I am sure, would have been justly proud when

309 of the 346 so treated were officially pardoned, leaving out only the thirty-seven who were convicted for murder. It was appended, however, that even though pardoned, the convictions still stood, presumably in order to avoid any 'misunderstandings'.

*

As already mentioned, the amount of documentation available to do with my grandfather's part in World War I is much more limited than that concerning Frank's and Syd's, but I have heard a great deal of recounted stories about him, mainly through my father. Even so things can sometimes appear a little distorted when viewed through the lens of time, and, like so many who went through that horrific experience and survived, my father often said that his father 'did not like to talk about it'. From what I have been able to glean, however, he certainly had a pretty rough time of things, not only during the war itself, but also through how he was affected by it, and the resultant circumstances in which he found himself after the war would dog him for the rest of his life.

My grandfather, Albert George Warren, was born in 1894 and, although I have searched high and low at the Wigston Record Office, I cannot find out for sure where he went to school. My money is on Mantle Road, as Frank, his next older brother, attended there when the family lived in Middle Street (now gone, as it was situated where the grounds of De Montfort University now stand). By the time Albert was old enough to begin school, however, the family had moved to Tewkesbury Street, but Tewkesbury Street is nearer to Mantle Road so the theory still stands. Although Syd, who was Granddad's next younger brother, appears to have gone to Narborough Road School, I think that this school had only been built (in or around 1901) around the time (or possibly a little later) that Albert would have been old enough to start his education. Maybe Albert started at Mantle Road and was then moved to Narborough Road, I simply cannot be sure.

Between 1900 and 1918, the official school leaving age was

fourteen, but, in the face of the needs of many families at the time, it was regarded as more the exception than the rule, and many children were as young as twelve years old when they left school. So, in view of my understanding of my family's circumstances at the time, I would think it unlikely that my grandfather, who would have been twelve in June 1906, would have returned to school for the autumn term that year. The 1911 Census has him down as 'Butcher', but I have seen another record, from just before the war, that has him down as a train carriage cleaner, so he obviously gave up butchering some time between 1911 and 1914 to work for the railways, and it would be the railways to which he would return following the war. I was always told that he worked on the left luggage counter and the railway records have him down as 'Cloak Room Attendant' so, unless the term 'left luggage' was being used euphemistically, this would appear to fit.

Unlike Frank and Syd, though, as far as I am aware, he did not join the Territorials in his youth.

For most of the service records that I have managed to track down about my grandfather, I am indebted to local historians, John Sutton and Adam Llewellyn, whom I met at an open event in Ibstock in 2018 and who very kindly took the time to dig them out from the bare details that I gave them. They mainly relate to his periods of hospitalisation, and it has to be said that they appear, at first sight, to be a little confusing. I put this down mainly to the severe strain that hospital staff must have been under, at a time when the completion of records would naturally have been regarded as much less of a priority than saving someone's life. However, back-calculating from them, I have concluded that my grandfather made the trip to the army recruiting office in Humberstone Gate and joined up some time in early January 1915. And since this must have been in or around the time that his first child was conceived – his daughter, Gwen, and probably only shortly after he had met his future wife, Marion, he may well have been a bit apprehensive about the decision. Alternatively, although there had been much talk about the war being over by Christmas and it clearly was not, he may well have decided that now was the time.

In any event, by 1 May 1915 he was 'Soldier No. 16652, 9th Leicesters' according to his marriage certificate when he married Marion Jack Blyth that day at Saint John the Divine Church, South Albion Street, Leicester. The church is situated just across London Road from the Midland Train Station, and although it still stands today, it has now been deconsecrated and turned into flats.

The 9ths formed part of Kitchener's Third New Army (K3) and along with the 6th, 7th and 8th Leicesters, the 110th Machine Gun Company and the 110th Trench Mortar Battery, became the 110th Brigade or 'Leicester Tigers Brigade' – a sort of 'Pals Battalion' you might say. I understand that after initial training at Aldershot they were sent to Salisbury, and then crossed to France on 29 July 1915, initially stationed at Tilques, near Saint-Omer, just over twenty miles behind the front. This would make sense, since there was a machine gun training school near Saint-Omer (within or attached to a convent I think) as, at around this time, my grandfather trained as a machine gunner. He must have volunteered for it, I suppose, and this was his role when, a year or so later, he was among those advancing towards Mametz Wood, near Fricourt on the Somme.

According to the official records, early on Friday 14 July 1916 the German positions were being heavily shelled when the 9ths joined the reserve line. A large number of casualties were sustained, including all the officers, when part of the Battalion, along with the 6th, 7th and 8th Leicesters, pushed northwards to Bazentin-le-Petit wood. By dawn, however, they had managed to make it through the wood and were able to consolidate. Throughout the morning the British made a concerted attempt to drive any remaining enemy soldiers out of the wood, but it was not entirely successful. Then, by the early afternoon, when the Germans began heavily bombarding the area, it started to look as though they were going to follow through with a counter-attack.

However, reinforcements were drawn and in the late afternoon orders were given to attack the remaining German stronghold in the north-western corner of the wood. Unfortunately, this resulted in many more British being cut down, particularly by machine gun fire, than there were German casualties, and the offensive stalled yet again. As the day drew to a close and the fighting stopped, it was clear that both sides had sustained a large number of casualties.

In the early hours of the following day, Saturday 15 July, the Battalion was sent back to Mametz Wood but the report then says they were 'ordered to return to their original post'. Which I presume meant back to Bazentin-le-Petit in order to try, yet again, to clear the wood. Unfortunately, that evening a subaltern and twenty men found themselves isolated in the German-occupied corner of the wood which had, by now, become a pretty inhospitable place to be. Sadly, they were mercilessly attacked with grenades by the Germans, and all were believed to have been either killed or wounded. Although a party from the 1st East Yorks. Regt. subsequently went out in search of the missing men, they were unable to locate any of them.

The following Sunday food and rum rations allowed for a brief respite, and it was with great jubilation that, over the next twenty-four hours, the Leicesters were ordered to fall back to Fricourt, having been relieved by the 64th Infantry Brigade. In total, eighteen officers and 349 other ranks had been either killed or wounded, and one of the wounded must have been my grandfather, who had incurred severe gunshot wounds to his left thigh, but I am not at all sure as to specifically how or when this happened or exactly where he was at the time.

As a young boy, when I used to ask my father about it, he would often simply reply that he was 'shot up on the Somme', or words to that effect. On one occasion, however, he added that after his father had been shot, he managed to make it to the comparative safety of an empty house, where he lay for some time, no doubt drifting in and out of consciousness. I understand that he sheltered in the house for several days because, apparently, he mentioned being aware that the Germans, having been initially pushed back, returned and then retreated again several times while he was lying there. In view of this, therefore, he must have sustained his injuries during the very early stages of the engagement. As it turned out he was rescued, of course, as otherwise I would not be writing this, but his suffering, I'm afraid, was to be far from over.

The first medical report is dated 16 July and from No.11 Stationary Hospital, Rouen – an ancient French city on the River Seine, some ninety miles to the south-west of the front and fifty-five miles from the port of Le Havre to the west. This hospital, along with several others, was situated at the city's racecourse (now a public park) in the southern outskirts of Rouen. Incidentally, around this time, a large brothel was said to have established itself in Rouen and the hospital, as well as receiving the wounded, was admitting more than its fair share of cases of venereal disease. So much so that if a soldier were to contract VD, they were often referred to behind their backs as 'a client for Rouen'.

My grandfather was not there for that, though, as on the report it clearly states, 'GSW. L thigh & comp fract femur' [*sic*], which I take to be gunshot wound to left thigh with compound fracture of femur. It may not have escaped your thoughts but when I first came upon this description and thought about all the possible consequences of being injured in this area of the body, it brought the full meaning of 'the butterfly effect' home to me. For that fraction of a second when the bullet or bullets that hit him were fired, not only his life, but both my father's and therefore, my future life hung in the balance. It all depends how souls are dished out, I suppose, but assuming that they are not simply given to the next conception that comes along, irrespective of family, had that butterfly not taken off in Brazil (or had, as the case may be), I would never have been born.

He stayed at Rouen for ten days, presumably under observation and in order to stabilise him both physically and mentally before being repatriated for further treatment. On 26 July he was discharged from Rouen and transported back across the Channel overnight, no doubt from Le Havre to Southampton, aboard the hospital ship HMHS *Gloucester Castle* and on the 27th he was admitted to the Royal Victoria Military Hospital, Netley, near Southampton, where he was to remain for over a year! Two days later his name appeared in the *Leicester Daily Mercury* amongst the many other casualties incurred by the Leicesters under the heading, 'A HEAVY LIST'.

Launched in 1911, the *Gloucester Castle* was later to have a bit of a rough time of things herself, firstly through being torpedoed by a German U-boat near the Isle of Wight in 1917. She was not sunk, however, and after being repaired, was recommissioned as a passenger ship following the war. During the Second World War, though, she was not so lucky. Now carrying cargo as well as passengers, she was considered fair game and in 1942, after coming under heavy fire from the German cruiser *Michel* off the west coast of Africa, she sank, killing most on board, including her captain.

Netley, also known as 'the Palace of pain' was a huge hospital, in fact one of Britain's largest hospitals during the First World War. Built at the behest of Queen Victoria in the mid-1850s, its primary purpose had been to treat the wounded of the Crimean War, but it certainly came into its own again when the vast numbers of casualties began to arrive back from France and Belgium. Conan Doyle's Dr. John Watson was supposed to have honed his skills as a surgeon here but he, of course, was fictitious, whilst the poet, Wilfred Owen, was a very real incumbent when he was treated here for shell shock. Owen's relatively short stay was just before my grandfather was discharged but I would doubt that they ever met.

On the outbreak of the Second World War Netley would again serve as a military hospital, notably treating many that had been injured during the Dunkirk evacuation.

There were anaesthetics, antiseptics, anti-inflammatory and antipyretic drugs of sorts around in 1916, along with painkillers such as morphine, that had been known down the ages. However, since Alexander Fleming did not happen on penicillin and its effects until 1928, there was no such thing as an antibiotic during the First World War. So, since one of the most serious risks posed by invasive injuries and subsequent surgery is infection, my grandfather was already in a much more dangerous situation than somebody similarly injured would be today. On top of this, the dirtier the wound, the more likely it was to be or to become infected and, having been incurred on the battlefield, my grandfather's was unlikely to have been the cleanest wound ever seen. In the worst cases, when such injuries become infected and the infections spread, even with modern antibiotics, they can prove very difficult, if not impossible, to treat and so my grandfather's eventual survival would have carried quite a measure of luck with it.

It is a sad fact, though, that many antibiotics are now becoming significantly less effective in curing bacterial infections due to their (often frivolous) overuse, having caused resistant strains of bacteria to develop over the years. From a personal perspective, I am convinced that without them I would not be here today.

Much to the concern of my parents, in my early childhood I experienced repeated bouts of tonsillitis. This eventually turned to quinsy, which severely obstructed my breathing. My mother said that she could clearly hear my gasps when she was downstairs, and I was upstairs in bed. Although I was very ill, the repeated doses of penicillin that the doctor prescribed eventually started to work and I slowly began to feel better. Shortly afterwards the decision was made to have my tonsils removed. Although new antibiotics are being developed, to lose the effects of such a 'panacea' brings Einstein's famous saying to mind. He thought that there were two things that may be infinite: the universe and human stupidity, but he was not quite sure about the universe…

The record I have of my grandfather's extended stay in Netley makes for some grim reading:

Disease *G.S.W. thigh Ampt^{n}*
Operations *Amputation – Re-amputation*
Result of operation *Fairly satisfactory*
Complications in order of occurrence *Double pneumonia*

Signature of Medical Officer [looks like] *J E Holden*

In other words, he had not only had most of his left leg amputated, but it seems that the first amputation was not good enough and they had to go back in and take more of his leg away. And as if that was not enough, he had contracted double pneumonia into the bargain! No wonder it would take so long before he was allowed to leave.

My grandfather's records go on to show that on 10 September 1917 he was transferred to the 'General Hospital Pavilion Brighton'. This is the Royal Brighton Pavilion, built for George IV in the early nineteenth century but used during the First World War as a hospital, initially for Indian troops, but later for the treatment of amputees. In view of the length of time that my grandfather was hospitalised, I'm sure that his parents and other available members of his family, but especially his wife, Marion, would have visited as and when they could. In all probability, although not as often as they would have liked, mainly on account of the cost of getting there, unless perhaps, they were entitled to any discounts on account of my grandfather having worked for the railways before the war. One thing that is certain is that Albert and Marion must have been together on or around 15 October 1917 because this was when my father was conceived as he was born on 10 July 1918 and always used to say, "When I was born the First World War was still raging."

It is hard to be completely accurate as time frames can vary, but on average the human gestation period lasts some 268 days (just over thirty-eight weeks) and 15 October 1917 is exactly 268 days before 10 July 1918. I have never heard anything to the effect that my father was born prematurely, or late, and before you ask, there is absolutely no doubt in my mind that my father was my grandfather's biological son. They were so alike that when, as a child, I looked at old photographs of my grandfather, I was convinced that they were images of my father. Could it have been that he was released for a short period then? Here again, there is no evidence that he was, since his hospital records suggest a continuous stay and, if he had been able to return, even for a short stay, then why could he not have been treated for the remainder of his issues nearer home? In short, I am as certain as I can be that my father's conception took place during my grandfather's stay in hospital at Brighton. But how did they manage it? In most of the pictures that I have seen of military hospitals at this time the rooms are packed with beds which are often spaced very close together. So it is unlikely that things were initiated on the ward. The only conclusion is that they must have found somewhere secluded during that visit – a linen store, perhaps? The mystery deepens when a glance at my grandfather's records for his time in the Pavilion shows up something that may have further complicated matters: 'Excision of femur at neck'. From what I can glean, this is more surgery to remove the head of the femur (or thigh bone) from the hip socket. As he was at the Pavilion until mid-December 1917, however, this operation could well have taken place after Marion's visit, but if the couple were hoping that she would conceive through this encounter, they must have had their doubts.

I have a picture of him seated between a Highlander to his right – this man missing the bottom part of his leg, though still standing on crutches, and a short chap – possibly a member of a Bantam regiment, to his left. Most likely taken during his time at Netley or the Pavilion, it clearly shows that there is very little, if anything, remaining of his left leg.

On 14 December 1917 my grandfather was moved again. He appears to have been initially bound for Queen Mary's Hospital, Roehampton – a military hospital situated near Putney, London, set up to care for wounded soldiers, particularly amputees. However, possibly due to logistical problems, he ended up in King George Hospital, nearer to London's city centre. The building had only recently been constructed and was originally intended to be a government stationery warehouse. However, on the outbreak of war, its situation, just up the road from Waterloo Station, made it very handy in facilitating the conveyance of the wounded arriving at the station from the Western Front, especially since the hospital and station were connected by tunnels, which meant the seriously wounded could be moved more safely and away from public gaze. By 1917 it too was one of the largest hospitals in Britain, and was taking in many who, like my granddad, needed to convalesce after prolonged periods of treatment. And it was said to have been a nice place to convalesce, there being a roof garden, recreation rooms and large grounds on which shelters had been built so that patients could relax and enjoy the view of the River Thames in all weathers. Excursions were even arranged as and when patients became more active.

The record I have of my grandfather's stay here is, no doubt, yet another example of the pressure that many hospital staff members must have been subject to at the time. Under 'Observations' after 'Disease' the MO has written: 'GSW Amp^{n}. L. arm' [*sic*], when it was his left leg that had been amputated. I am absolutely sure that neither of his arms had been affected in any way.

After some six weeks here, in late January 1918 he was discharged 'as an invalid' and returned home to Dunkirk Street, Leicester, to be reunited with his wife, Marion, and daughter, Gwen, who by now would have been nearly two and a half years old.

In all, my grandfather had been hospitalised for over eighteen months and undergone at least three highly invasive surgical procedures since sustaining his injuries. Nevertheless, he had pulled through and even managed to father another child into the bargain. He must have been made of some tough stuff, but then he needed to be as, although he could not have foreseen it at the time, his struggles were still far from over.

*

The first of these subsequent struggles arose when something strange happened about his military discharge. You need to understand, though, that all this comes from my father's anecdotal account of the matter, which he could not possibly have witnessed for himself as he would either not have been born or, if he had, would only have been a baby. So he must have been told this, most probably by either his father or his mother, or both, and, as I say, the fogs of time can often distort recollections. Additionally, all the attempts that I have made to research the story more fully have, so far, shed very little, if any, further light on it.

On the '(E1615) Army Form W.3243A' issued from King George Hospital, London it clearly states that he was discharged 'as an invalid 26-1-18' [*sic*] and I can find no prior gaps between his periods of stay at different hospitals. In another record, though, his discharge date is down as '15.2.18' [*sic*] so whether this has anything to do with it I do not know. Anyway, the story goes that shortly after he arrived back home two policemen turned up at his front door and arrested him for being absent without leave – effectively desertion, and we all know what that could lead to. The fact that he only had one leg and that he had been in hospital for eighteen months did not appear to faze them. Whether or not he was held in custody I do not know but, under the circumstances, I hope not and would have thought it highly unlikely but it did go to court with my grandfather in the dock, in front of the judge. As the story goes, the police gave their evidence, after which my grandfather was allowed to speak and, after explaining that he had been in hospital since 1916, demonstrated that he only had one leg. At this point the judge's face was said to have dropped and, turning to the policemen, told them in no uncertain terms, not to be 'so bloody stupid'!

Quite why this matter came to court in the first place, I have no idea, and can only guess that with conscription having been introduced, and the demand for fighting men at this stage of the war so great, anyone even slightly suspected of avoiding 'their duty' would be pursued most vigorously. Still, pretty poor treatment, though, for one who had already given so much for his country, I feel.

Epilogue

'Does it matter? – losing your legs?
For people will always be kind...'
'Does it Matter?' – Siegfried Sassoon

After my grandfather finally came home, although he had been badly wounded, the household began slowly to return to what passed for normal in those times and, when his 'brush with the law' was out of the way, unfortunately, a long line of other sad issues still lay ahead. As well as the losses of Frank and Syd, my grandfather's two other brothers, John (Jack) and Arch, had also been wounded and Marion had lost one brother, with another wounded. So, even in the absence of anything else, for those members of the family who had returned, life could never be quite the same again.

By 1918, although the Russians had now packed up and left to fight a revolution, the United States had entered the war and become heavily involved, sending large numbers of troops to Europe. Also, with the determined counter-attack by the Allies following Germany's 'Michael Offensive' and the civil unrest within Germany, it was now beginning to look unlikely that the Central Powers could possibly prevail.

In early August 1918, the Battle of Amiens began what was to become known as the 'Hundred Days Offensive': a concerted effort by the Allies to regain lost ground and to push the Germans yet further back. Shortly afterwards the Americans and French attacked in Meuse-Argonne and, although costing many casualties, these assaults did drive the Germans back to the extent that they lost significant areas of previously occupied France and Belgium.

Then, in the Middle East, when General Allenby's forces succeeded in overcoming the Turks in Palestine and the tide of the war had swung well and truly in favour of the Allies, the Axis powers began to sue for peace.

We tend to take the First World War to have been a victory for the Allies and essentially it was, leading to the downfall of no less than three enemy empires. Technically, however, it was an armistice (a negotiated ceasefire) that drew the conflict to a close. And, although Allied occupations followed, including a partial occupation of Germany, there was nothing on the scale of the occupation of Germany after the Second World War.

When the German delegation came face to face with Marshal Foch in that train carriage in the forest near Compiègne, a few miles to the north-east of Paris, they found him in no mood to compromise. With Germany's collapse, both at the front and at home, threatening her very existence, Foch knew that he was on solid ground. In addition to the proposed occupation of Germany, the swift withdrawal of all German troops that remained in occupied France, Belgium and Luxembourg, as well as the return of Alsace-Lorraine to France (which had been retained by Germany after the Franco-Prussian War), were demanded. The Germans were also required to withdraw from various other territories including Austria-Hungary (which would also have to be split up), Turkey and Romania. Additionally Germany was required to pay war reparations and many of her ships, planes and trains, along with her armaments, were to be confiscated.

Foch was right to stand his ground and very early on the morning of Monday 11 November 1918, the Armistice was signed. It was to come into effect later that day at 11am GMT (British and French clocks being set the same then) and, although it would be the following year until the Treaty of Versailles was signed, apart from a very few remnants of hostility, it was the day that the guns fell silent on the Western Front and, therefore, effectively the end of the Great War. However, because of certain outstanding details, at least as far as America was concerned, it would take until 1921 for the US Government officially to recognise the end of hostilities in every respect!

Foch was pretty perspicacious about something else too. When it came to the final draft of the Treaty of Versailles he was not at all happy with the detail and felt that it was far too liberal when it came to putting an end to Germany's belligerence. He was said to have exclaimed, "This is not a peace, it is an armistice for twenty years!" Although technically wrong (the 'Armistice' would last for twenty years and sixty-five days to be precise) he wasn't far off, was he? A certain Corporal Adolf Hitler of the 16th Bavarians pictured sneering towards the camera in many a World War I photograph and another useless 'scrap of paper', this time signed by him, saw to that. Against the backdrop of the desperate economic and social mess that Germany found itself in at the end of 1918, Hitler was able to garner increasing popular support for the idea that Germany's failure had lain at the hands of scapegoats and thus history was to repeat itself. In other words, the 'unfinished business' of World War I turned into the horror that was World War II, which was to claim globally some three times as many lives!

*

Everyone must have seen those pictures of smiling people standing on every surface possible of those old B-type double decker buses or in town squares, waving handkerchiefs and flags etc. that symbolised the joy and relief that only the end to that fierce and bloody First World War could have brought. But, as the war was drawing to a close, another threat was just emerging, one that would end up killing many more people than the war had. Estimates vary, but World War I was reckoned to have cost something like twenty million lives worldwide, whereas some claim that the so-called 'Spanish flu' pandemic cost fifty million plus, rivalling even the number of those taken during the 'Black Death' pandemic of the late Middle Ages! The earliest cases of Spanish flu in the UK were detected in Glasgow during May 1918, the virus having presumably arrived via the port there. The same city having suffered a small outbreak of bubonic plague during what was dubbed the 'third pandemic' only eighteen years before, which probably originated in the same way. But, unlike the outbreak of plague in 1900, which was contained, Spanish flu soon spread southwards and was to turn up in London only a few weeks later. It was a sort of 'perfect storm' in that it was caused by a highly infectious virus that arose when so many people, often crowded together and completely stressed out by the effects of over four years of privation, were mixing with very large numbers of war-weary soldiers returning home from the front. It did not help that, although viruses were known to exist, their close scientific study was still very much in its infancy and this virus could kill very quickly, especially if it led to pneumonia. 'Sore throat at breakfast – dead by teatime!' was a saying of the time. For many it must have seemed like the final straw.

Although initially detected in Spain, the true origins of the virus are unclear. Some have suggested that, like several other viral diseases that have emerged since, including COVID-19, it may have come from the Far East, possibly China, whilst others thought North America or Europe itself, but the truth is that nobody really knows. A 'zoonotic virus', meaning that it can spread from animals to man, its genetic makeup suggested avian origin, possibly from intensively reared domestic fowl.

A nursery rhyme penned at the time went:

> I had a little bird,
> Its name was Enza,
> I opened up the window,
> And in-flu-enza.

The close proximity of the troops at the front meant that once one of them caught the disease it would soon start to infect many more. The symptoms of the earliest infections seemed mild. Although affected troops and other initial victims experienced the usual fever and aches and pains, these tended to subside after a few days, and almost all those infected began to recover. In response the medics began to call it 'three-day fever' and the full effect of the pandemic was only to become clearer when the troops started to return home, bringing the infection with them. As it spread, this 'second wave' seemed to have a much more serious effect on the body, in the worst cases leading to suffocation as the lungs filled with mucus and blood. Before long an increasing number of victims began to experience these severe breathing difficulties, many dying within hours!

The deaths of Frank and Syd, relatively early on in the war, the repatriation of my grandfather in 1916 and both Jack and Arch being wounded (out of the war?) left only Fred and Ernest, who I believe returned unscathed and, presumably, not carrying the virus. So, as far as I know, none of my family contracted Spanish flu during the 1918–19 pandemic. Nevertheless, they cannot have escaped every single aspect of it as infection levels and death rates due to Spanish flu in Leicester were among some of the highest in the country.

Despite its decline during the early 1920s, influenza of any kind was and still can be a very serious disease and, although probably a different strain of the infection, it was to rear its ugly head again towards the end of the decade; this time leaving the Warren family entirely unable to escape its attention.

*

In view of the way that shell shock was regarded by some as mere cowardice back then, I suspect that the idea of any connection between birth defects and the levels of stress previously experienced by the parents would not have been widely considered. Nowadays, however, it is thought that there may well be something to it, particularly, but not solely, if it is the mother who has been affected. So, since my grandmother, Marion, with her husband away fighting, as well as (I understand) one brother being wounded and the other lost, would surely have suffered her fair share of stress on top of all that experienced by my grandfather. And it is because of this that I have always wondered whether what happened next might, at least in part, have been an added consequence of the traumas of war.

Some five and a half months after my grandfather returned home, my father was born, and although otherwise healthy, he was born with a clubbed foot. In this type of birth defect, the foot or feet are twisted inwards and the sole or soles, instead of being flat towards the floor, are at an angle, sometimes even at right angles to it. Although a fairly common birth defect, its exact cause is still not fully understood. There is a slight hereditary correlation, though, and since my maternal grandfather was also born with the condition, when I was born, naturally the first thing my parents did was to examine my feet. Both my feet were normal, I am pleased to say.

With modern techniques, in most cases, and where treatment is started as soon as possible, it is relatively easy to restore the foot to a good degree of normality. Back when my father was born, however, the treatment was not quite so effective. He spoke of several operations and having to wear a leg brace, which he hated, but this treatment would continue until he was about ten years old. I have seen photographs of him as a young boy, some with his leg brace on and others, taken at a similar age, with it off. Whether that was because he was reluctant to be photographed with it on or whether it was during a period when he did not have to wear it, I do not know, but his legs do look a little bent without the brace. As he got older, he suffered from more aches and pains in and around his affected foot than would normally be expected, and I recall that his foot remained a distinctly abnormal shape throughout his life.

*

Following the General Strike of 1926, towards the end of the 1920s the Great Economic Depression began to descend on the world. But, as far as my grandfather's family was concerned, these events must have seemed mere asides in comparison to the misery that was about to befall them.

It may have been during the winter of 1929–30 or, perhaps more likely because it was a very cold winter, that of 1928–9. The story goes that my grandfather had made a sledge for the kids, who would have been aged between something like six and thirteen at the time. One day, after a heavy snowfall, they went off to the local park to try it out. Climbing to the top of a hill they all got on: Gwen, more than likely at the front as she was the eldest, my dad; Albert, his younger brother; Harry (possibly) and the youngest; Charley. As the snow was thick and hard the sledge soon gathered momentum and sped down the hill, only to plough straight into a tree. All were relatively unscathed except for Gwen who had hit her head and, by all accounts, had either been knocked out or, at least, 'gone very limp'. The other kids raised the alarm, and she was taken back home. Although with time Gwen appeared to recover, my Aunt Doll always used to say that she seemed much slower than she had been before and 'never really got back to her old self again'.

During the summer of 1930, however, she must have taken a serious turn for the worse, as she was admitted to the Leicester General Hospital, Evington, where, sadly, she died. Her death certificate, signed by Dr. Ernest C. Hadley, gives the cause of death as *Encephalitis lethargica* – an inflammation of the brain.

Although thought by some to be a possible side effect of Spanish flu infection, the general consensus was that the blow to her head, sustained during the sledging accident, had led to the inflammation, which had then slowly increased to a fatal level. Even today nobody knows exactly what causes encephalitis and there is no known cure, although some drugs can be effective in the short term.

Albeit that I doubt Gwen's death was a direct result of the stresses imposed on her parents by the horrors of the war, as may have been the case with my dad, they certainly would not have helped.

I understand that Gwen, being the eldest, and Charley, being the youngest, were particularly close and that she may well have 'mothered' him to a degree. So there can be little doubt that the eight-year-old Charley would have felt the loss of his big sister every bit as much as the rest of the family, if not more so. Indeed, the bond between them must have been very strong, as my Uncle Charley would mention Gwen 'coming to him' when he knew that he was dying, almost sixty years later.

Thankfully the type of encephalitis that affected Gwen now appears to be much rarer than it was during those years following the First World War. And it may well have been that its prevalence, relatively shortly after the Spanish flu pandemic, could have been down to some link between the two diseases.

From the pictures I have of Gwen, she was a beautiful young girl and her loss to the family must have been every bit as devastating as those of Frank and Syd, during the war. I often wished that she had survived and that I could have known her but alas, these matters are decided by higher powers than we.

Rest in peace Gwen.

*

Believe it or not, though, there was yet more misery to come when the winter of 1932–3 saw another outbreak of influenza. And, with the memory of Gwen's demise still raw, Harry, now coming up for thirteen and for reasons soon to become clear, being unlikely to have been the easiest youngster to live with, my grandmother catches the disease. At the same time, despite the successes of his operations, my grandfather was still suffering, particularly, as often happens, when the shrapnel and other debris that remained inside him, tended to move about. But as they say, one tragedy does not preclude another and in early February 1933 my grandmother's infection led to pneumonia and she too died.

She was only thirty-nine, and the family must have been devastated. The boys, especially, would have been totally stunned at the loss of their mother, especially so soon after the loss of their sister, and my grandfather must have felt suicidal. How they got through it all I just do not know. Perhaps a belief in heaven, influenced by Marion, who had been a Sunday School teacher, helped, because they did manage to get through it. Nevertheless, the extent of the misery that must have clouded the rest of that winter and beyond is difficult to imagine.

My grandfather did not remain single for long, however, as in the autumn of that same year he married Bess (Bessie Thompson; née Rudman, I think) who had also lost her first spouse. I do not know whether my grandfather had known Bess while he was still married to my grandmother, and I am not altogether sure what the rest of the family made of this, especially in view of the relatively short time interval, but the new arrangement seems to have worked, as they remained married until my grandfather died, over seventeen years later.

Although my grandfather died before I was born, I can still remember Bess. When I was only a very young boy, I recall my father taking me to see her from time to time. I can vaguely remember that you used to have to go through a door in the wall near to the old Great Central Railway viaduct that crossed over Northgate Street. Behind this were rows of Victorian buildings, mainly sorts of tenements, as I recall, and Bess lived on the first floor in one of these. There was always a warm welcome, but I must admit that I found the place a bit depressing. My dad obviously cared about her, but my mum said that she was always asking him to lend her money. Knowing my father as I did, believe you me, this sort of thing would in no way have served to endear her more to him.

The only picture of Bess that I have is of her standing proudly in her ARP (Air Raid Precautions) Warden outfit together with armband and a tin helmet slung at her side, obviously taken some time during World War II. Interestingly there is more than a passing facial resemblance between Bess and Marion, so I wonder whether this had some bearing on the new relationship. She certainly does not appear undernourished, though, and if, during the blackout, I had been ordered by her to close my curtains, I would certainly not have argued!

*

Just over eighteen months after my father was born, his brother, Harry, came into the world; Harry Sydney, to give him his full name. Although on his birth certificate his name is spelt with an 'i' rather than a 'y', I believe that he had been named after Syd and indeed, on most of the other documents relating to him, his name is spelt with a 'y'. In fact, these sorts of errors are more common than you may think on official documents: my Uncle Charley's birth certificate, for example, has him as 'Charles Frank', whereas he was, in fact, 'Charles Frederick'.

By all accounts, from a toddler, Harry started to develop into something of a 'difficult child', even to the extent that people began to think he might have psychological problems. I recall that my father was always reluctant to go into too much detail when I asked him about Harry, even when I was an adult. I remember one specific time when I enquired, my mother interjected to the effect that Harry was always in trouble. My father responded, as he typically did when he strongly disapproved of what was being said or done, by grimacing and tutting, and although I went on to ask my mother what she meant, she had by then got the message and refused to say anything more. The reason, no doubt, was the 'stigma' that mental health issues attracted back then, and in some notes I have, that my father had written about our ancestry, he may well have felt this intensely because, with regards to Harry, his detail is not as accurate as I would normally have expected from him.

Harry died when he was just over eighteen and a half years of age, in 1938. I know that for a fact; I have both his birth and death certificates. Yet my father has him down in some notes as having died in 1934. Then he would have been just thirteen or fourteen and on the rare occasions that he did speak about him, he always used to imply that Harry died at around this age. As I recall, he said that some stone-throwing incident with other kids had set it off. How likely would it have been for him to make such a mistake about his slightly younger brother? My father certainly was not prone to such levels of inaccuracy, and with Harry's death happening only the year before the Second World War broke out; a pretty significant event, not some five years before, I am left struggling even more. There were certainly no such misapprehensions about Gwen's fate.

The reasons why my father may not have wanted to recall the tragedy in too great a detail perhaps become clearer when you realise what had affected Harry and why he died so young. His death certificate makes for some grim reading, and he must have suffered terribly. His lungs were congested, his appendix was badly inflamed, and he was covered in boils, but the underlying cause of all this was severe degeneration of the liver as a result of Wilson's disease. And, sadly, it may well only have been after his death in this way that the true reason behind Harry's issues in life became clear.

Wilson's disease (or Kinnier Wilson disease as it was originally called – after Dr. Samuel A. Kinnier Wilson who first described it in detail) is a rare genetic disorder that prevents the body from metabolising copper. Left untreated, copper builds up in the body, particularly in the liver and brain. As a result, the sufferer not only appears physically ill but, since the brain is involved, also experiences personality disorders that could, especially in those days, be regarded as 'madness'.

Nowadays, if detected early enough, Wilson's disease is easily treatable, and sufferers can expect to go on to live comparatively normal, healthy and full lives. One of the telltale signs is sometimes that dark rings appear around the irises of the eye, as a result of the build-up of copper there. Whether or not these were noticed in Harry or, indeed, whether he had them at all, I have no idea. In any event, back in the twenties and thirties, the exact nature of the disease was still under investigation so, even if they were present, they may just have been put down to 'normal variation'. My fear, though, is that Wilson's disease was never even considered and that neither the family nor anybody else had the slightest inkling that Harry was suffering from it. In any event, his condition seems to have been misunderstood rather than treated and, if left untreated, Wilson's disease almost always proves fatal.

The condition having finally overwhelmed him, Harry died in the Leicester General Hospital, where Gwen had died some eight years earlier and I would be born some fifteen years later. As was Gwen's, his death certificate is also signed by Dr. E.C. Hadley and, in view of the considerable discomfort that he must have endured, the end may well have come as a 'blessed relief'.

At times I have wondered whether, when the family finally realised exactly what had affected Harry and that it was a physical disease, not 'madness', they felt any less 'stigmatised'. Although there is no doubt in my mind that they dearly loved him, did they now fully understand the reasons for his bad behaviour? Was it ever fully explained to them? In those days, when formal interactions were perhaps a little less compassionate than they may be today, I am not so sure. Under 'Occupation' the death certificate simply gives his address: '25, Harding Street, Leicester', below which it coldly states 'No Occupation'.

Rest in peace Harry.

*

The youngest child, Charles Frederick, my Uncle Charley, served in the Royal Navy during the Second World War and I think that my father was rather envious of him in that respect. Although I knew my dad desperately wanted to serve, he had been unable to join the regular forces on account of his deformed foot. When he first received his call-up papers and duly reported, the recruiting officer is reputed to have told him, "Get you into a pair of army boots, soon cure that!" After a medical, however, the Army rejected him shortly afterwards, a decision possibly reinforced by the fact he was a mechanical engineer, which was a reserved occupation. Not easily put off, though, he then tried to join the Navy but was again rejected, this time curtly being told that, "If the Army don't want you, we bloody well don't!" He did, however, get to do his bit in the end when he joined the Home Guard, and he always used to say, about the TV series, *Dad's Army*, that, "It wasn't far from the truth!"

Before long he was made lance corporal and became an accomplished marksman. After he died, I came across his Certificate of Service, which I framed, and which now hangs from a wall in my house. Each time I look at it I cannot help but feel proud that he was eventually able to do his bit for our freedom.

Uncle Charley fought bravely during World War II and survived unscathed, apart from his tattooed forearm, that is. He rose to the rank of Chief Petty Officer but sadly died of bowel cancer in his mid-sixties. Somewhat coincidentally, his grandfather, Richard, also died at a similar age of a very similar condition, both having worked in the hosiery industry. However, as to whether the contraction of bowel cancer, especially in later life, can be in any way connected to previous circumstances must remain a matter for speculation. Even the degree to which it is inherited is unclear, and so this may just have been pure coincidence. My father thought at the time that Uncle Charley's illness may have been down to the great number of vaccinations that he had received on account of travelling far and wide in the Navy, but I am left struggling with that one as well. Yet perhaps to suggest that his death, too, could have been influenced by long-past parental ordeals may be pushing things a little too far. In the end, though, who can say for sure?

Despite the problem with his leg, my dad lived the longest of the four children. At almost eighty-nine he collapsed and died from heart failure, at home in Markfield, just to the north of Leicester, during May 2007, having outlived my mum by some fourteen years. And his longevity and stoic attitude to life make me think that, if there were anything at all in the theory alluded to, that stress in parents can affect the health of offspring, I cannot possibly see how it could have had anything at all to do with *his* death. Despite his problems (as a result of his deformity, he had a greater number of aches and pains, mainly in his back and legs, than you would normally expect) he was a 'tough cookie' and certainly not one to readily complain. In fact, the only time I saw him cry was when my mum died, and at one point during that outpouring I heard him mention his father. "What that man went through!" he said. Funny how one sadness can bring out another.

Nevertheless, my grandfather, despite his war wounds and all the terrible things that subsequently affected him and his family, would certainly have agreed with Winston Churchill when he said, 'if you are going through hell, keep going'. With a war pension, an invalid carriage (such as they were in those days), along with being able to return to work at Leicester Central Station, he remained solvent and as active as he could for the rest of his life. My mum always used to say that he had a good sense of humour (an oblique implication that he was unlike my father in that respect), and this is clear from the photographs I have of him. In one, he is obviously parodying Bud Flanagan, posing in front of a large billboard, dressed in a fur coat with an umbrella tucked under his arm. Looking at him then, nobody could possibly guess the torments that must have lain behind the broad smile he has on his face. He was also clearly not afraid of taking the odd risk or two, my father often recounting the story of him receiving a marvellous train set once for Christmas, after his father's horse had come in at 10/1!

I always remember, as a very small boy during the winter, since there was no central heating in our house in those days, my dad would place one of my grandfather's old overcoats over my bed sheets. It was a thick herringbone design and an extremely good insulator, but I can't help thinking that, although my dad was far from maudlin, there may well have been something a little bit more to it. I rather suspect that throughout all the ordeals that his family had to endure, my dad's father looked after him and loved him the best way he could. In other words, it may well have been that in laying his father's coat on top of me, my father was passing some of that love on to me and, if so, it worked. As was my father, I am tremendously proud of my grandfather and what he sacrificed for the good of mankind. I have his trio of medals – Pip, Squeak and Wilfred as they are popularly known – in a frame alongside a picture of him, taken still in uniform but after he had lost his leg. The 1914–15 Star (Pip), the British War Medal (Squeak) and the Victory Medal (Wilfred) are not really much when you consider all the suffering that he endured. But they are testament to his great bravery, and I will treasure them for ever.

My grandfather passed away, aged fifty-six, the day before Christmas Eve 1950, essentially of circulatory failure. No mention was made on his death certificate about the effect that his war wounds may have had on his relatively early demise.

*

So, what of everybody else? I have records of Richard and Louisa collecting Frank and Syd's medals in 1921 which, like before, when the war had finally come to an end, for any family having lost loved ones to it, must have been yet another bittersweet experience for them.

Sadly, Richard died of bowel cancer in 1927 but Louisa lived on for another twenty-two years and made it to just over ninety years of age, dying in September 1949. Flo, the eldest child, would have an even longer life; she lived to 101. Towards the end of her life, though, she had not realised just how old she really was. Apparently when Flo was coming up to what she had thought was her ninety-ninth birthday in 1983, her daughter, Ida, had done some research and found out that it would, in fact, be her 101st! She had totally missed out on her hundredth birthday the year before and all that would have gone with it! The error was put down to her 'modifying' her age slightly when marrying her husband, Sam, all those years ago, who was somewhat younger than she was. A family trait?

Flo was survived by her sister, Doll (Doris Mary), the youngest child, but only by a further two or three years. Nevertheless, reaching eighty-two years of age, she too 'did not have a bad innings' as they say.

Although I had met my Great-Aunt Flo on one or two occasions and knew my Great-Aunt Doll well, I never knowingly met any of my great-uncles from Richard and Louisa's family, even though some did survive until well after I was born. Over the Internet, however, I was able to trace some of their descendants and through these contacts have been able to glean a little bit more about these 'lost relatives'. My thanks to Dave Williams (Flo's grandson) for a great deal of additional information about Flo and Doll. Also, thanks to Malcolm Woodcock, the grandson of Arch (as my grandfather always used to refer to him but Malcolm knew him as Richard) who told me about Arch's family. And, last but not least, my thanks to Vicky Wilson for the information about Fred – her great-grandfather.

As an incidental bonus to my research, I also learned a little more about some of the famous people to whom I am evidently related. Mainly through marriages, to name but three: Firstly, there is Ted Williams (Dave Williams's father), the showjumper famous in the 1950s and '60s, who was Flo's son-in-law. Then there is Arch's (Richard's) father-in-law who was Ted Pritchard, the famous boxer of the 1880s and '90s. Apparently Henry Cooper's grandfather was his sparring partner. And, by all accounts, as I was told from a very early age and which was repeated by some of the lost relatives with whom I have been able to re-establish contact, I am related to one of the Dallas Boys. I know… you would have to be of a certain age, but they were a group of Leicester lads who formed what could perhaps be described as the first 'boy band' in the 1950s – quite famous in their day, often appearing on TV. Despite some considerable research, I still have absolutely no idea to which member I am supposed to be related or through whom. Again, it is no doubt through marriage, since none of the band was named Warren and it does not help that two of them were a Smith and a Jones. Maybe one day I will find out.

As for John (Jack), Ernest and Leonard (Joe) I do not know what became of them. Jack, being the eldest son, had a family (I think) even before the First World War and I assume that Ernest and Joe (the youngest boys) went on to have families too. Yet, for some reason or other, I never recall my parents talking about them in any great detail. Then again, you don't always pay a lot of attention when you're young, do you?

In any event, everyone must now be dead so may they, along with the other members of my family who have 'passed beyond the veil', all rest in peace.

*

Albert Einstein is said to have predicted that he did not know with what weapons World War III would be fought but that World War IV would be fought with sticks and stones! An obvious cognition that there now exists weaponry capable of returning civilisation to the Stone Age. Not least for this reason, I hope, as all should, that there will never be another world war and that all the misery and loss from the two we have already had, stops there. It is a sad fact that since the outbreak of the so-called 'war to end wars' there has continuously been some sort of conflict raging somewhere in the world and if something were to arise closer to home again, I do worry that we are not nearly well enough prepared for it.

Although not entirely without its problems, in the main, Europe has enjoyed relative peace since the end of World War II, with the measures imposed on the Axis powers, particularly Germany, the establishment of the United Nations (UN) which provides an alternative to aggression, the North Atlantic Treaty Organisation (NATO) alliance and then the establishment of the European Union (EU) (formerly European Economic Community – EEC). All were attempts to draw nations closer together, including many, it has to be said, that had previously been at each other's throats down the ages. They do not always work, of course, Hitler having withdrawn Germany from the League of Nations (the predecessor of the UN) in 1933, but they have certainly increased interaction and, global pandemics excepted, international travel is now safer and easier than it ever has been. With first-hand experience of World War I now having passed out of living memory, as that of World War II soon will, however, the question arises as to whether all this is enough to guarantee our future stability. Or is it always a case of 'what goes around, comes around'? Although we may be reluctant to recall some aspects of the past, as the philosopher George Santayana once said, 'Those who cannot remember the past, we are condemned to repeat it'.

For the better or the worse (depending on your standpoint) we have already seen cracks appear in certain of these 'modern regimes'. The angry reactions to strict economic measures imposed on poorer eurozone members who have had to be bailed out by the richer ones for example. (Particularly aimed at Germany, by far the richest member.) And then came Brexit of course.

Perhaps wars will be fought along entirely different lines in future, say involving cyberattacks on large-scale computer systems etc. And with our ever-increasing dependency on these, especially with regard to defence, health and energy, and the like, it is not difficult to imagine how devastating this could be.

Nevertheless, the ever-present threat of the use of nuclear weapons is not going to go away. Some maintain they are not necessary and should be destroyed, whilst others insist that they are the very reason why there has not been another world war. Different peoples and cultures will always think differently, have varying takes on matters and some will be more upset by certain issues than others. Our only hope is that common sense prevails and that it is possible to compromise and learn from our mistakes. But I must admit, I have my doubts…

Syd (standing) – probably taken on his way to France February/March 1915.

Arch in (what I believe to be) his Royal Marines' uniform.

Frank – the only picture I have of him.

Flo in later life.

Doll as a young woman and in later life.

Fred.

Gwen when a young lady.

Uncle Charley in later life.

Bert – my dad, in later life.

My grandfather – Albert George Warren (seated centre), presumably in the grounds of a hospital.

My grandmother – Marion Jack Warren (neeé Blyth).

Albert George (my grandfather) & family – left to right: Albert (my father), Marion (my grandmother), Charley, Gwen, Harry and Albert George.

My grandfather – Albert George Warren, posing as Bud Flanagan 1940s?

Bess – Albert George's second wife. Obviously taken during WW2.

Albert George's and Marion's children on the beach (probably either Skegness or Cleethorpes), around 1929. Left to right: Albert Richard David (my father), Charles (my uncle Charley), Gwen and Harry. Charley and Gwen pulling a face and smiling and Dad and Harry more serious – generally the norm...

The slagheaps (crassiers) near Auchy-les-Mines in present times.

The pithead (puits de mine) near Auchy-les-Mines in present times.

Map of Europe at the Outbreak of World War I in 1914.

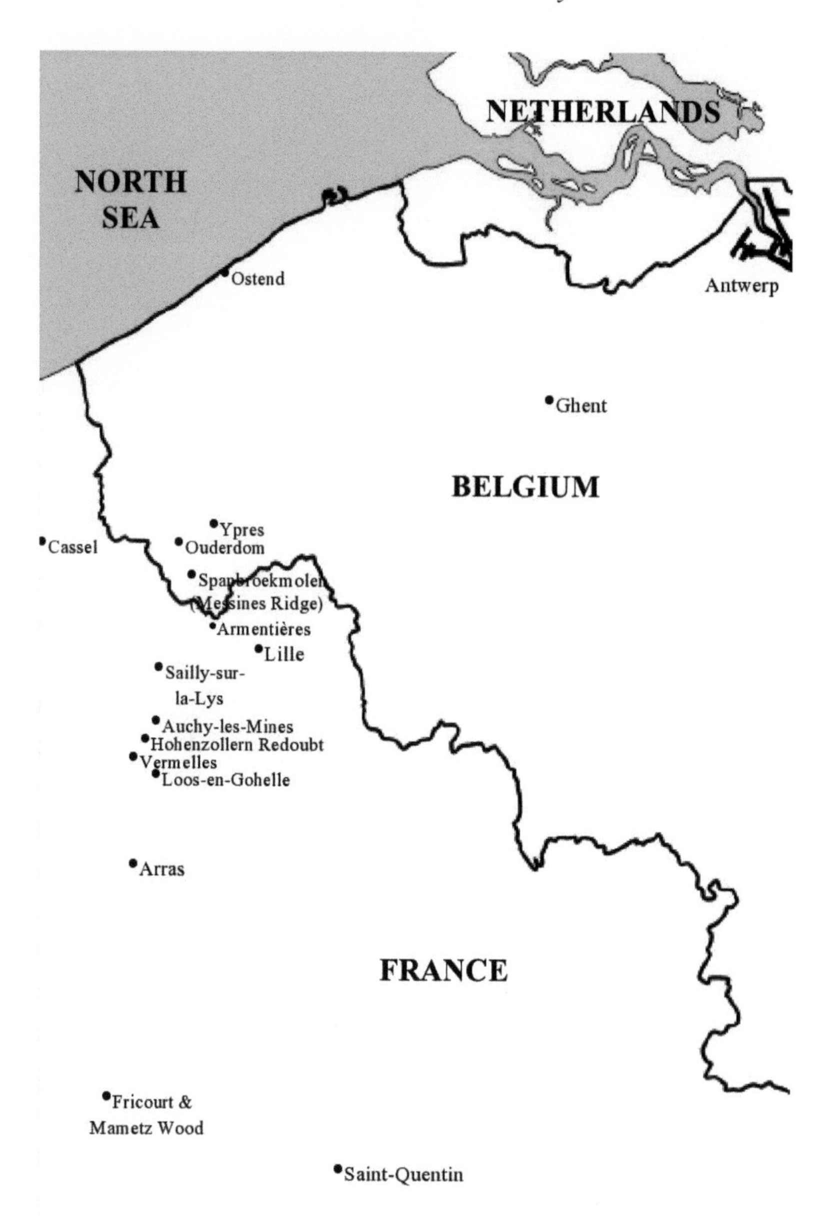

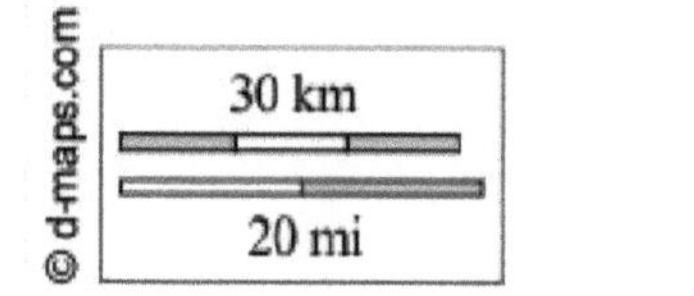

https://d-maps.com/carte.php?num_car=2080&lang=en

The Northern European War Theatre 1915/16

Acknowledgements

In addition to those mentioned in the body of this book I would like to extend my gratitude to the following for their valuable assistance:

Professor Keith Snell of the University of Leicester History Dept. and Malcolm and Jennifer Elliott for their guidance on life during nineteenth-century Leicester.

My cousin, the local historian and writer, Joanne Vigor-Mungovin, for correcting many a false assumption and enlightening me on various aspects of the lives of our mutual ancestors, several of which are relayed in this book.

All the staff at the Leicester, Leicestershire and Rutland Record Office in Wigston for their assistance, particularly Helen Sullivan for her guidance on several of my ancestors' burial sites in and around the city and Clare Underwood and Jenny Morgan for permission to use the images on the jacket.

Virginia Wright, Historical and Heritage Advisor at St. Mary de Castro Church, Leicester for her clarifications about burials there.

Alison Mott of the Loughborough Archaeological and Historical Society and Lynne Dyer, Accredited Leicestershire Tour Guide, for their information about the village of Desford.

Canon Barry Naylor for his clarifications about St. Andrew's Church, Leicester.

The staff at Wigston Library as well as Margaret Warren; a fellow descendant of Richard Ward Warren, for their guidance on the Freemen of Leicester.

The staff at the Derbyshire Record Office in Matlock and the Staffordshire Record Office in Lichfield for all their assistance.

All the long-lost relatives, both in Britain and around the world, with whom I was able to establish contact through Genes Reunited, the Internet or other means.

The staff of the Framework Knitters Museum, Ruddington, Notts. for their clarifications during my visit there.

All the authors of the many relevant publications that I read in order to understand the various aspects about which I have written. Far too long a list to mention individually, I must add.

My wife, Nicky and my brother-in-law and sister-in-law, Mervyn and Claudy, for their dedicated proofreading and, last but not least, my thanks to everybody else who has assisted me in the writing of this book either knowingly or not.

David C. Warren
February 2022

This book is printed on paper from sustainable sources managed under the Forest Stewardship Council (FSC) scheme.

It has been printed in the UK to reduce transportation miles and their impact upon the environment.

For every new title that Matador publishes, we plant a tree to offset CO_2, partnering with the More Trees scheme.

For more about how Matador offsets its environmental impact, see www.troubador.co.uk/about/